DARTMOOR
A New Study

DARTMOOR
A New Study

EDITED BY CRISPIN GILL

Contributors:

Denys Brunsden
John Gerrard
James Barber
John Somers Cocks
Frank Booker
Michael Havinden
Freda Wilkinson
Robert Groves
Michael Ewans
Brian Le Messurier

 David & Charles: Newton Abbot

ISBN 0 7153 5041 2

Set in 11/13pt Baskerville
and printed in Great Britain
by Clarke Doble & Brendon Limited Plymouth
for David & Charles (Publishers) Limited
South Devon House Newton Abbot Devon

Contents

List of Illustrations

Plates

continued on page 10

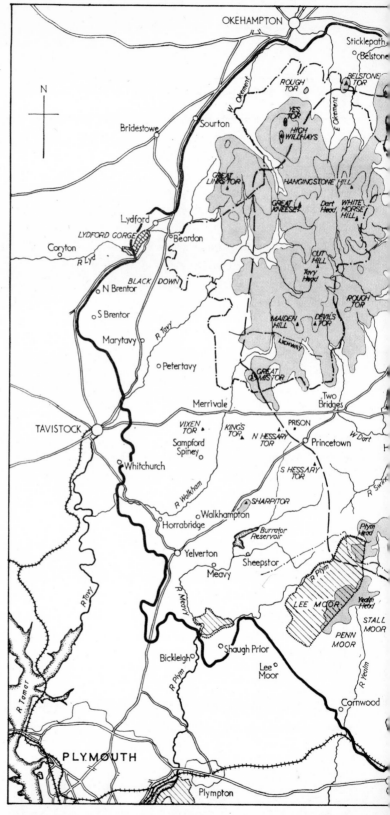

Fig 1. A ge...

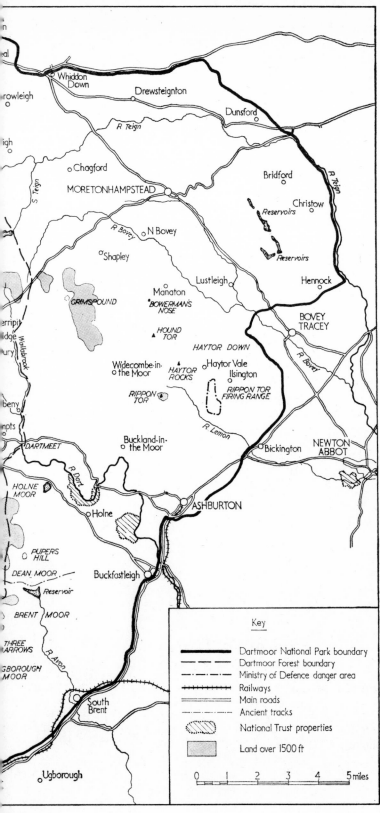

Key

▬▬▬▬	Dartmoor National Park boundary
▬ ▬ ▬	Dartmoor Forest boundary
▬ · ▬ · ▬	Ministry of Defence danger area
⊦⊦⊦⊦⊦⊦	Railways
══════	Main roads
▬ · · ▬ · ·	Ancient tracks
▨	National Trust properties
▨	Land over 1500 ft

0 1 2 3 4 5 miles

Figures in Text

Introduction

By Crispin Gill

THIS BOOK WAS born out of discussions on a proposed reprinting of Worth's *Dartmoor*. It had already gone through two small editions and some people, while acknowledging Worth's authority and value, argued that his was essentially a work of record and that the need was for interpretation, for an examination of current theories on the geology and prehistory, in which much new work had been done. It was also felt that many other Dartmoor subjects—land use, recreation, industry, intrusions, for example—all needed re-examination; in some cases they had never been adequately dealt with.

Out of this debate came the ideal solution, that Worth should be reprinted and that a new work should be set in hand. The lack of a full history of the Moor has always been one of the biggest gaps in West Country literature. William Crossing devoted much of his life to collecting historical data, but this was unfortunately destroyed before it could be put into circulation. When this work was projected in 1966 it was felt that the range of knowledge was more than could be found in any one person, and so the present contributors, each with specialised knowledge, were enlisted.

They were told that the basic aim was to present as far as was possible in one volume a survey of modern knowledge of Dartmoor. Clearly one book could not contain every detail, but it was felt that it should be possible to contain the essential facts and the broad sweep. The book was to meet the need of the ordinary reader and not the specialist, but the reader was assumed to be an intelligent person who would not be written down to, although he might not have the specialised knowledge or even the private vocabulary of the scientist writing for scientists. In some subjects, of course, technical terms have to be used because in no other way can the precise meaning be conveyed, but this has been kept to a minimum.

For the purpose of this book Dartmoor was defined as the area of the National Park, with the exception of the part east of the Bovey Tracey to Whiddon Down road, and with the addition of the moorland of the china clay area south-west of the Cornwood to Cadover road. The National Park boundary, which is roughly marked by the main roads

13

encircling the Moor, seemed a logical as well as a convenient arrangement, but the book was to be concerned with the wilderness and its settlements, leaving the border towns such as Ashburton and Tavistock to be dealt with only in so far as they were essential to the main story. The park boundaries excluded the china clay area because it was felt that such an industrialised district could not be subject to park planning requirements, but it does overflow the park boundaries and is an essential part of the historic Dartmoor. The area east of Moretonhampstead, although included in the park, is really approach country and contains little true moor or downland.

The other boundary problem was between contributors, and this was resolved by the synopsis and mutual discussion as the work progressed. Inevitably there is a little overlapping where certain events and developments are relevant to different subjects, and these have been left so that the flow of argument is not impeded.

Two chapters have not materialised. One, on Dartmoor books, became to some extent superfluous as each contributor refers either in his chapter or his list of sources to the writers in that field. The Dartmoor Preservation Association is also publishing an extensive Dartmoor bibliography of non-fiction works, compiled by John Somers Cocks with assistance from Brian Le Messurier. This leaves the novelists untouched, but Eden Phillpotts, Sabine Baring-Gould and John Trevena are about the only ones to have produced works of consequence. A. J. Coles (Jan Stewer) has written plays and a vast number of dialect stories, and there are some Dartmoor novels by Vian Smith, though his following has been mainly in the United States. Galsworthy lived for some years at Manaton but only touches on the Moor in one play. Nor have the painters been dealt with, but as with too many of the novels one has the feeling that they have only a superficial understanding of the Moor, and add little to one's knowledge or appreciation.

The other unwritten chapter is on Dartmoor politics. In the West of England there has been no hotter field since the war, or one in which passions are so vehemently aroused. This is understandable because, as a growing population builds up an increasing land hunger, so the agriculturists seek to increase the Moor's output, the foresters see it as marginal farming land which would be more productive under trees, the Services see it as ideal training country where the minimum of people are disturbed, and the townsmen who park theirs cars round Burrator and Holne Reservoir on a Sunday afternoon not only see the Moor as a natural source of water for their taps but regard the artificial lakes as actual improvements on the barren scene.

Ranged against all these would-be developers are those who argue that, with the increasing urbanisation of England, the last pieces of surviving wild country have an increasing value as places where overcrowded people can find peace and quiet, the challenge of natural forces and the solace of loneliness. As the developers account as perversely unrealistic those who would preserve inviolate the Moor's 'barren acres', so those who defend them cannot in turn understand the insensitivity of those who want to plant trees or houses or pylons or reservoirs with their attendant roads in this last wilderness in southern England.

It is this lack of understanding, and the fact that appreciation of the Moor for itself is a comparatively new idea, which has made the fight so bitter. It has been interesting to watch the Dartmoor National Park Committee, the main chamber in which the debate has been conducted. Devon County Council nominates twelves members to this Committee (not necessarily, but usually, members of the county council) and the Minister of Housing and Local Government nominates the other six, who have then to be elected by the county council—which thereby in theory retains a veto. In practice the 'nominated members' are recommended to the Minister by the Countryside Commission or its predecessor, the National Parks Commission, and might roughly be called defenders. This background has not produced the cut-and-dried responses that might have been expected. At regular intervals the county council has not been happy with decisions presented to it by the Dartmoor Committee, and from time to time county councillors have sought to get people elected to the committee who would present what they felt to be rational views and fight the stranger elements. Many county council members of the Dartmoor Committee have been as strong defenders of the Moor as any nominated members; and over the years the other county representatives, as they have sat and learned about the problems, have often gradually moved away from the viewpoints they were sent to put forward. They have tended to do this or to cease attending meetings. The Park Committee has slowly become very much the conscience of the county council over the Moor; it has at times stubbornly and courageously fought the county council. Sir Henry Slesser, for many years chairman of the Park Committee, did not always win the approval of the Dartmoor Preservation Association, but on his retirement he could write such cynical verse as

> Bring forth bulldozers, swift to turn
> Our mossy immemorial peat
> That Bingo halls, for which folk yearn,
> Arise in every new-found street.

> Let operatives, skilled, press on
> With roads and wires, cement and sand
> That we may build New Babylon
> On Dartmoor's hard concreted land.

The verses were published anonymously but the authorship was an open secret.

The usual sneer is that worse things have happened to Dartmoor since it became a national park than ever before in its long history. One might also ask what would have happened, how much worse would things be, had there been no National Park. Its committee members have felt that it has been crippled by the Act of Parliament which created it, a compromise which paid lip-service to the idea but which had impossible checks written into it during its passage into law. Above all the committee has been short of money. Nothing is free, not even amenity or beauty, and those who want to keep Dartmoor basically as it is (no one wants glass-case preservation, or even the American-style park where the only permitted change is the encouragement of recreational activity) must pay. If Parliament wills a National Parks Act it must provide the money for it, or see that the money is provided. A Park Committee cannot stand before a developer and plead that he shall not do what he wants to do, when it would make or save money for him and the committee can offer no compensation in exchange. Yet that is a fight into which the Park Committee is so often plunged; and astonishingly it has often reached some measure of success.

Undoubtedly the preservation of Dartmoor in the last quarter-century has owed more to one individual than will ever be realised. Sylvia Sayer, grand-daughter of Robert Burnard, founder of the Dartmoor Preservation Association, and herself chairman of it since the end of the war, has built it up into one of the most powerful amenity societies in the country, and has been its most indefatigable worker and its most powerful voice : 'the shield of the moor', in Henry Slesser's phrase. Her knowledge is enormous, her industry unbelievable. If her battles have taught her to be ruthless in her methods she has never lost her natural charm and good humour. Sometimes it seems as if in her the issue polarises and becomes personal; she has earned the kind of venom usually reserved for party politicians of the most successful kind, yet she has seen her DPA followers grow to over a thousand, and perhaps her greatest achievement is that she has roused the conscience of an even vaster number of people.

It may be that if the Maud reforms for local government come about and Dartmoor falls into the area of two unitary authorities, Devon and Plymouth, there will be a change of control. The Maud proposals for

Page 17 (above) *The 'sugar-loaf' form of Saddle Tor is dominated by the prominent vertical and horizontal joints. The striking contrast between the vegetation-clad moorland slopes and the bare rock is vividly portrayed; (below) central Dartmoor from Great Mis Tor. The high residual masses of north and central Dartmoor rise above the Summit Erosion Surface. In the foreground the northern extremity of Great Mis Tor slopes down to the River Walkham*

Page 18 *Great Mis Tor:* (above) *a mass of granite boulders that has been broken off the main tor and deposited in the form of a complex lobe. Frost action under past climatic conditions is the suggested mechanism;* (below) *the closely spaced horizontal joints give this tor its characteristic appearance. Under past conditions they were the means by which first chemical weathering penetrated the rock underground and then frost action attacked exposed surfaces*

Park boards (on the pattern of the Peak Park board) rather than joint committees (as for Exmoor) were accepted by the Wilson government. If this ever comes about, the new Dartmoor park authority will precept for its financial needs, as do regional police forces, and will not be subject, as at present, to the overriding authority of Devon County Council. The argument is that Dartmoor is a national park, part of the national heritage, that it should be cared for by the nation, not by local authorities, and that in the last resort its control should not necessarily reside with the residents. It is this last point which produces the most heat and alarm.

As the largest landowner on the Moor, in its holding of the Forest proper, the Duchy of Cornwall is in an invidious position. The monarchy is very properly above politics, whether national or local, but what happens on the Moor increasingly tends to draw it into the Dartmoor struggle. It is not easy for the Duchy, over whose Council the Queen presided until the Prince of Wales came of age, to resist claims on the Moor advanced by government departments such as the Ministry of Defence, when their spokesmen are the ministers who are also, in law, the Queen's advisers. In fact a great weight of responsibility lies on Parliament and the various ministries, for half the battles are between the ministries carrying out the conflicting policies that Parliament has passed into law. It seems incongruous to have the Minister of Housing and Local Government encouraging the Countryside Commission and the National Park Committee to preserve the amenities and the character of Dartmoor when the Minister of Agriculture is at the same time paying subsidies to farmers to fence and plough large tracts of land, the Minister of Transport wants to straighten out the narrow little lanes, and the Chancellor of the Exchequer makes it possible for people who have never seen Dartmoor to pay for trees to be planted there as a way of escaping death duties. Parliament, and the people for whom it speaks, must make up their minds on the value they place on Dartmoor and all the national parks.

Not all the contributors to this book are on the same side in these political arguments. They are stated here because to offer a modern study of Dartmoor and ignore the arguments about it would not be honest. The contributors have presented their essays objectively but, where their own views have crept through, their divergence is apparent.

Perhaps one last word may be said. Dartmoor has survived all its improvers and developers; it has buried not only the men but the mines they dug, the roads they made, and the houses they lived in. Even airfields can be removed. Wire fences will fall down as the acres they enclose cease to be viable farmlands, and trees will in the fullness of time fall under

B

the axe and the weather. But the vast concrete dams stretched across the valleys will not just ruin a corner of the Moor for two or three human generations, but for centuries after they have outlived their usefulness. The danger of each proposed development should be costed not just in its immediate amenity effect, but in its cost to the succeeding generations as yet unborn. Dartmoor does not need a glass case, but it does need care.

Yelverton, April 1970

1

The Physical Environment of Dartmoor

Denys Brunsden and John Gerrard

THROUGHOUT the long human occupation of Dartmoor man's perception of the area has changed and this has influenced his behaviour and achievements. The response to these changing attitudes has a visual expression in the form of landscape changes such as farming patterns or forest clearance. In 1586, William Camden described Dartmoor as 'Squalida Montana, Dertmore'. Today our twentieth-century taste regards it as an area of great natural beauty and it has been designated as a national park, preserved as part of our heritage.

In view of these contrasts, it is important that when the reader attempts to interpret the Dartmoor landscape he is aware both of his own attitudes, which may colour his own interpretation, and of the attitudes of the people at the time the landscape was created, for this may lead to a deeper understanding of the forms which are studied. In this chapter an attempt is made to describe the environment from an unbiased point of view, where opinions are expressed they have been reached only after very careful assessment of the available evidence.

The National Park boundary encompasses a region of contrasts between the tor-crowned ridges and peat-filled valleys; moorland waste and agricultural land; royal forest and medieval settlement; which provide a rich diversity of interest. In this area man has assessed and utilised the varied resources of soil, water, woodland and minerals and so created the changing landscape patterns which today are regarded as 'typical' Dartmoor. An important part of this type of study must therefore be a scientific description of the physical environment in which man lives, as a framework within which to examine how he has influenced and changed the landscape.

The granite massif of Dartmoor forms the most prominent morphological element in the landscape of south-west England. The upland is everywhere over 700ft in elevation, with the highest summits reaching heights of over 2,000ft. Although the area as a whole may be regarded as a plateau, it is dissected by deep valleys which possess a relative relief of up to 500ft. The ridges slope from 1,900ft in the north to 1,500ft in the south and are defined by a complex series of basin-like valleys and narrow gorges. They are often bevelled by remnants of erosion surfaces, are occasionally surmounted by tors and are frequently fringed by rock buttresses. The moorland edge slopes steeply down to the incised streams of the lowland which have a relative relief of over 1,000ft. The streams possess mature upland reaches and vigorous lowland courses which, where they cross the granite boundary, are separated by deep gorges.

The area surrounding Dartmoor is dissected by closely spaced streams, but the lowland ridges characteristically show a bevelled appearance composed of a series of erosion surfaces. Many of the main drainage basins are of an elongated shape but the total length of stream per unit area of the basin is low in comparison with many parts of the country. It seems as if the Dartmoor rivers are able to remove the available water with a minimum of channel development. In consequence the area drained must be large before further stream extension can take place.

That both the number of streams should be small and their length relatively short for an area of upland Britain is due to a combination of the permeability and homogeneity of the granite and the water holding capacity of the peat and weathered rock, which together ensure a steady rather than a spectacular discharge of water.

Geology

The National Park includes the whole of the Dartmoor granite outcrop, the metamorphic aureole rocks formed as the molten granite was intruded and a rich mineral zone set within a varied assemblage of sedimentary rocks. (Table 1 and Fig 2). These rocks influence the patterns of relief, soils and vegetations.

The granites of south-west England occur as six large outcrops lying on a continuous ridge from Dartmoor to the Isles of Scilly. The Dartmoor granite is an intrusion which rises steeply from the south to spread northward into the sedimentary rocks. To the west it is linked by Kit Hill and Hingston Down to Bodmin Moor. In the east it has been eroded to form the dissected area of lowland Dartmoor.

The Dartmoor granite is composed of several distinctive rock types. First, there are the contact rocks which cooled at the margin of the granite intrusion and have different properties from the rocks in the centre of the intrusion and those beyond the zone of contact. Secondly, the coarse grained 'Tor' or 'Giant' granite, forms most of the tors and high level ridges. This granite contains large crystals of felspar set in a coarse

Table 1

THE SEDIMENTARY SUCCESSION

Recent		Peat, Alluvium, Valley gravels, Estuarine deposits, Blown sand	
Pleistocene		Head, Raised beaches, Terrace gravels, Cavern deposits	
Middle Oligocene		Bovey Beds	Ball clays, Lignite
Eocene		Haldon Gravels	Cobbles, Sand matrix
Upper Cretaceous		Upper Greensand	Gravel, Sands, Chert
		Unconformity	
Trias		Upper Sandstone Group	Red sandstone
		Pebble Beds	Pebbles cemented in sand
Permian		Lower marls with sandstone	Red marls, Sandstone in lower part
		Lower sandstone and breccia	Red sandstone and rock sand
		Breccia and conglomerate	Igneous rock and Culm debris
		Clays with sandstone (Watcombe C.)	Red clay, Sand and breccia bands
		Stages	Unconformity	
Carbon-iferous	Upper	Stephanian	Not represented	
		Westphalian	Not represented	
		Namurian	Sandstone Group	Sandstone, Grit, Shale
	Lower	Viséan	Calcareous Group	Shales, Limestone, Cherts
		Tournaisian	Shales and Quartzite Group	Shales, Quartzite, Siltstones, Tuffs
Devonian	Upper	Famennian	Slate Series	Grey, green, red slates
		Frasnian		Grits, Shales, Limestones
	Middle	Givetian	Limestone Series	Massive grey limestones Thin limestones with coral and crinoids, Shales, Lavas
		Couvinian		
	Lower	Emsian	Staddon Grits	Red-purple grits, Shales
			Meadfoot Beds	Shales, Grits, Calcareous bands
		Siegenian	Dartmouth Slates	Purple-green slates, Grits
		Gedinnian	Not represented	

Sources: Memoirs and one-inch maps of the Geological Survey; K. F. G. Hosking and G. J. Shrimpton (1964); I. G. Simmons, ed. (1964).

matrix of quartz and biotite. Intruded into the 'Tor' granite is the 'Blue' granite, a fine-grained rock, underlying the Tor granite and visible in quarries, the west face of Haytor and on the side of the Dart Valley at Bench Tor. The last type consists of veins and dykes of a fine-grained rock called aplite which crosses all other forms.

Other variations were caused by the processes of mineralisation, such as

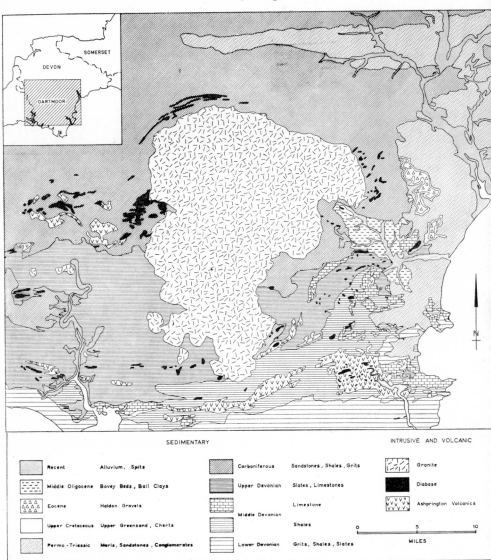

SEDIMENTARY   INTRUSIVE AND VOLCANIC

	Recent	Alluvium, Spits		Carboniferous	Sandstones, Shales, Grits		Granite
	Middle Oligocene	Bovey Beds, Ball Clays		Upper Devonian	Slates, Limestones		Diabase
	Eocene	Haldon Gravels			Limestone		Ashprington Volcanics
				Middle Devonian			
	Upper Cretaceous	Upper Greensand, Cherts			Shales		
	Permo-Triassic	Marls, Sandstones, Conglomerates		Lower Devonian	Grits, Shales, Slates		

0   5   10

MILES

Fig 2.   Solid geology (simplified). Based mainly on the 1in and ¼in maps of the Geological Survey. The outcrops of the Devonian and Carboniferous rocks have been generalised. Small occurrences of volcanic materials have been omitted for clarity.

intrusion of black tourmaline, the veins of which can be seen in most quarries, facing the sides of the joints and staining the granite pink or red. Occasionally the tourmaline combines with quartz to produce schorl, a very resistant rock which can be seen at Leigh Tor, Holne Chase and Lovers Leap below Ausewell rocks. Another common process is kaolinization which has produced the extensive deposits of kaolin at Lee Moor.

These processes also resulted in large deposits of tin, arsenic, copper, iron, wolfram, quarzt and fluor. Tin was found at such sites as Haytor, Holne, Lustleigh, and Vitifer (Fig 13, p 101). Copper was not common on the moorland, but rich deposits were found at Ashburton, Hingston, Marytavy and Tavistock. Similarly, lead, iron, silver, zinc, arsenic and wolfram were more commonly found on the granite margin. At some centres the minerals were found in an ascending sequence of tin, copper, lead and arsenic zones and were emplaced in fissures which follow the north-south, east-west, and north-east, south-west directions corresponding to the joint patterns of the granite. Tin and copper lodes cross Dartmoor from west to east but lead fills north to south cross-courses which often displace the tin. Today these minerals are no longer exploited and the sites of the original deposits are indicated only by disused shafts and buildings.

The granite is surrounded by rocks altered by the granite as it was intruded, which, because of their variable resistance to erosion, form an inaccessible country of steep slopes and dissected heathlands on the granite margin. The texture of these rocks is complex and depends on the nature of the original rock as well as the processes of change they have undergone during the emplacement of the granite. Sandy beds are usually recrystallised into grits and quartzites; clay beds have become shales and siltstones; cherts are unchanged or form quartzites, and calcareous rocks form calc flinta.

The contact between the altered rocks and the granite is usually sharp but may show an interleaving of sedimentary rocks with the intrusive material. Examples can be clearly seen at Burrator, in the surface rocks at Leusdon Common and in the exposed river bed of the Mardle.

The Dartmoor area owes much of its form to the structural patterns which determine the disposition of the rocks. The most striking features originated with the earth movements which disturbed the whole of south-west England at the close of the Carboniferous period. The rocks of the lowland area surrounding Dartmoor were folded along east-west lines and the Dartmoor granite was intruded at or towards the close of this uplift.

This ancient pattern was further disturbed by the earth movements of the Tertiary period, which caused widespread dislocation on north-west—south-east lines, notably in the Bovey Tracey, Lustleigh and Stickle-path areas. These lines of weakness run along the valleys at Lustleigh and Moretonhampstead. The Bovey Basin is a deep, faulted basin now infilled with ball clays, gravels and lignite of Middle Oligocene age derived from early erosion of the Dartmoor granite.

The joints of the granite also affect the topography. Vertical joints are abundant, with all orientations. Locally dominant trends often determine the relief patterns, and are followed by the streams (for example, the Dart at Hexworthy and the Okement at Kneeset Nose) and control the processes of weathering and subsequent tor formation.

The History of the Landscape

The history of the erosion of Dartmoor and the development of its drainage pattern, is a complex problem which can only be studied by either examining the landforms or the deposits which contain dateable remains. The early rivers eroded the granite to produce flood plains and eventually wide open valleys. Since Dartmoor was uplifted several times, the rivers were forced to cut new valleys inside their old ones and so a terraced landscape was produced in which each level represents a long period of erosion of the landscape. Erosion surfaces of this type can be seen at various heights: on the high moor 1,900–1,700ft and 1,650–1,500ft; and at several levels between 1,300 and 750ft along the valleys of the main rivers. To the experienced eye these terraces accurately record the history of how the rivers have cut into the granite (Figs 3 and 4).

At lower elevations there is convincing evidence that the sea was once at a much higher level and has fallen by stages to its present level. These stages are represented in the landscape by flat surfaces and steeper slopes which are the remains of old shore platforms and cliffs. They can be grouped on the basis of altitude and are believed to represent evidence of landscape evolution under the influence of a falling sea level.

On Dartmoor the highest level may be traced at a constant height of 700 to 680ft OD and is everywhere backed by a steeper slope which may be interpreted as the degraded cliffs of the shoreline. The marine origin of the surface is confirmed by the way it cuts across complex strata of various ages and is little affected by changes in rock resistance. The best examples of this surface are found on Roborough Down (map reference 514680) and Green Down (715687).

Below 700ft OD similar evidence is available for a sequence of levels at 590ft, 430, 325, 150, 50, 24 and 14ft OD which marked stages in the retreat of the sea. This evidence is supported by an equivalent sequence of extensive flood plains and river terraces, such as those clearly visible at Staverton (790642) and Totnes (802609).

The history of erosion is also revealed by a study of the evolution of the drainage pattern. The earliest rivers flowed east and removed the cover rocks of the Dartmoor granite to produce the highest surface on the summit of the Moor. Some of the debris removed by these rivers was later deposited in the Hampshire Basin and Dorset. Traces of this drainage pattern are still preserved by the east-west moorland sections of the Dart and Teign.

During the earth movements of the mid-Tertiary geological period,

Table 2

EROSION SURFACES

Area	Dartmoor	River Dart	S. Dartmoor, S. Hams	River Exe
Early Tertiary	Upper Surface 1,900–1,700ft in north 1,650–1,500ft in south	Summit Plain 1,900–1,700ft in north 1,650–1,500ft in south	Summit Plain 1,620–1,520ft in south	
Mid-Tertiary	1,350–1,050ft	1,300–1,100ft	1,375–1,300ft	
Late Tertiary	950–750ft	1,000ft 920ft 800ft 750ft	930–875ft 820–730ft	925ft 825ft
Early Pleistocene	690ft marine	690ft marine 590ft 480–475ft 445–430ft 325ft 270ft 230ft 180ft 150ft 110ft 50ft 25ft 10–14ft	700–690ft marine 600ft 550ft 475ft 460ft 430ft 400ft 375ft 350ft 327ft 300ft 280ft 150ft 126ft 25ft 14ft 0 −36 to −50ft −140 to −150ft	690–686ft marine 424ft 334–330ft 287–283ft 232–230ft 185ft 127–122ft 91–85ft 50–48ft 30ft

Sources: Brunsden (1963) Brunsden *et al.* (1964); Kidson (1962); Orme (1964); Waters (1960).

Dartmoor was tilted to the south and the south-flowing Tamar, Plym, Avon, Erme and the long north bank tributaries of the Dart were initiated. This explains the present pattern of the Dart drainage, with its eight large north bank tributaries and only two small rivers flowing north.

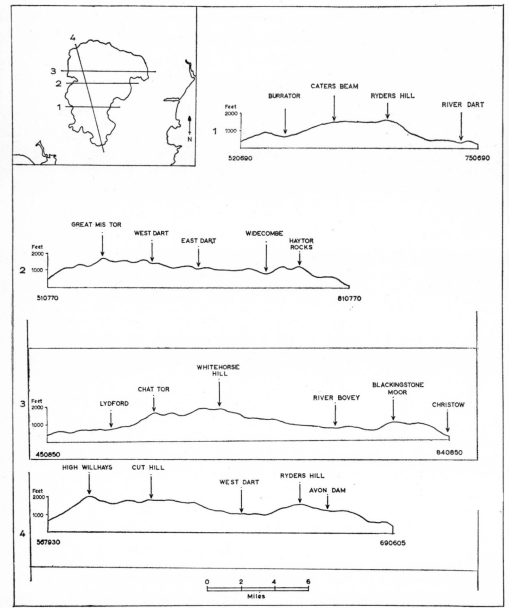

Fig 3. Summit profiles. These illustrate the dominance of erosion surfaces in the Dartmoor landscape, with occasional higher residuals (High Willhays, Whitehorse Hill) and incised valleys (Dart, Bovey) breaking the skyline.

The rejuvenation of the drainage continued spasmodically throughout the Tertiary period until interrupted by the rise of the sea to the 690ft level, isolating Dartmoor as an island. When the sea retreated again, the rivers extended across the emergent sea floor where they occupied new courses and cut discordantly across the rock structures. Some, eg the Tamar, Avon and Erme reoccupied their old valleys but the ancient course of the Dart, eastward past Ashburton to the mouth of the Teign was re-occupied only until, at a later stage, a river capture took place at Holne diverting the Dart into its present course (Fig 47).

This drainage pattern is essentially the same as that on today's maps and only small changes have taken place. Some east-west streams have eroded weaker banks in the rocks. River captures have led to an integration of the drainage pattern with good examples at Ashburton (755709) where the Ashburn has been diverted by the Dart, at Blackabrook Head (575777) where the Walkham has beheaded the Blackabrook and at Lydford where the Lyd has captured the River Burn. For an alternative viewpoint see British Association (1969) *Exeter and its Region*.

Weathering of the Granite

The moorland surfaces are dominated by massive rock outcrops or tors which frequently overlook wide shallow basins. They are believed to be produced by differential weathering and removal of the granite. These processes and the topographic trends of the land accurately follow the underlying structures, which are of three main types—first, fault zones which control the outline of Dartmoor, especially between Bovey Tracey (815786) and Chagford (707876); secondly, vertical joints which divide the granite into blocks spaced at 1- to 20-foot intervals; and thirdly, horizontal joints and curved joints which run parallel to the surface of the hillsides. These structures control the evolution of the granite landscapes by guiding the processes of weathering and erosion.

Three processes, chemical and physical weathering and changes produced by the circulation of the hot fluids from depth, have followed the structures to alter and attack the granite. These together produce a transportable regolith (or loose mantle of transportable soil and broken rock) by selective weathering of the rock. This debris is then removed by erosion to form valleys and basins and the unweathered areas remain as tors, hills and steep gorges.

The processes of breakdown and erosion are significantly influenced by the joints. Closely spaced joints allow thorough removal, whilst widely spaced joints define large blocks which resist weathering and are there-

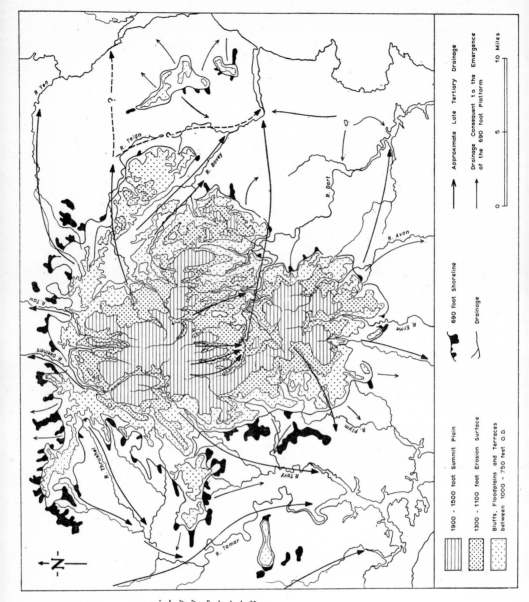

Fig 4. Geomorphology. A simplified geomorphology map based mainly on published accounts by D. Brunsden (1963, 1964), C. Kidson (1962), A. R. Orme (1964) and R. S. Waters (1962, 1964). Surfaces below 600ft not shown.

fore more difficult to erode. Where two or more closely spaced joint systems cross, hollows or river basins can be formed by intense weathering and erosion. Where resistant elements cross, the streams will only be able to form steep narrow valleys, and on the ridges tors will stand out above the surface. This landscape is the result of a delicate balance between breakdown and removal of the granite.

The effect of chemical weathering may be seen in most quarries on the Moor. Here the three main minerals of the granite, biotite, quartz, and felspar, are weathered under the action of weakly-acid ground waters. The weathering begins at the surface and decreases downward towards the water table as the weathering agents are used up. Biotite is oxidised and the felspars are broken down to form clay minerals which are slowly moved along the joint planes. The carbonates are washed away in solution. The quartz and some of the clay minerals remain to form the gravel deposit known as growan which can be seen in almost every gravel quarry on Dartmoor. The process is accompanied by colour changes from grey to pink, white or yellow as the 'pallid' zone is produced. In addition, the permeability of the granite is increased, the original structure of the rock is lost and the only solid granite remaining is in the form of rounded core-stones set in the weathered matrix. The final product is a sandy or silty soil layer that is rich in iron minerals.

These physical changes make it possible to identify several weathering zones. The upper layer is a disturbed soil zone of quartz fragments, felspar, silt-clay and organic debris. It is in this layer that the soils of Dartmoor are produced. Beneath is the residual product of weathering that has not been moved by denudational agents and is represented by the pale coloured decomposed rock. Here the granite is often incoherent, although the original structure is maintained and core-stones of fresh rock persist. The lowest layer consists of bedrock in the form of angular joint blocks. The joint edges may be rounded and some residual debris may be found along the joint faces. This limit of weathering often coincides with the water table, except where closely-spaced joints allow the rapid passage of water and weathering agents. The irregular boundary between weathered and unweathered rock may be called the weathering front or the basal surface of weathering.

The chemical changes should not be confused with the effects of physical weathering. Where erosion has removed rock from a hillside the removal of weight allows the underlying rock to expand, with a resulting fracturing of the joints in lines parallel to the ground surface. This process is called stress release jointing and has affected most outcrops. It has produced thick layers of granite which run parallel to the

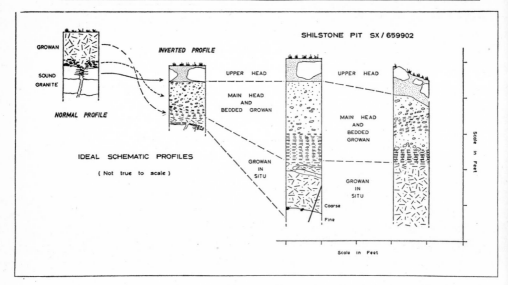

Fig 5.   Dartmoor weathering profiles. The idealised profile of granite weathering and
the inversion of the profile by solifluction processes with an exposure from north Dartmoor. Based on the work of R. S. Waters (1964, 1965).

surface, eg Slipper Stones (563889), and which control the shape of tors,
eg Bellever Tor (645765). Organic activity is of minor importance, but
the effect of frost action is not to be underestimated.

The landscape of Dartmoor shows unmistakable evidence of three
types of Pleistocene frost action. First, frost-shattered rock outcrops and
boulder-strewn slopes are present throughout the Moor. Secondly, frost-
produced soil layers occur on nearly every surface and in most river
valleys. Thirdly, small-scale benched landforms have been cut into steep
upland slopes by frost processes.

The coherent granite outcrops and altered rocks were readily destroyed
by differential frost action. The rock masses were fractured by the growth
of ice, especially in areas of close spaced jointing. Large blocks were
pushed aside by frost thrusting at East Mill Tor (599898) and Oak Tor
(613900). Elsewhere frost shattering has completely destroyed tors to produce extensive clitter or boulder slopes. The boulder fields below Staple
Tors (543760), Great Mis Tor (563770), Sheepstor (565683) and Hen
Tor (594694) represent rock masses which have been broken down and
even sorted into stripes by frost action. Subsurface shattering is visible
in most gravel pits where typically the rock is broken into small plates
(1–5in), which form part of the head deposits. Such frost penetration extends downwards 3–8ft beneath the surface.

Frost processes are always selective in their attack on rock masses, as each rock type gives rise to a different expression in the landscape. Coarse-grained granite resists frost action except where the joints are closely spaced. Fine-grained granite is usually removed to form rock shelters as at Hay Tor and Bench Tor (690719). The altered rocks on the granite margin are reduced to small fragments to form steep scree slopes as in the Dart gorge (710715) or form angular tors cut by steep rock faces, eg Cox Tor (531620).

The products of chemical and physical weathering were sorted out by frost and moved downhill to infill the valleys and form patterned ground and debris lobes. Most gravel pits, eg Shilstone (659902), Blackabrook (596752) and Lakemoor (657764), show evidence of a frost-disturbed layer called head, which overlies decomposed or solid granite. Sometimes two layers may be distinguished which may be representative of two cold phases. A coarse layer with angular blocks is typical of the upper head and this overlies finer disturbed materials and bedded deposits. At the bottom contortions and involutions in the deposit mark the limit between the disturbed and undisturbed materials.

On the edges of Dartmoor the slates and other altered rocks were selectively eroded to form benched hill slopes which are known as altiplanation surfaces. Examples may be seen at East Hill (597940), Sourton Tors

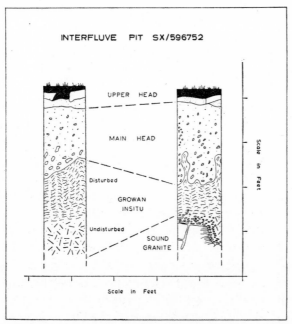

Fig 6.   Interfluve pit. An exposure of soliflucted material resting on decomposed granite or growan. After R. S. Waters (1964, 1965).

(543897), Lake Down (540810), Southerly Down (535878), Smeadon Down (522792), Peak Hill (555700), Brent Hill (700617), Black Hill (705786) and Cox Tor (531762). Here the hillsides are cut into steps produced by spring sapping and frost shattering of the exposed rock surfaces. Cold climate processes were so extensive that many of the features of the Dartmoor landscape must be regarded as relict features of Pleistocene time when Britain experienced a colder climate than today. Slopes were modified by removal of the weathered mantle. Valleys were infilled with debris and tors destroyed.

The processes of chemical and physical weathering have affected materials which at an earlier date may have been partially changed by mineralisation. These processes took place in precisely those areas most affected by chemical change. Because of this it is difficult to determine the origin of the altered material. However, where the changes decrease downwards towards solid rock the agents probably originate at the surface and chemical weathering is suspected. It should be recognised, however, that both processes may be seen in the same section, since any lines of weakness which exist in the granite are those which both agents would follow.

Origin of the Tors

An understanding of the processes of differential weathering and erosion is essential to an understanding of the Dartmoor landscape. This is particularly so when the origin of tors is discussed. Various theories have been put forward to explain tors, including an hypothesis relating to deep weathering and erosion, a suggestion that they may be of periglacial or cold climate origin and that they may even be man-made, relict sea-stacks or features produced by wind action. Of these suggestions those concerned with weathering and periglacial action have received most attention.

In 1955 Linton suggested that the production of a tor involved a first stage of sub-surface weathering and a second stage in which the debris is removed to reveal outcrops of unweathered rock. Core-stones which remained in the weathered matrix were let down to pile one on top of the other and form the upper separated boulders of the tor. Linton defines a tor as 'a residual mass of bedrock produced below the surface level by a phase of profound rock rotting effected by ground water and guided by joint systems, followed by a phase of mechanical stripping of the incoherent products of chemical action'.

In 1962 Palmer and Neilson attributed the formation of tors to

Page 35 (above) *Finds from Dartmoor and its vicinity now in Plymouth City Museum and Art Gallery:* (left) *Beaker period: left, long-necked beaker, lignite button and flint knife from Fernworthy; top right, bell beaker from Watern Down, 10 in high; bottom right, stone axe-hammer from Crockern Tor:* (right) *Bronze Age: top left, overhanging rim urn from Hurston Ridge, 18¾ in high; top right, drinking cup from the Dewerstone; bottom left, cooking pot from Raddick Hill; centre, bronze rapier from Fice's Well, Princetown; bottom right, part of a stone mould for casting a bronze palstave, from Burgh Island:* (below) *Stone row leading to the retaining circle of a burial mound on Down Tor*

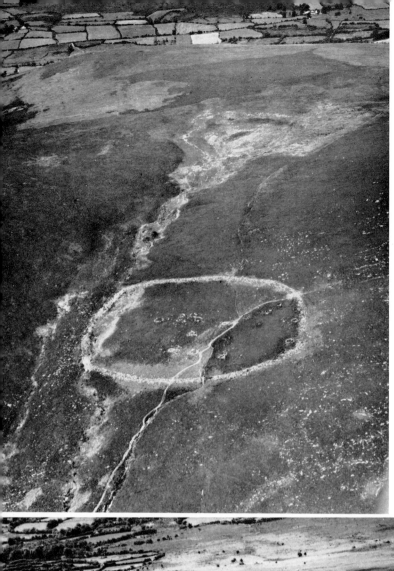

Page 36 (left) *Grimspound: aerial photograph of the famous Bronze Age enclosed settlement, looking east;* (below) *Foales Arrishes: a typical arable settlement with 'Celtic' field system of Late Bronze Age or Early Iron Age period*

mechanical weathering under periglacial conditions. They define a tor as an 'upward projection of granite left behind when the surrounding bedrock was broken up by frost action and removed by solifluction. Their shapes are controlled largely by joint spacing and orientation and have been slightly modified by post-glacial atmospheric weathering.'

Space does not allow a full discussion of these problems, which have been adequately covered in other publications, but some additional observations may be made. First of all, tors show a decrease in weathering towards the base, accompanied by an increase in angularity. These features are compatible with the theory of chemical weathering and are supported by the presence of sections of weathered granite close to tor formations. Secondly, there is considerable evidence of solifluction processes on Dartmoor which might easily have removed any weathered rock that once existed.

These agents may also be responsible for the second stage of Linton's hypothesis. Thirdly, frost action is clearly visible on many tors, but it must be pointed out that these processes, when operating, may have been involved in destroying tor formations which were produced by the two phase process of chemical weathering and erosion. It is obvious that elements of both hypotheses can be accepted.

Fourthly, attention must be drawn to two aspects of tor morphology that have not been adequately explained. Nearly every tor on Dartmoor possesses curved joints that run parallel to the surface of tor or hill. Similarly, many of the tors consist of more than one rock mass, arranged round an avenue which has clitter or boulder-strewn slopes leading from its entrances. It may reasonably be suggested that the centres of the tors have been removed to leave a characteristic 'empty middle', and that if the material in the clitter slopes were replaced in the centre, a dome-like structure could be produced. The curved joints would then be linked as continuous sheets of granite. Examples may be seen at Great Staple Tor (543760), Chat Tor (558852), and an undestroyed dome still exists at Blackingstone Rock (786856). It can be argued that the original form of tors was neither the pile of corestones of Linton's hypothesis nor the soil covered hill of Palmer and Neilson's, but a granite dome with curved joints running parallel to the hillside.

The Soils

The parent material for soil development is provided both by the weathering of bedrock and by the head layer which covers most of the slopes. There is a close relationship between soil and rock type, together

c

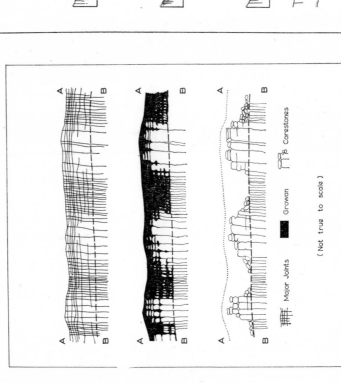

Fig 7.

(i) Granite landforms. The evolution of tors and granite landscapes based on the diagrams of D. L. Linton (1955).

(ii) Dartmoor tors. The evolution of the tors based on the drawings of J. Palmer and R. A. Neilson (1962).

with the influence of climate, slope, drainage and the biome. In addition
the soils have been influenced by man's activity, vegetation clearance and
land management. The evolution of the soil types can only be understood in this context. The most important sources of information are
A General View of the Agriculture of the County of Devon published
in 1809 by Charles Vancouver and the recent work of Clayden *et al* and
the Soil Survey of England and Wales.

The Dartmoor soils as reported by Vancouver were described as either
cultivated loam soils or uncultivated peaty earth which were developed
on the reddish-brown clay in the 'Granite gravel district'. This division
is essentially that followed by Clayden and Manley, who have mapped
brown earths and peaty soils on a parent material of granite, growan (or
decomposed granite) and head. The peaty soils are divided into blanket
bog with associated peaty-gley soils, valley bog and peaty ground water
gley soils and peaty gleyed podsols. Gley soils are defined as those which
develop under water-logged conditions.

The brown earths are found in the Moretonhampstead area and the
Webburn valleys. They are developed under both farmland and moorland pastures at altitudes of 1,100–750ft OD where there is an annual

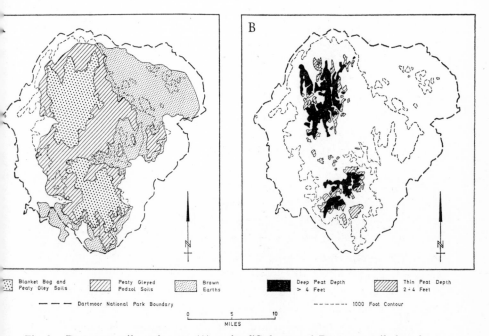

Fig 8. Dartmoor soils and peat. (A) a simplified map of Dartmoor soils based on
the published map of B. Clayden and D. J. R. Manley (1964); (B) the occurrence of
peat based on a survey by I. G. Simmons (1963).

average rainfall of 35 to 50 inches. The soil has a surface horizon of dark brown loam interspersed with bleached quartz grains. This is followed by a light brown layer which is transitional to a gritty friable loam and yellow brown gravelly head. These soils, although acid, are usually cultivated and are known as the Moretonhampstead Series.

The blanket bog and peaty gley soils are found on the northern and southern moorland where rainfall is in excess of 80 inches a year. Two divisions of peat, thick (greater than 4ft) and thin (2 to 4ft), may be recognised and peat only forms where slope angles are less than 15°. The most common altitudes are 1,800–1,500ft in the north and 1,550 to 1,200ft in the south. A few wet areas, eg Taw Head (610860), East Dart Head (681855) and Caters Beam (625690) are still accumulating peat, but elsewhere it is being eroded.

Where the peat is less than sixteen inches thick the soils are described as peaty gley soils. The peat contains abundant fibrous dead roots and the mineral horizon is an organic, grey loam which is followed by an olive-grey clay loam. Iron pans are usually absent.

The valley bogs and peaty groundwater gley soils are always formed where there is excess ground water, but they show thin peat development. They are known as the Laployd Series, and a typical profile shows thin black peat overlying grey clay loams. Yellow mottling and iron oxide staining can be found throughout the profile. On many streams this profile has been distributed by stream tinning.

Peaty-gleyed podsol soils are typically found on the hillslopes which descend from the high surfaces. These soils, known as the Hexworthy Series, are overlain by a few inches of peat which contains bleached sand grains. The bulk of the profile, which is usually quite thin, is a black loam which merges downward to a leached horizon and an iron pan. These soils are acid, and local waterlogging occurs where there is an iron pan.

The Dartmoor soils have formed under the influence of several factors. Relief and parent materials have remained fairly constant, but climate and vegetation have changed since glacial times. Soil types cannot always be related to present conditions. The influence of man since the Bronze Age is very important. His actions in clearing the vegetation may be responsible for changing the brown earths of Moretonhampstead into the present areas of peaty-gleyed podsols. Peat erosion may be caused by peat cutting, burning and grazing. To understand the soils a knowledge of the history of the vegetation and vegetation clearance is essential.

This activity can be partially reconstructed from archaeological remains and pollen analysis of the peat deposits. At the end of the last glacial period the climate improved to allow tree growth. Hazel, oak and elm became established, with Quercus robur as the Dartmoor forest cover and Quercus petraea on the surrounding sedimentary rocks. The ensuing periods of vegetation history are measured by numbered pollen zones and pollen zones V to VII B contain spores of bracken, grasses, compositae and light demanding trees, such as rowan. This evidence correlates with the Mesolithic cultural period and the beginning of deforestation.

Between 3300 and 2500 BC Neolithic settlements were established in clearings in the forest. The soils began to be leached, and this allowed blanket peat (zones VII A, VII B) to develop. By the beginning of the Bronze Age (2500–1500 BC) peat was accumulating on high ground and the temporary clearings had semi-permanent hut sites. Pollen evidence suggests that forest clearances, agriculture, pastoralism and peat growth continued during the Bronze Age. Recent evidence from Cholwich Town (586619), where an earlier Bronze Age stone row is buried by peat, shows that the oak forest was cleared and cereals introduced. The Hexworthy soil series probably originated by leaching of the cleared forest brown earths.

The middle to late Bronze Age (1500–450 BC) continued this process and pollen diagrams of zones VII B to VIII shows that pollen of Plantago lanceolata Pteridium and Compositae all increase.

Cooler summers and wetter winters renewed the growth of hill peat, and around 900 BC, when the Eriophorum moors were finally established, Sphagnum and Molinia appeared and the grazing capacity of the uplands was reduced. The Sphagnum moorlands increased in area following a change toward even wetter conditions at approximately 500 BC, when the first Iron Age settlers arrived in Britain. The Iron Age people settled around the moorland fringe and clearance of the vegetation must have continued in the vicinity of their camps. The Dartmoor landscape of this time included many field systems and farming settlements where seasonal grazing allowed continued leaching of the soils, prevented forest rejuvenation and increased the area of peaty-gleyed podsols.

Vegetation

The present Dartmoor landscape was now clearly evolving, and during Roman, Saxon and medieval times the forest clearance continued. Therefore, although the terms 'wild' and 'natural' are often applied to the vegetation of Dartmoor, few sites can be found where the communities have not been altered by human activity. Indeed it is more likely that the vegetation pattern is a direct result of anthropogenetic changes.

The moorland communities can be divided into wet and dry moor. The wet moors include purple moor grass, bog cotton grass (Eriophorum spp.), cross-leaved heath (Erica tetralix), ling (Calluna vulgaris) and bell heather (Erica cinerea). The dry moors are divided into grass, heather and whortleberry moors. True grass moor is uncommon. It includes western furze (Ulex gallii), bracken (Pteridium aquilinum), the grasses Nardus stricta, Agrostis setecea and Deschampsia flexuosa, heath bedstraw (Gallium saxatile) and wood sage (Teucrium scorodonia) are also common.

True grass moor always includes sweet vernal grass, sheep's fescue, fine bent grass and heath bent grass, while eyebright (Euphrasia officinalis) and lady's bedstraw (Gallium verum) appear where grazing is heavy.

The heather moors are dominated by Calluna vulgaris but are rarely perfect since they are affected by burning or swaling in order to stimulate new growth for pasturage. Where this is carried to excess, bracken colonises the burnt areas. The full community, which to the casual observer has a remarkably uniform appearance, contains some 250 species.

Whortleberry moors consist of an open community in which the dominant plants are Vaccinium myrtilus, with fine-leaved grasses on better drained sites. On the open moor whortleberry occurs as small patches among the heather.

The blanket bogs carry a restricted flora which is characterised by Eriophorum species, bog asphodel and tormentil, with sphagnum in wet areas and cross-leaved heath or heather in dry patches. Sedges (Larex panicea, Rhynchospora alba) are common.

The Eriophorum moors are surrounded on the steep slopes by the dry moors. These descend to the valley bogs where a lush cover of rushes is mixed with sphagnum, cross-leaved heath, sundews (Drosera rotundifolia), bog asphodel, pale butterwort, bog violet, cotton grasses and the ivy-leaved bellflower (Wahlenbergia hederacea).

The tors carry mosses and liverworts in their deep crevices and the exposed faces are colonised by lichens. Humus patches may have the black spleenwort (Asplenium adiantum-nigrum).

Unusual communities are found where the moorland streams cross the granite margin. These sites are heavily wooded and very rich in bryophytes. Golden saxifrage (Chrysosplenium oppositifolium) and sphagnum species are found in the boggy areas. Higher plants are represented by stone crop (Sedum anglicum), daffodil (Narcissus pseudo-narcissus), wild garlic (Allium ursinum) and flax-leaved St John's wort (Hypericum linarifolium). At Holne Chase (720715) fine stands of sessile oak (Quercus petraea) cover pale butterwort, flax-leaved St John's wort, wavy-leaved St John's wort (Hypericum undulatum) and skullcap (Scuttellaria minor). Yarner Wood (780790), a National Nature Reserve, where research is carried out in forest management, possess Quercus petraea and hazel.

In some of these sites the royal fern (Osmunda regalis) has been decimated by collectors and is now very rare. Protection of this species is now urgent.

Finally, attention must be drawn to the woodlands of exceptional interest. These are Wistman's Wood (613774), Black Tor Beare (565892) and Piles Copse (644620). These woodlands contain low stunted trees and abundant epiphytes which occupy a west-facing clitter slope habitat. The dominant tree is the pedunculate oak (Quercus robur) with occasional mountain ash (Sorbus aucuparia), holly (Ilex aquifolium) and Salix spp.

The trees are very distorted and average 10ft in height with occasional specimens reaching 25–27ft. Rich epiphyte floras hang from the branches and polypody ferns, wood rushes, whortleberry, mosses, lichens and liverworts all compete for light. These protected woodlands are among the most interesting vegetation relicts in Britain. It is sad that Wistmans Wood is beginning to be affected by too many visitors, due to its proximity to one of the main roads across Dartmoor, the Dartmoor National Park Information Caravan where leaflets may be obtained, and recent publicity. Perhaps a time is coming when the woodland will need to be fenced off.

Climate

The climate of Devon, although complex, may be described in general terms as oceanic. The western position, extensive coastline and the inland penetration of the estuaries, ensure a high annual precipitation and humidity, but its southerly latitude affords more than the national average of sunshine hours with diminished frost and snow.

On low ground the average annual rainfall is below 40in, but the western areas are wetter (45·5in at Okehampton) than the south-east (35in at Torquay). Dartmoor itself achieves a higher average of 60in, ranging from 82in at Princetown to 34in at Fernworthy. 100in a year are common, Princetown, for example, receiving a record of 115in in 1882. The average number of wet days in Devon is 161 with a maximum of 199 rain-days recorded in 1929. The corresponding figure for Princetown is 214 rain-days. The maximum monthly rainfall usually occurs in

January and the minimum in June. Thunderstorms are rare, but severe
and heavy rainfall followed by serious flooding may result (eg 5·4in in
twenty-four hours at Princetown). Catastrophic climatic conditions are,
however, rare and local. Famous floods took place on the Cowsic in 1890,
the Okement in 1917, the Yealm, Meavy and Teign in 1929 and the
Exe in 1964.

Temperatures are usually mild. The average daily maximum and minimum temperatures for Princetown are 5·6°C and 0·6°C in January and
17·2°C and 10·0°C in July. On the coast this range is reduced, but on
the Moor extremes from 30°C to −10°C have been recorded. The number of days with frost is high and some very severe cold spells have been
recorded with 30° of frost in Cullompton in 1940. Temperatures above
32·25°C are rare. The daily average of sunshine varies from three to four
hours on Dartmoor to 4·87 hours at Torquay. There is usually a high
number of 'summer days', (ie days on which the maximum temperature
rose to or above 25°C) due to the frequency of anticyclonic conditions
affecting the area.

Winds are generally strong with a prevailing direction of west to south-
west. Gale force winds frequently occur on the coast and on the higher
summits. Fog or low cloud is common on the Moor, but rarer on the
lower areas. The effect of altitude on rainfall, storms and temperature is
always evident. Snow is rare on the lowland, where it lies far less than
five days in the year. It is, however, common on the Moor, lying for an
average of 15–20 days over the open moorland and more than 30 days
on the summits. Falls can be very heavy and farms are frequently isolated. Heavy stock losses are recorded at these times. In the famous
storm of 1891 the Princetown train's engine was buried to its funnel for
several days.

Altitude also affects evaporation rate and transpiration. Increased
cloudiness, humidity and rainfall lead to an average summer surplus of
the water budget of 3in over Dartmoor but an average deficit of 3in in
the lowlands. If the need for irrigation and the heavy use of water by the
coastal resorts is considered in the light of these figures, the real need to
use the water catchments of Dartmoor for reservoirs becomes very
apparent. The basic climatic and hydrological data clearly support the
case for judicious planning of the water resources of Dartmoor.

Fauna

The map of Dartmoor in J. C. Bellamy's *Natural History of South
Devon*, 1839, shows the Moor as the domain of eagle, bustard, goshawk,

Table 3

PRINCETOWN (height 414 metres)

	Jan	Feb	Mar	Apr	May	Jun	Jul	Aug	Sept	Oct	Nov	Dec	Year
Average daily maximum °C	5·6	5·6	7·2	9·4	13·9	16·1	17·2	17·8	15·6	11·1	8·3	6·1	
Average daily minimum °C	0·6	0·6	1·1	2·8	6·1	8·3	10·0	10·6	8·9	5·6	3·3	1·7	
Absolute maximum °C	12·2	15·6	19·4	20·0	24·4	26·7	28·9	30·0	28·9	23·3	16·7	12·2	
Absolute minimum °C	−10·0	−10·0	− 8·9	− 5·6	− 1·1	2·8	4·4	2·8	0·6	− 2·2	− 6·1	− 8·9	
Number days with air frost	14·3	13·8	11·3	4·3	1·3	0·0	0·0	0·0	0·0	1·9	4·1	10·4	61·4
Number days with ground frost	15·0	14·0	13·0	7·0	2·0	0·0	0·0	0·0	0·0	5·0	8·0	18·0	82·0
Average No days with fog at 09ʰGMT	9·0	9·0	7·0	5·0	3·0	3·0	4·0	4·0	6·0	8·0	9·0	9·0	76·0
Average No rain days ≥0·01in	21·0	18·0	19·0	16·0	14·0	14·0	17·0	16·0	15·0	21·0	20·0	23·0	214·0
Average No days with snow/sleet	4·0	6·0	5·0	2·0	0·0	0·0	0·0	0·0	0·0	1·0	1·0	3·0	22·0
Average No days snow lying at 09ʰGMT	5·0	5·0	2·0	0·2	0·2	0·0	0·0	0·0	0·0	0·2	0·1	1·0	13·7
Average No days with thunder	0·3	0·1	0·4	0·5	0·8	0·5	1·0	0·9	0·9	0·6	0·7	0·6	7·3
Maximum rainfall in 24 hours inches	4·2	2·7	2·1	1·7	2·2	5·0	2·8	4·2	2·7	3·4	5·4	2·8	

Generalised climate data for Princetown. *Source:* British Association 1969, *Exeter and its Region.*

kite, raven and other 'exotic' species. At the other extreme Carrington, a
Dartmoor poet, has written :

> Nothing that has life
> Is visible;—no solitary flock
> At will wide ranging through the silent moor,
> Breaks the deep-felt monotony . . .

Reality regarding the avifauna lies somewhere between the two. Dartmoor is still dominated by large birds but the raven (Corvus corax) is the
only one of the species listed by Bellamy still present. The bustards, eagles
and goshawks have given way to rook (Corvus frugilegus), buzzard (Buteo
buteo), carrion crow (Corvus corone), kestrel (Falco tinnunculus) and the
occasional wandering bird of prey such as the merlin (Falco columbarius),
hobby (Falco subbuteo) and harrier (Circus sp).

The raven is, however, the undisputed master of the moorland scene.
For some obscure reason, perhaps due to thermal currents, Beardown
Tors have been chosen as its late afternoon meeting place in late spring,
when as many as twenty-five may be present.

The buzzard inhabits the wooded moorland fringe, though it may be
seen over the moorland. It usually prefers a tree nest site and, owing to
the scarcity of cliff nesting sites, the raven is also forced to nest in trees.

Rooks, carrion crows and kestrels also prefer tree sites but range far
in their feeding habits. In the lowlands carrion crows build their nests
high in trees, but there are very few high trees on Dartmoor and the crow
has to make the best use of low rowans, oaks, willows and hawthorns. The
carrion crow is generally solitary, but large parties of rooks are com-
monplace well into the central moors where they join with starlings
(Sturnus vulgaris) in following the roaming cattle.

The kestrel is also a frequent visitor to the open Moor, although it stands
a better chance of finding the small mammals and insects it preys on
near woodlands. Most other birds of prey are scarce visitors with the
exception of the tawny owl (Strix aluco) which is relatively numerous.
Montagu's harrier (Circus pygargus) was until 1958 a Dartmoor breeding bird, but the young plantations which it favoured gradually disappeared with continued growth of the forests. But any British bird of
prey is likely to appear on Dartmoor at least once a year.

If it is the large birds that catch the eye, it is the small ones that provide the majority of Dartmoor's species. Summer is the time when the
Moor is most frequented and this season is dominated by the skylark
(Alanda arvensis) and meadow pipit (Anthus pratensis). Both are conspicuous while singing in flight, but once on the ground they are elusive

and it takes hours of patience to track one to its nest. Unfortunately for the meadow pipit the cuckoo (Cuculus canorus) does not appear to have the same difficulty.

The abundance of these two species is demonstrated by a sample by Lack of 326 acres of Dartmoor, in which he found 94 meadow pipits and 78 skylarks.

Exotic species such as the thick-kneed plover have long disappeared but Dartmoor still possesses a few rare breeding species. The diminutive dunlin (Calidris alpina) and golden plover (Pluvialis apricaria) are two of these and number only a few pairs. Golden plover are common enough in winter, and in spring when the numbers are swollen by migrants returning north. But most years a few remain in the central Moors to breed. The dunlin is even more elusive in the breeding season and is rarely seen by chance. Summer visitors include the whinchat (Saxicola rubetra), redstart (Phoenicurus phoenicurus) and wheatear (Oenanthe oenanthe). The spotted fly-catcher (Muscicapa striata) is relatively common near human habitations and is one of the few species that can be found in the ancient oaks of Wistman's Wood.

These species are fairly widespread, but the ring ouzel (Turdus torquatus) is far more local, as it prefers old mine workings and areas of clitter in which to breed. It may, however, be seen anywhere after the breeding season when the young begin to disperse.

Dartmoor with all its heather moors might be expected to possess excellent game birds. However, partridge (Perdix perdix) and pheasant (Phasianus colchicus) are scarce and prefer the small areas of cultivated land. Red grouse (Lagopus scoticus) breed sparingly on the central moors, but black game (Lyrurus tetrix) are almost extinct, with only the occasional bird being seen.

Winter sees an influx of a different bird population, with numbers depending to a large extent on the weather. The local population is augmented by hard weather movements of fieldfares (Turdus pilaris), redwing (Turdus musicus), lapwing (Vanellus vanellus), golden plover (Pluvialis apricaria), snipe (Capella galinago) finches and pipits. In winter the reservoirs provide wildfowl with shelter.

It is difficult to estimate bird populations, and yet terms such as 'scarce', 'common', 'numerous', are unsatisfactory. It is for this reason that the study of birds of the Postbridge area by Dare and Hamilton is so valuable. In their area of 15 square miles (9,500 acres) they have recorded 75 breeding species and 41 non-breeding species. Of the 75 breeding species no fewer than 60 breed annually. They have also been able to make a few statements about the decline of some species. Three species—black grouse, common sandpiper (Tringa hypoleucos) and little owl (Athene noctua) no longer breed, and mallard (Anas platyryncha), red grouse, lapwing, common snipe (Capella galinago), curlew (numenius arquata), barn owl (Tyto alba) and cuckoo (Cuculus canorus) are widely reported to have decreased during the last twenty years. It seems that the first five species, which are ground nesters, may have been plagued by an increase in predators such as foxes, crows and magpies. The barn owl was reduced in the winter of 1947 but has recently begun to re-establish itself.

The changes which man has made to the natural environment by creating reservoirs and planting conifers have been especially beneficial to bird life. The coniferous plantations have provided habitats for many new breeding species including, near Postbridge, the sparrow hawk (Accipiter nisus), merlin, Montagu's harrier, chiffchaff (Phylloscopus collybita), siskin (Carduelis spinus) and redpoll (Carduelis flammea) in fir plantations, and three others—nightjar (Caprimulgus europaeus), coal tit (Parus ater) and goldcrest (Regulus regulus) which are virtually confined to coniferous plantations. Only the redstart (Phoenicurus phoenicurus) and starling show increases unrelated to conifers.

In a similar way the reservoirs have provided new areas for water fowl, Burrator and Fernworthy being the most important. These waters are more important in winter when the duck have dispersed from their breeding areas. Tufted duck (Anas fuligula), pochard (Aythya ferina), mallard (Anas platyryncha) and teal (Anas crecca), are common with goldeneye (Bucephala clangula), goosander (Mergus merganser) and canada goose (Branta canadensis) on some reservoirs. Also the occasional rarity appears in some winters, especially when the weather has been hard. The reservoirs also have their populations of gulls, and provide a base for occasional forages deep into the heart of the Moor. The same is true for herons (Ardea cinerea), Burrator being especially important. Herons are well known for their long feeding flights, and when young fish are plentiful can be seen high in the central moor.

The birds are usually conspicuous, but mammals are rarely prominent either on the open moorland or in the more sheltered wooded valleys; the region, however, is sufficiently wild and diverse in character to include most of the British mammals. Dartmoor is conspicuously lacking in deer, although at one stage this was far from the truth. A jury at a survey court for the Forest of Dartmoor did present 'that one Edward Ashe in the somer tyme of 1607 was (by his own confession) at the rowsing of a stagge and was at huntinge of the same dere with hands till he was killed about Blanchdon which was not lawful to be donne without licence'. The same jury also found that William Chastie 'kild a stagge with a pece or gun . . . about Blacktorebeare'.

A little later Samuel Rowe, quoting Mrs Bray, reported that 'towards the end of the eighteenth century red deer (Cervus elephas) were very plentiful on the moor, so much so that in consequence of the complaints of farmers, they were exterminated by the staghounds of the Duke of Bedford sent down from Woburn for the purpose. Tavistock was so glutted with venison that only the haunches of the animals killed were saved, the rest being given to the hounds.' The last indigenous deer was killed about 1780, but there was an eyewitness account of one at Fernworthy in August 1962.

Most of the mammals prefer the shelter of woodlands for feeding and breeding but foxes (Vulpes vulpes) are common on the open moor. Reliable estimates place their density at about three or four to the square mile. Rabbits (Oryctolagus cuniculus) are making a comeback in certain areas and even the otter (Lutra lutra) may be seen frequenting Dartmoor streams. The badger (Meles meles) more usually digs its sett in the woodlands, but it regularly patrols the open moors and occasionally a sett may be found far from woodland, such as those at Lur Tor, near Broadown and Bellever Tors. Stoats (Mustela erminea) and weasels (Mustela nivalis) are common among the clitter, and mice such as the long-tailed field mouse (Apodemus sylvaticus) may be active.

But generally speaking the smaller mammals, mice, voles, hedgehogs and rats prefer a woodland habitat, often choosing young conifer plantations. The three commonest species in these localities appear to be the bank vole (Clethrionomys glareolus) long-tailed field mouse and common shrew (Sorex araneus), but accurate figures are difficult to obtain. Less common are the short-tailed vole (Microtus hirtus), pygmy shrew (Sorex minutus) and water shrew (Neomys fodiens). The red squirrel occurs sparingly, and the grey squirrel is now beginning to colonise the fringe valleys, but this does not mean that the grey squirrel will eventually oust the red.

A parish-by-parish survey in Dorset showed that behind the general statement that greys were moving in and reds dying out lay detail that disagreed with a simple theory of competition for food or nest sites. The red squirrel died out before coming into contact with greys in some places. It now appears that a disease known as 'Squirrel 'flu' may have been responsible for the decline of the red squirrel. Thus there is little need for alarm at the thought of grey squirrels invading the fringe valleys.

Bats are a part of the mammalian fauna that are often overlooked. Old tin workings, deserted farmhouses, caves and quarries such as those at Buckfastleigh provide ample nesting places for greater (Rhinolophus ferrum-equinum) and lesser horseshoe bats (Rhinolophus hipposidorus), natterers (Myotis nattereri), long eared (Plecotus auritus) and pipistrella bats (Pipistrellus pipistrellus).

Dartmoor has lost the pine martin (Martes martes) and polecat (Mustela putorius), but gained the North America mink. Ever since the rearing on farms was established in 1929 mink have escaped, but there were no records of their breeding until 1957 when young mink were seen on the Teign. Since then they have spread to other parts of the country as well as penetrating well into Dartmoor. They are bolder than most mammals and family parties can be seen swimming in the rivers or leats. They have multiplied to such an extent that the first organised mink hunts have just been started.

The characteristic reptiles of Dartmoor are the common lizard (Lacerta vivipara) and adder (Vipera berus), with slow worm (Anguis fragilis) and grass-snake (Natrix natrix) less common and usually confined to woodland and dense bracken-covered hillsides. Lizards may be seen anywhere among the heather and whortleberries, but adders are more localised, preferring sunny, boulder-strewn hillsides.

In addition to these reptiles there are three common species of amphibia. The common frog (Rana temporaria) is frequently seen near pools, and in a good year the surrounding moor may be covered with hundreds of their young. These pools are also the home of the palmated newt (Triturus helveticus), which is the newt of highland Britain. The third species is the common toad (Bufo bufo) which is also conspicuous at ponds during the breeding season.

Any treatment of the insect fauna over such a wide area as the Dartmoor National Park must of necessity be selective and consequently only the common species are mentioned. Insect species tend to be more restrictive in their choice of habitats, and for the sake of simplicity Dartmoor will be divided into moors and tors, woodlands, rivers and pools.

The insect fauna of the open moors shows the least variety of species. Probably the commonest Lepidoptera is the fox moth, the young larvae of which are conspicuous with their ringed pattern of dark brown and orange. The emperor moth is less conspicuous, as its larvae normally live deep in the heather fronds. The oak eggar moth is another species whose larvae include heather in their diet, but it is not as common as the fox or emperor moth.

The commonest butterflies are the meadow brown, gatekeeper and small heath, whose larvae are all grass-eating. Small copper and common blue are more local and the grayling prefers drier hillsides. As with birds, butterflies now travel long distances over the open moor from the woodlands they normally inhabit. Silver-washed, high brown, and pearl-bordered fritillaries can all be seen on occasion. The peacock and small tortoiseshell prefer cultivated stretches, but, like the migrant red admiral and painted lady, are notorious wanderers and late in summer may be seen in great numbers on the blossoming heather.

Many species are less prominent on the moors than they are in the surrounding lowlands. The Hymenoptera—ants, bees and wasps are of this type. Bumble bees, are common, and hive bees are numerous during the heather season. Several species of ant occur on the drier parts and the wood ant may extend its foraging lines well out into the heather. Beetles are plentiful but inconspicuous and generally come alive only at night. The commonest seen are bumble dors and the rose-spotted green common tiger beetle.

The valley woods with their mixture of oaks, ash, beech, alder and scrub such as holly, hazel, blackthorn and hawthorn support a rich insect life. The prevalence of leaf litter and rotting branches provides a large variation of habitat. The wood ant is ubiquitous in these localities and its nests are frequently found beside paths. In their industrious efforts to find food and nest materials their foraging lines thoroughly impregnate the area.

Many insects dwell under leaf litter and below logs and stones and are easily discovered. Springtails, mites, millipedes, centipedes, spiders, wood-lice, earthworms and beetles are all present. The generally acid soils are not to the liking of snails, but slugs are common.

The leaves and twigs of the trees and shrubs house a different insect life. Panorpid flies and hover flies are frequent in the glades and paths, together with nocturnal moths and glade-hunting butterflies like the hair-streaks the fritillaries and the speckled wood. Less conspicuous are the lace-wing flies, plant bugs, long horn grasshoppers and snake and alder flies.

The rivers and ponds provide two contrasting habitats for water-loving insects. The former are usually clear and swift flowing while the latter provide stretches of stagnant, weed-covered water.

There has been very little published work on the ecology of Dartmoor streams; this is a little surprising in view of the importance of these streams for salmon and trout. The salmon (Salmo salar) and sea trout only spend part of their life cycle in the Dartmoor streams, but the brown trout (Salma trutta), grayling (Thymallus thymallus), minnow (Phoxinus phoxinus), common eel (Anguilla anguilla) and three-spined stickleback (Gasterosteus aculeatus) spend most of their lives on Dartmoor and rely on the river fauna for their diet.

The fauna of the rivers generally include species of the following insect orders: Plecoptera, Ephemeroptera, Megaloptera, Trichoptera, Odonata, Diptera, and Coleoptera. Compared with lowland streams this is an impoverished fauna and reflects the acidity of the water and its low organic content. The fauna is to a large extent cryptic in its habits. Some species live on the surface of boulders or even creep or swim over the bottom, but the majority are sedentary in crevices, on the interstices of stones or buried in vegetation, gravel or mud. It has been shown that before these insects are available to the fish they have to be detached from their niches. Thus in this instance the speed of the river is important.

It is the swiftness of the water that makes the streams totally different from the stretches of stagnant water. Standing water may be found for a variety of reasons: flooded mine workings, bomb impact craters, disused leats, or even some sections of rivers when the flow of water is very low. In these sections water skaters are common, Velia cumens and Hydrometra stagnorum being usually seen. When the innumerable imagines are emerging from their various aquatic larval forms, a small part of the ecology of these habitats may be discerned. These imagines are preyed upon by dragonflies, by many of the bird species that inhabit the banks; such as wagtails, flycatchers, and if they happen to drop on the water, fish rise from below! Other insect species likely to be encountered in these waters are Haliplid beetles, back-swimmers and great water beetles.

Thus the landscape of Dartmoor is shown to be the result of an interaction of a complex series of factors operating over a long period of time. Although the dominant elements of the physical landscape are due to natural processes, the flora, fauna and soils owe much to the influence of man. The characteristic beauty which is admired today by the summer tourist is in many cases a man-made phenomenon and it is to be expected that in the future man will continue to develop and change the scene. Now that the area has been designated as a National Park certain elements will be preserved, but today the physical environment is being increasingly affected by tourism, industry, agriculture, forestry and water undertakings. These activities are sometimes regarded as intrusions on the Dartmoor scene, but there have been aesthetic benefits where the plantations and reservoirs have considerably enriched the fauna of the region. Perhaps the important point is to make certain that present-day changes are managed in such a way that the physical environment is not dominated by man's actions, but to stop all change would be an arrogant attitude, implying that only that which man did in the past is good or interesting, and all that is of the future is inevitably bad.

Notes to this chapter are on pages 283–286.

Page 53 (above) *The hamlet of Michelcombe, Holne, from the air. The layout of the fields indicates the presence of former strip cultivation;* (below) *isolated farmsteads at East Combe, Chagford. With its near neighbour West Combe this settlement lies in a sheltered side valley running down to the South Teign*

Page 54 (above) *A deserted medieval village; houses at Houndtor before excavation;* (below) *medieval cultivation terraces and lynchets on Challacombe Down, Manaton*

2

Early Men

James Barber

> The earliest records respecting the history of Dartmoor must be sought
> on the moor itself, and that with no small diligence and labour.

THE VISIBLE remains on Dartmoor of human occupation in prehistoric
times—the burial mounds, ceremonial stone rows and circles, house
foundations, cattle pounds and arable field boundaries—are now acknowledged to form one of the richest concentrations of such monuments in
the British Isles. The significance of Dartmoor in this respect, together
with its special interest for natural historians and its great scenic beauty,
makes it an area of unique national importance, whose conservation
seems to many a matter of vital concern.

Realisation of the Moor's exceptional wealth of archaeological interest
dawned relatively recently. In this connection one can certainly discount
the activities of the medieval treasure-seekers who, from the reign of
Edward II[2] if not even earlier, rifled numerous barrows and cairns in
what must have been, one imagines, usually a fruitless quest for gold
artifacts. The ancient monuments of Dartmoor were overlooked by the
earliest English antiquaries, John Leland, William Camden, and William
Stukeley, who in the sixteenth, seventeenth and eighteenth centuries
located and recorded so many prehistoric remains elsewhere in the
country. They were also ignored by the first historian-topographers of
Devon itself, John Hooker, Tristram Risdon, Thomas Westcote and Sir
William Pole, whose works were written between about 1599 and 1635
and who could trace the history of Dartmoor no further back than the
early Middle Ages. They thought of it as a remote and inhospitable
tract of country, supporting a sparse and uncouth population of tin
streamers and peat cutters, and farmers making a precarious living in
adverse circumstances. According to Hooker '. . . this one thinge is to
be observed that all the yere through out commonly it rayneth or it is
fowle wether in that more or desert'.[3]

The early cartographers of Devon were equally oblivious of Dartmoor's
antiquities. As late as 1765, when Benjamin Donn issued his *Map of
the County of Devon*, and 1789, when Gough published an edition of

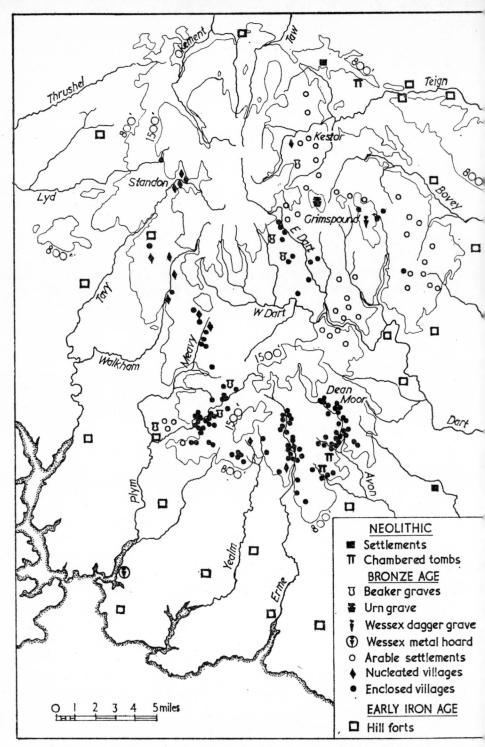

Fig 9. Distribution map of prehistoric settlements and notable grave groups on and near Dartmoor. The map is based on figures 20, 22 and 23 in *Exeter and its Region*, published by the University of Exeter for the British Association, 1969, from the chapter 'Prehistoric and Roman Settlement' by Lady Fox. Reproduced by permission of the University.

Camden's *Britannia* including a map of Devon closely based on Donn's, Dartmoor is shown completely devoid of archaeological features. Just beyond the north-eastern boundary of the Moor, however, the legend 'A Druid Cromlech' indicates on each map the position of Spinsters' Rock, the denuded Neolithic tomb chamber at Shilstone, Drewsteignton, frequently referred to in subsequent literature,[4] and Wooston Castle and Hembury Castle, two of the Early Iron Age hill forts which encircle the Moor, are also shown. Even in 1809, when the Ordnance Survey published the first edition of its one-inch map of Devon, no ancient monuments are shown on Dartmoor itself, although the Drewsteignton 'cromlech' is marked and several more of the neighbouring hill forts such as Cranbrook Castle and Prestonbury Castle.

Not until the last years of the eighteenth century and the beginning of the nineteenth, when Dartmoor was opened up by the construction of the Tavistock–Moretonhampstead turnpike and when ambitious schemes of moorland enclosure were begun in the Prince Hall–Tor Royal area, did educated observers begin to penetrate Dartmoor. For the first time its prehistoric settlement and ritual monuments were noticed and ascribed (as was inevitable in the prevailing climate of archaeological opinion) to the Druids. So were certain natural features like rock basins, logan stones and Wistman's Wood.[5] This formative phase of Dartmoor archaeological studies was devoted to the location by fieldwork and to the preliminary classification of the more prominent monuments, actual excavation being rarely undertaken. As early as 1790, however, a correspondent informed the Rev Richard Polwhele that 'a gentleman hath lately opened some of the barrows on Dartmoor, and found urns either filled with ashes, or with the bones of a human body; together with ancient coins and instruments of war.'[6] In 1832, the Rev E. A. Bray excavated a kistvaen on Beardown, discovering a small fragment of coarse earthenware.[7] These early finds cannot now be traced and interpreted.

The first reference in a history of Devon to a prehistoric site on Dartmoor proper appeared in 1797, when Polwhele described Grimspound, among the most accessible and best preserved of the Bronze Age settlement sites, and speculated wildly about the purpose for which it had been built.[8] Grimspound was again mentioned, more soberly, by Lysons in 1822,[9] and the first and very accurate survey of the settlement was drawn and published by Mr A. C. Shillibeer in 1829. A landmark in the development of Dartmoor studies was the publication in 1830, in the first volume of the *Transactions of the Plymouth Institution*, of Samuel Rowe's paper 'Antiquarian Investigations in the Forest of Dartmoor,

Devon', a record of fieldwork carried out during 1827 and 1828 by
Rowe, John Prideaux, Henry Woollcombe and Major Hamilton Smith.
The different types of ancient monuments then recognised are described
and discussed, and all the known sites are listed in topographical, not
typological, order. Illustration is confined to a picturesque but somewhat inaccurate plan and reconstruction drawing of the complex of ceremonial and habitation remains at Merrivale.[10] Rowe published a revised
and expanded version of his paper in book form in 1846,[11] and a further
edition of this work, revised and enlarged by J. Brooking Rowe in 1896,
ranks as the definitive statement of knowledge about prehistoric Dartmoor on the eve of a new phase of exploration and discovery by archaeological excavation.

An intensive programme of excavation, involving both settlement and
ceremonial sites, was carried out between 1893 and 1906 under the aegis
of the Devonshire Association. Its Dartmoor Exploration Committee
tackled the ancient habitations. 'The hut circles . . . of Dartmoor had not
been submitted to examination with pick or shovel till . . . 1893, when
Mr R. Burnard and the Rev S. Baring Gould . . . felt that the time was
come when an end must be put to haphazard conjecture, and positive
results should be sought and, if possible, obtained, in the only way by
which the purport of these rings could be established, and their approximate date determined'.[12] The Association's Barrow Committee, formed
in 1879 to investigate the barrows of Devonshire except Dartmoor, extended its brief in 1882 to include Dartmoor as well, and embarked
upon a series of vigorous campaigns of barrow digging.

The excavations did not entirely realise the aim of ending specula-
tion and replacing it with factual knowledge. By present-day standards
the work was done over-quickly and with insufficient record. Yet pottery
and other objects were amassed which to this day form the basis of our
understanding of the Bronze Age and Early Iron Age communities on the
Moor. In the same way the material extracted from the burial mounds
of Wiltshire at the beginning of the nineteenth century by Sir Richard
Colt Hoare and William Cunnington remains the fundamental archive
of the Early Bronze Age Wessex Culture. The results of the Committees'
researches were published year by year in the Devonshire Association's
Transactions, additional material being printed independently by Robert
Burnard,[13] and the excavated finds deposited in the Municipal Museum
at Plymouth.[14] The Dartmoor Exploration Committee remained in being
as late at 1950 but, after the initial impetus at the turn of the century,
little excavation was attempted, and none after 1933. The Barrow Committee continued to add by fieldwork to the known distribution pattern

of funerary sites on the Moor, but with it, too, the conduct of major excavations ceased.

The information about prehistoric Dartmoor derived from both field-work and excavation was summarised first in 1906, in the first volume of the *Victoria County History of Devonshire*,[15] and subsequently by J. W. Brailsford in 1938.[16] The 1950s were marked by particularly significant advances in Dartmoor prehistoric studies, fresh excavations being undertaken and new interpretations based upon the earlier discoveries. In 1952 Dr C. A. Ralegh Radford[17] surveyed the whole picture from the standpoint of a wide and fully up-to-date familiarity with general British prehistory, and published the first comprehensive set of drawn and photographic illustrations of the pottery from the Dartmoor settlement sites. A further landmark was the publication in 1953 in book form of the papers contributed to the Devonshire Association Transactions between 1930 and 1950 by Mr R. Hansford Worth.[18] The continuing value of this exhaustive body of information about the monuments raised by early men on Dartmoor can be judged by the recent demand for its re-issue.[19] Dramatic new light, moreover, was shed on the prehistoric period by Lady Fox as a result of her excavations—the first to be conducted on the Moor in the modern scientific manner—at Kes Tor and Dean Moor.[20]

The present emphasis in Dartmoor studies lies partly in continued field-work; new settlement and ritual sites are still being located on foot and from the air, and are being systematically given the same protection as the more familiar monuments, namely scheduling by the Ministry of Public Building and Works. Reinterpretation of the accumulated evidence is also proceeding; Arthur ApSimon, for example, in a study of the pottery found in the mid-nineteenth century in the Ash Hole Cave, Brixham, has reviewed the Dartmoor wares and placed them in their chronological and cultural context in the prehistory of south-west England.[21] Environmental studies, too, thanks to the pioneering work of Dr I. G. Simmons,[22] are beginning to make an important contribution to our understanding of prehistoric life on the Moor, by defining the successive stages of its vegetational history and by illustrating the effects of man's increasing impact upon his natural surroundings.

A great deal of the current fieldwork on Dartmoor, and almost all the excavation, is being devoted to the Anglo-Saxon, medieval and later phases of its occupation, but there is no doubt that the lines of future research, by excavation and in the laboratory, into the problems that still remain about the prehistoric period are steadily becoming clearer, and that the time is ripe for a fresh impetus in this sphere.

How is one to account for Dartmoor's abundance of prehistoric remains? As an upland area of light soils from which the original forest cover could readily be cleared, it offered just the sort of terrain attractive to the earlier prehistoric settlers, whose techniques of agriculture were rudimentary. The scarcity of trees suitable for building timbers, combined with a natural profusion of granite boulders of assorted shapes and sizes, resulted in structures, made elsewhere in wood, being built here in imperishable stone.[23] Above all, as a result of climatic deterioration the Moor largely escaped intensive agricultural and industrial development, until the modern period. The tide of human settlement on Dartmoor receded on the onset of colder, wetter conditions during the Iron Age in the last centuries BC, and the Moor was left a largely untenanted wilderness, with the foundations of the buildings of its earliest inhabitants weathering down into the landscape.

In the nineteenth century some prehistoric monuments were cleared away in the making of newtake fields, their stones being incorporated into the new boundary walls. Sheer vandalism, too, is not such a purely contemporary phenomenon as might be supposed.[24] Only in our own time, however, is the whole character of Dartmoor and the survival of many of its antiquities threatened by massive encroachments for military training, china clay extraction, reservoir formation, afforestation and intensive hill farming, in spite of the designation of the area as a National Park, and in spite of the protection by scheduling of countless individual monuments.

Hunters and Food Gatherers

During the great Ice Age of the Quaternary geological epoch, from about 600000 to about 15000 BC, when the climate of Europe fluctuated over millenia between arctic and tropical conditions, and when animals like the mammoth, woolly rhinoceros, elephant, lion, hippopotamus and hyena roamed in turn over a Devon connected for much of the time with the Continent, Palaeolithic or Old Stone Age men congregated in limestone caves and rock shelters at Stonehouse, Cattedown, Oreston, Yealmpton, and Torbay, but left virtually no trace of their presence on Dartmoor. A single flint hand-axe found by Mr Worth in 1931 at Brent Moor, on the watershed between the Avon and the Erme near Western Whitaburrow,[25] if indeed it was dropped there in ancient times, is alone in suggesting occasional forays of hunting parties on to the Moor. The hand-axe is of Acheulian type, similar to examples found in Kent's Cavern, Torquay.[26] Since Dartmoor was never engulfed in the British ice sheet, intermittent use of it as a hunting area can fairly be postulated.

The first unequivocal evidence for human life on Dartmoor dates to the latter part of the ensuing Mesolithic period, which ran from about 15000 to about 3500 BC. The evidence consists of quantities of worked flints, collected on the surface without excavation at a number of spring-side sites such as Postbridge, Gidleigh Common and, most notably, East Week[27] on the north-east foothills of the Moor, where artifacts of Mesolithic character form a significant proportion of the 30,000 flints picked up after ploughing. The Moor, indeed, is as prolific in surface finds of prehistoric flint implements and waste chippings as it is in the more conspicuous monuments of stone and earthwork. Flint is not of natural occurrence on Dartmoor, and every scrap of it found there must have been brought in by human agency, usually in ancient times.

These scatters of Mesolithic flints indicate the presence of temporary camping sites of people still entirely dependent upon hunting, fishing and the gathering of edible fruits and roots for their livelihood. Future excavations where the flints occur may reveal the shallow scoops in the ground, once provided with flimsy superstructures of branches and turves, which served these men as dwellings. Recent research by Dr Simmons into the vegetational history of Dartmoor, on the basis of a series of pollen analyses, suggests that the Mesolithic hunters found a forest environment rich in game, and that, by lighting fires to break clearings among the trees or to help drive animals during the chase, they began the long process of forest clearance which was to lead, before the end of the prehistoric period, to the establishment of the treeless moorland landscape with which we were familiar before the conifer plantations.

The Dartmoor sites of this period have numerous counterparts elsewhere in Devon and Cornwall, at coastal sites like Westward Ho!, at Dozmare Pool on Bodmin Moor, and on the heights of Maker and Staddon on either flank of Plymouth Sound.

The First Farmers

From around 3500 BC Neolithic or New Stone Age settlers familiar with the basic principles of cereal cultivation and stock breeding, bringing with them certain novel crafts like the making of pottery and weaving, were colonising the British Isles after crossing from the Low Countries in the north to Spain and Portugal in the south. Late in the Mesolithic period, possibly about 5000 BC, the flooding of the North Sea and the cutting of the English Channel had finally detached Britain from Europe.

Immigrant Neolithic settlements have been detected widely in the south-west, at Carn Brea in Cornwall for example, and in Devon at Haldon and Hazard Hill, where undefended village sites have been located, and at Hembury, where traces of a Neolithic fortified enclosure were found buried beneath more massive Iron Age ramparts thrown up some three millenia later.

Numerous examples of Neolithic flintworking, and particularly specimens of the characteristic beautifully-flaked, leaf-shaped arrowheads, have been found on Dartmoor, many of them in the northern sector where monumental remains are infrequent. The flints may denote the existence of hunting camps analagous to those of the previous period, for agriculture did not immediately and altogether oust hunting from its place in the economy, but they could also attest the seasonal movement of herdsmen with their cattle from winter quarters to summer pastures.

In the present state of our knowledge, not one of the Dartmoor settlement sites with visible monumental remains is demonstrably of Neolithic date. The Dartmoor Exploration Committee excavators at the end of the nineteenth century initially attributed the dwellings they examined to the New Stone Age, on the ground that no objects of metal were found within them. It is now realised that this is fortuitous, resulting from the predominantly acid soil conditions of the Moor. Dr Ralegh Radford suggested in his 1952 paper[28] that some of the pottery found in the settlement at Legis Tor could be of Neolithic tradition though of Bronze Age date, but subsequent examination of the sherds has shown that they are straight-sided, flat-bottomed vessels of Bronze Age type, not round-bottomed ones of Neolithic character. The hypothesis advanced by Professor Piggott in 1954[29] that certain settlements, for example Trowlesworthy Warren, might be of Neolithic date remains to be tested by excavation.

That forest clearance on Dartmoor continued during the Neolithic period is certain; it is evidenced by pollen grains carefully collected from sections through peat deposits, identified under the microscope, and then counted. The proportions of different species of trees and grasses at different periods can thus be ascertained, and deductions made about changing climatic conditions and the extent of man's activities nearby. The possibility that Neolithic settlements may one day be identified on the Moor derives some support from the fact that two chambered long barrows of probable early Neolithic date are known at Coringdon Ball and Cuckoo Ball. It is to be hoped that excavation will reveal the original plans of these now much-ruined burial chambers, together, perhaps, with some fragments of datable pottery or other grave goods. Just beyond the north-eastern boundary of the Moor, as mentioned previously, stands the 'Spinster's Rock', Drewsteignton, the completely denuded chamber of a similar tomb, re-erected in its present form after collapsing last century.[30]

The Neolithic surface finds include examples of axe-heads made of several different types of igneous rock. During the Neolithic period a regular prospecting and trading system grew up; suitable outcrops of igneous rock were located in south-west England, Wales, and north-west England, and the axes were distributed to settlements in the south and east. A reflex trade brought westward axe-heads made of flint quarried at Beer Head in East Devon or mined in the more extensive chalk lands of Wessex.

Late in the Neolithic period, during the second half of the third millenium BC, a different cultural complex can be detected in Britain, with artifacts of types which suggest that their makers were Mesolithic people adopting and adapting the way of life and material possessions of the Neolithic immigrants. Characteristic late Neolithic flint arrowheads and other implements are indeed found among the surface gleanings from Dartmoor, at East Week for example, but none of the distinctive pottery in use among these communities has yet been brought to light on the Moor, or indeed in Devon or Cornwall, nor have any settlement structures been located.

There can be no doubt that the Neolithic era witnessed a significant improvement in material culture on Dartmoor and generally in the south-west, and probably also some increase in population, but it should be borne in mind that already by 3000 BC fully literate, metal-using urban civilisations were arising in Mesopotamia and Egypt, and that written history, in the form of king lists and annals of significant events, was being compiled there.

Early Metal Users

The monumental record of Dartmoor begins in earnest with the Bronze Age, from shortly before 2000 to around 500 BC. At the end of the third millenium BC, knowledge of the identification and working of copper was introduced by itinerant craftsmen and prospectors from the Continent, and before long sources of tin were located, so that implements and weapons could be made of bronze—copper alloyed with some 10 per cent of tin. It has long been believed that a key part in the introduction of primitive metallurgy into the British Isles was played by people distinguished archaeologically by a particular type of pottery vessel or beaker which was frequently interred in their graves. Actual metal objects, however, are rarely found in Beaker Folk graves.

Though direct evidence of tin-streaming on Dartmoor at any period in the Bronze Age is at present lacking, it may be significant that Beaker influence was evidently strong on the Moor. The surface finds include many examples of the finely pressure-flaked barbed-and-tanged arrowheads introduced by the Beaker Folk, and several specimens of their massive shaft-hole axe-hammers or battle-axes.

Several characteristic Beaker burials, moreover, have been discovered in Dartmoor barrows fortunately undisturbed by earlier pillagers. At Watern Down a fine bell-shaped beaker was found in a kistvaen, though the flexed skeleton had as usual decayed away, owing to the same acid soil conditions which are so harmful to metal objects buried or discarded on the Moor. Another kistvaen, at Fernworthy, contained a beaker of the later, long-necked type, accompanied by a lignite cloak button, the greatly decayed remnant of a copper knife with a wooden hilt, and a flint knife. A perforated stone wrist-guard, worn on a leather strap to protect an archer's wrist from the recoil of his bow-string, came from a kistvaen on Lakehead Hill, this time without an accompanying beaker, while at Redlake some scraps of a once fine beaker decorated with the impressions of a comb-like stamp were all that survived of a burial which had previously been ransacked. Other robbed barrows on the Moor, their contents long since dispersed without record, can fairly be attributed to the same people.

More problematical, on the scanty evidence available, is the ascription to the Beaker Folk of many of the ceremonial monuments on Dartmoor, the stone rows and the stone circles. The rows are frequently aligned towards and terminate at burial mounds, and often occur in groups of sacred structures including other barrows and large, non-funerary stone circles. In some cases, for example Fernworthy, conclusive proof of Beaker involvement has come from one of the barrows in the complex, though never from one directly related to a stone row. It was unfortunate that when the Cholwich Town stone alignment was excavated from end to end, prior to its obliteration under waste products of the china clay industry, no dating evidence was encountered, while the barrow at its extremity was found, as all too often, to have been rifled. Of great interest, however, was the discovery through pollen analysis that the alignment had been erected in a woodland clearing where cereal cultivation had previously taken place.[31]

A further pointer to an Early Bronze Age dating for the Dartmoor rows and circles is provided by analogy with related ceremonial complexes elsewhere in the country where excavations have been more productive—notably Avebury in Wiltshire and the groups of monuments, surprisingly similar to the Dartmoor ones, at the opposite extremity of Britain, in Caithness and Sutherland.[32] Related alignments associated with barrows of Beaker date, but constructed in timber, have been revealed by excavation both in eastern England and in the Netherlands. The relationship often postulated between the Dartmoor alignments and those like Carnac in Brittany can, it appears, be discounted. The Breton monuments differ significantly in layout, and presumably in purpose, from their British counterparts.

The stone rows can fairly be interpreted as processional ways, many of them with funerary significance. Some, however, do not appear to be associated with burials, and a few exceptional examples are built across country for considerable distances, up to two-and-a-half miles. These must be related to the earthwork monuments known as cursuses which are found in southern and eastern England and appear to be of late Neolithic date and of ceremonial or social function, possibly even race tracks! The longest known cursus, in Dorset, extends for the astonishing distance of six miles.

Some of the stone circles on Dartmoor are simply the retaining circles of barrows or cairns, erected to keep the material of the mound in place, but those with considerable diameters of up to 110ft, occasionally, like the Grey Wethers, occurring in pairs, can only be temples. Nowadays it is impossible to accept any connection between them and the Druids— the priesthood of the Celtic tribes of Britain in the centuries immediately before the Roman Conquest—but otherwise, for all the progress in archaeological techniques and interpretations and in spite of attempted astronomical solutions, one can add little to the comments of Mrs Bray in 1836. 'Where extensive stone circles are found near what may be called . . . cursus or via sacra . . . or near cromlechs . . . we may fairly conclude such to have been erected not as . . . habitations . . . but as temples sacred to those Gods whose worship would have been considered as profaned within any covered place, and whose only appropriate canopy was held to be the Heavens in which they made their dwelling.'[33]

It may seem strange to ascribe to the Beaker Folk, at the very beginning of the Bronze Age, the bulk of the ritual monuments on Dartmoor when none of the settlement sites, not even those like Merrivale situated in the immediate vicinity of ceremonial complexes, are demonstrably of the same culture and antiquity. Yet evidence elsewhere in Britain and on the Continent, where the Beaker Folk wandered extensively from Spain to Czechoslovakia, indicates that they were a people constantly on the move, practising pastoral not settled agriculture, and settlement sites attributed to them are rare. Beaker sherds were, however, found in hut circles at Muirkirk in Ayrshire early in this century,[34] and this may be a pointer to discoveries still to be made on Dartmoor. Some sherds from the 1905 excavations at Watern Oke, a village settlement of some eighty houses on the Tavy, belong, indeed, to vessels similar to beakers in size and shape, but are decorated in the plaited cord technique more appropriate to a later phase of the Bronze Age in the middle of the second millenium BC.

Traders and Prospectors

A developed form of Early Bronze Age culture, known to archaeologists as the Wessex Culture, flourished in Wiltshire and adjacent counties between about 1700 and 1300 BC. The presence in the south-west and on Dartmoor of representatives of this rich and powerful ruling caste is attested by a series of barrow burials with characteristically exotic grave goods. From barrows grouped in cemeteries at Farway and Upton in East Devon came cups of Dorset shale and Baltic amber and blue faience beads of East Mediterranean origin, and a necklace found in a grave at North Molton was made up of beads of shale, amber, and faience.

This was the heyday of the Mycenaean Kingdom in distant Greece, and its prospectors penetrated deep into the west Mediterranean region in search of tin, copper, and gold. Indirect stimulus from this quarter must have had much to do with the genesis of the Wessex Culture and of a closely-similar culture established at the same time in Brittany, though there was also influence from the flourishing bronze industry of Central Europe. It is probably no accident that the gold cup found in a barrow at Rillaton in east Cornwall was worked in a corrugated technique similar to the gold and silver vessels found in the royal shaft graves at Mycenae itself. One classic Wessex Culture burial has been excavated on Dartmoor, in a cairn on Hameldon Hill, overlooking Grimspound. The grave goods included a poorly-preserved bronze dagger of characteristic ogival outline; its wooden hilt had perished but the pommel survived, fashioned of amber and decorated with hundreds of tiny gold pins hammered into it in a simple geometric pattern. This ornamental technique can be matched on other contemporary dagger handles of different shapes found in Wiltshire and in Brittany, but the actual form of the Hameldon pommel is more reminiscent of Central European examples cast in bronze. This was one of the finest specimens of Early Bronze Age craftsmanship ever found in Britain, and its loss through

enemy action in 1941, with most of the rest of the archaeological collections of the Plymouth Athenaeum, was a disaster of much more than local
significance.

Settlement sites of the Wessex Culture are unknown, even in its homeland, so it is not surprising that none has been recognised on Dartmoor.
But barbed-and-tanged arrowheads of Wessex type, larger and more
regularly shaped than those associated with beakers, have been found
on the surface of the Moor; one was picked up in recent years within
Grimspound itself, where the Dartmoor Exploration Committee's first
excavation in 1893 failed to produce any datable objects.

Some at least of the large ceremonial stone circles on the Moor may
have been used or even erected at this time; certainly in Wessex itself this
was the period when Stonehenge was remodelled as we know it today.
The Wessex Culture devoted the profits from its far-flung commerce to
the worship of its gods and the commemoration of its dead, not to
elaborating the habitations of the living.

A number of hoards of bronze weapons and implements, each representing the stock-in-trade of an itinerant bronzesmith active late in the
Wessex Culture period, probably in the fourteenth century BC, have been
discovered in southern England, one of them near Oreston in 1868. The
siting of this hoard on the estuary of the Plym, a natural highway from
the sea to the Moor at a time when transport by water was the general
rule, since thick forest occupied most low-lying ground and all river
valleys, must surely be significant. The hoard comprised sixteen flanged
axeheads with typical crescent-shaped cutting edges, three dagger blades,
a tanged spearhead and a chisel.[35]

Stockbreeders and Husbandmen

During the Early Bronze Age the basic indigenous population, partly
of Neolithic, partly of even older Mesolithic ancestry, seems to have gone
its own way largely unaffected by the comings and goings of the alien
Beaker Folk and by the activities of the Wessex Culture chieftains and
merchants—a small if influential élite whose rich material possessions
attract perhaps a disproportionate amount of attention in the archaeological record. In the British Isles as a whole the native population is
attested most clearly by exceedingly numerous cremation burials, either
accompanied by or contained in large pottery vessels or urns of several
different types, some of which have a restricted regional distribution. The
most common type, found throughout Britain, is the overhanging rim or
collared urn; on the other hand, ribbon-handled urns are confined almost

exclusively to Cornwall. All the urn varieties began in the Early Bronze Age, and can be shown to persist through the Middle Bronze Age until at least 1000 BC, but individual burials are difficult to date with accuracy because grave goods were only very rarely buried with the urns.

Although many of the Dartmoor barrows and cairns are likely to have been raised over enurned cremations, few of the large, ill-fired, easily broken vessels have survived. A characteristic collared urn, however, was found in shattered fragments within a ruined cairn on Hurston Ridge, Chagford, in 1900. It had been inverted over a small heap of cremated bones laid on a granite slab, which covered a pit dug into the subsoil to contain the sifted ashes from the funeral pyre. Not until 1962 were the sherds reassembled and consolidated, enabling the height of 18¾in and the rim diameter of 16in to be ascertained. No objects of bronze or bone had been placed with the cremation, but the style of the vessel and the elaboration of its decoration, carried out by pressing a twisted thong into the surface before firing, suggest burial in the fifteenth or fourteenth century BC. At much the same time, about 1350 BC, but in a country at an unbelievably different level of civilisation, Tutankhamen was being laid in his splendid tomb.

The chronology of the Dartmoor settlement sites has been notoriously difficult to determine. Metal objects have never been found in them because of the acidity of the soil, though whetstones occur frequently, and no instance has been recorded of a stratified site with one layer of occupation clearly later than another. Dating has thus had to depend almost entirely upon pottery typology—a far from straightforward criterion. The soil conditions which have destroyed bronze and iron on the Moor have also seriously weakened the poorly-fired domestic pottery made and used by its Bronze Age inhabitants, and it has been possible to reconstruct only a few vessels completely. Only in the last decade has the sequence of the wares found in the hut circles been fully understood, by reference to the finds from two settlements in Cornwall; Trevisker, St Eval; and Gwithian, Hayle. The latter has proved particularly informative, being at last a stratified site, with three separate layers of occupation. None the less, it is to be hoped that in future the dating based on successive pottery styles will be checked and supplemented by radio-active carbon (C14) determinations from specially gathered charcoal samples. The early excavation reports, with their frequent mention of charcoal-filled cooking holes and hearths, give grounds for hope that similar deposits remain to be found; their recovery and scientific examination are matters of urgency.

Meanwhile, however, the pottery evidence suggests that the Dartmoor settlements are the domestic counterparts of the funerary mounds raised over enurned cremations, starting in the Early Bronze Age but persisting throughout the Middle Bronze Age and on into the Late period beyond 1000 BC. The earliest wares so far recognised are characterised by plaited cord-impressed decoration related to that found on many collared urns and on their Cornish ribbon-handled counterparts. The vessels are usually barrel-shaped, with internally bevelled rims. Later wares have simpler decoration, effected either by single-strand cord impressions or by incision. Later still the vessels, now usually straight-sided and often flat-rimmed, are decorated exclusively by sharp incisions or shallow toolings, often combined with massive cordons and lug handles. The Dartmoor domestic wares used to appear very much as a class on their own; now they can be seen to belong to a much larger south-western scene, embracing funerary as well as domestic pottery, which presumably had racial, social and political as well as merely ceramic significance. Similar wares are known, not only from the North Cornish sites already mentioned, but also from coastal sites in South Devon, among them Kent's Cavern, Torquay, the Ash Hole Cave, Brixham, and also probably Mount Batten, Plymstock.[36] Related finds have also been made in west Somerset and Dorset. Beyond, in Wessex and the south-east, quite different ceramic traditions prevailed.

The Dartmoor Bronze Age settlements are divisible into three types which, judging by the sherds found in association with them, appear to be broadly contemporary. Each type, however, has a different distribution pattern, which suggests that each represents a different response to the natural environment and had a different economic basis. It is regrettable that knowledge of prehistoric agriculture on the Moor will always be handicapped by the fact that the acid soils which rot pottery and eliminate metal also destroy bone, both human and animal, unless it has been burnt. We can never know exactly which species of animals were herded, nor in what relative proportions they were kept, nor whether the hunting of wild game for food played a significant part in the economy. We can only make certain broad inferences from the settlement types themselves and from their characteristic locations.

As yet, too, no carbonised grain has been found on Dartmoor, though the practice of grain-drying, attested there during the Middle Ages, may well have been necessary in the Bronze Age in spite of the generally more favourable climatic conditions which then prevailed. Nor, so far, have grain impressions been recognised and identified, as elsewhere, on pottery surfaces from the Dartmoor settlements, though such discoveries may well be made in the future. Nor is it known what cereals were grown on Dart-

moor in prehistoric times and in what proportions, though pollen analyses
derived from soil samples collected near settlement sites may in time provide convincing information.

On the southern and western slopes of the Moor, the warmer and
wetter region then as now, two types of village settlement are found.
They are believed to represent two variant pastoral economies, based
on stock-breeding with but little attention paid to the growing of cereals.
One type consists of the familiar and conspicuous pound, a non-defensive
enclosure intended to protect stock from wolves and other marauding
animals, the houses of the inhabitants being either scattered within it or
clustered around its margin. The other type is the nucleated village—a
group or a long string of dwellings with no encircling wall but with short
lengths of walling linking certain houses, forming small enclosed areas
which could be used either as individual rather than communal cattle
pounds or as little garden plots where some cereal could be grown to
allow variation in diet. The main accent in the economy was again
stock-breeding. In each type of settlement the individual dwellings are
usually small, about twelve to fifteen feet in diameter, and consist of a
dwarf stone wall with a single entrance, often protected by a windbreak,
the rafters resting on the wall and meeting in wigwam fashion over a
central hearth.

A third main settlement type occurs chiefly on the drier, more sheltered
eastern and south-eastern slopes of the Moor, and appears to represent
a way of life based chiefly on arable farming. The houses are found in
small groups or hamlets, associated with small square fields of 'Celtic'
type, once believed to be exclusively of Early Iron Age date but now
known to have originated during the Middle Bronze Age at the latest.
Drove roads are provided between the fields in many settlements, indicating that some flocks and herds were kept and that the economy was
mixed. The dwellings themselves are usually large, up to thirty or thirty-
five feet in diameter, and the rafters, in view of the larger span, were
supported by a ring of posts, with or without a central pillar to secure the
apex of the roof. In one case, on Shaugh Moor, excavation has revealed
evidence for a timber windbreak outside the entrance;[37] elsewhere
standard stone-built ones are present. The distribution of this settlement
type complements almost exclusively that of the pastoral villages, a fact
which suggests contemporaneity of occupation as well as difference in
economy. The only area where the distribution patterns overlap significantly is in the Plym valley, where there is a patch of 'Moretonhampstead' soil of the kind favoured by the arable farmers on the eastern flank
of the Moor.[38]

Page 71 *Two pictures taken in the early 1900s show a block of granite being taken from a hedge near Yeo Farm, Chagford, to Moretonhampstead railway station; such blocks were widely used for building and memorial purposes*

Page 72 (above) *Lee Moor clay workings;* (below) *peat drying and stacking on Dartmoor in the early 1950s*

By the Late Bronze Age the evidence of pollen analysis and soil study suggests that several centuries of intensive pastoral and arable husbandry had largely eliminated the original forest cover of Dartmoor, woodland being confined to the lowest slopes and the valley bottoms, and perhaps to a few small areas of high ground between the settlements and the blanket bog which was forming over the high peaks as the climate steadily worsened.

Finds of bronze articles are unknown in the settlements, and only a few chance specimens have come to light elsewhere on the Moor. A rapier of Middle Bronze Age type was found at Fice's Well, Princetown, and a Late Bronze Age spearshaft ferrule at Gawler Bottom. A particularly interesting discovery was made in 1965, when a bronze palstave of Central European manufacture was found in a prehistoric field on Horridge Common, Ilsington. The palstave, a form of axehead, was discovered on the surface after a track had been bulldozed through a field system, with drove roads and three dwellings, of the sort just described above. Although the palstave is not closely datable, it was probably imported from the Continent between about 1300 and 1100 BC.[39]

Other Middle and Late Bronze Age bronzes have been found on the fringes of the Moor, a palstave of normal south-western type, for example, at Drewsteignton, and a group of Late Bronze Age barbed spearheads and spearshaft ferrules at Bloody Pool, South Brent. Examples of the stone moulds used in casting bronze artefacts have also been found near by : half of the mica schist mould for a Middle Bronze Age palstave of south-western type was picked up at Burgh Island, Bigbury-on-Sea, and a hoard of four pairs of moulds, also made of mica schist, for casting rapiers and bracelets of Middle Bronze Age character, was found last century at Hennock in the Teign valley. Bronze implements, scrap metal, and founder's ingots of the eighth and seventh centuries BC have been discovered at Mount Batten at the mouth of the Plym, close to where the Wessex Culture Oreston hoard was found.

Iron Age Communities

Not until Lady Fox's excavations at Kes Tor in 1951 and 1952 was it possible to demonstrate conclusively that one of the arable settlements on the Moor, complete with 'Celtic' fields, drove roads and large houses, was occupied in the Early Iron Age. Part of a large shouldered pot of Late Bronze Age or Early Iron Age type had indeed been found by the Dartmoor Exploration Committee in one of the dwellings of a similar

E

settlement at Foale's Arrishes, but at Kes Tor the evidence for iron working was irrefutable, with the iron smelter's combined house and workshop separated in its own pound from the rest of the community, perhaps to ensure that the industrial mysteries could be performed away from prying eyes. In the absence of Carbon 14 determinations, it can only be said that the settlement at Kes Tor is likely to have flourished during the fifth century BC.[40]

Epilogue

At this point the record of prehistoric Dartmoor comes, for the present, to an abrupt halt. There is no trace on the Moor proper of settlements with pottery of the types introduced later in the Iron Age, after 300 BC, with curvilinear decoration, best known for its occurrence at the lake villages of Glastonbury and Meare in Somerset, but also widely scattered, though with regional variations of ware and decorative motifs, throughout the south-west, including both Devon and Cornwall. Is one to assume that depopulation of the Moor accounts for this phenomenon; or prolonged survival there of residual Bronze Age or earliest Iron Age folk, unaffected by changes in material culture all around them; or is it simply a case of sheer chance in the sites so far subjected to archaeological scrutiny?

In the present state of knowledge the weight of the evidence favours depopulation as a consequence of climatic deterioration. The concept of Highland Zone retardation no longer seems valid in the later prehistoric periods in this country, when new cultures and technological innovations, whether native or imported, appear to have spread as rapidly into highland fastnesses as they did across the lowlands.

The presence on the margins of Dartmoor of Iron Age hill-forts, one of which, Cranbrook Castle, was briefly explored by the Dartmoor Exploration Committee and produced potsherds decorated in the Glastonbury style, might seem to imply that newcomers around the Moor were hemming in an older community surviving on the higher slopes. It is, however, just as likely that the hill-forts represent the need for defence in inter-tribal conflict among the later Iron Age peoples themselves. The chance finding of a single prehistoric gold stater on Bellever Tor is in itself totally inadequate evidence for occupation of the Moor during the period of the first centuries BC and AD to which the coin belongs.

Certainly, as Polwhele recognised as early as 1797,[41] there is no hint of occupation on Dartmoor in Roman times—only, again, the odd coin dropped by some chance wayfarer. If Roman pottery and glass reached

the native Iron Age communities in the north of Scotland and the Ork-
neys, it is surely inconceivable that it would fail to appear among the
material possessions of native communities on Dartmoor, had any existed
there, especially since flourishing Romano-British settlements are known
to have existed near by, at Stoke Gabriel, for example, and Mount
Batten, where continuous occupation is attested throughout the Iron
Age and Roman periods, from about 400 BC to about AD 400.

There is, then, no evidence at present for settled habitation on Dartmoor between about 400 BC and the period of the first Anglo-Saxon
settlements about AD 700.

Notes to this chapter are on pages 286–288.

3

Saxon and Early Medieval Times

John Somers Cocks

The Coming of the Saxons

So FAR AS present knowledge extends, Dartmoor apparently remained an uninhabited region for several hundred years until the Saxons under Cenwealh pushed their way westwards into Devon in the middle of the seventh century and began to settle the land. Small groups of Britons may have remained here and there around the moorland edge, but no actual evidence has yet been found for it.

The chronology of the invasion of the south-western counties is a difficult question. A recent reappraisal, though not universally accepted, seems a much more plausible interpretation of events than any previously put forward, and places the battle of Peonnan in 658 as being fought just east of Exeter and that of Posentesbyrig in 661 at Posbury, a commanding hill-fort a little north-east of Dartmoor. Centwine's encounter at an unnamed place in 682 must have been further west still; it resulted in the British being pushed to the Atlantic coast of north-east Cornwall with all Devon north of Dartmoor falling into Saxon hands. Some such sequence must have been followed to fit in with the known date of 670 for the foundation of a monastery in Exeter.

Once Exeter had been secured, the way was clear for the invaders to sweep around the south of Dartmoor, coming not only by land but also along the coast by boat, penetrating up the creeks and estuaries of the southward-flowing rivers. No battles from this phase have been recorded before the year 710 when Ine and Nunna defeated Geraint of Dumnonia, probably somewhere near the Tamar, and completed the conquest of Devon.

So far as Dartmoor rather than Devon is concerned, one can learn very little about the pattern of settlement from a study of the distribution of the commonest place-name elements. Except for some rivers and streams, names of Celtic origin are almost totally lacking, indicating the completeness of the Saxon settlement. It is also possible to see that a group favouring the ending -cott for their settlements (very commonly met with in north Devon) swung southward to colonise the north-eastern side of the

Moor as far south as about Manaton. Throughout Dartmoor, names ending in worthy are frequently encountered, but the early -ingtun ending, indicating a group settlement under a local leader, is almost unknown. Ilsington, which was probably founded by one Ilfstan on the very eastern edge, is an exception.

There is no evidence that these earliest settlers made their homes on the open moorland above about the 1,000ft contour line, and the lower lands and deep valleys were heavily wooded or ill-drained and quite beyond the primitive means of clearance at first available. It was the middle heights from about 500 to 1,000ft that would have attracted them, particularly when it is remembered that they may well have come on to land previously cultivated in some form.

From about the latter quarter of the seventh century, then, the colonising of the moorland edges went on, gradually increasing in momentum. The land originally appears to have been granted in large blocks or estates, with smaller estates being later carved from them. As early as 739 a charter included the Drewsteignton region in a vast area given to Crediton minster, and had other charters survived from this period the pattern would no doubt be seen to be repeated. Others from the tenth and eleventh centuries (sometimes perhaps copies of earlier ones) make it clear that even at that stage huge grants were being made. One such is known as Peadingtun's land boundary; though dated about 1050, it is likely to be a copy of a grant made about a century earlier to the bishopric of Crediton. The bounds quoted make it clear that the land ran right up into Dartmoor and included the modern parishes of Ashburton, Buckland, Widecombe and most of Manaton and Ilsington, apart from lowland parishes. Another relates to the western half of the parish of Meavy in 1031, which must itself have once formed part of an even larger estate.

On the smaller scale, what would the pioneer settlers have found on their arrival in the area? There were large tracts of forest or brushwood extending well up the valleys on the Moor itself, but open moorland there would have been in plenty, which could have been used as grazing without any clearance at all. Water would normally have presented no problem, so that choice of sites was not too limited. Moreover, there is considerable circumstantial evidence that they were not coming to virgin territory.

The possibility of the continuity of farming from Celtic to Saxon times is a vexed question, for despite emigration to Brittany Dumnonian remnants could have remained even on the Moor's edge. Centuries of subsequent farming have not always completely obliterated traces of prehistoric barrows which must have been erected not far from settlements and fields, while field names such as Borough, Roundy Park and Stone Barrow are highly suggestive of what lay in them when the Saxons first enclosed them. Celtic or British river names such as Teign, Dart, Avon, Meavy and Tavy could have been passed on by the Celtic inhabitants living near their courses well off Dartmoor, but the Wallabrooks, derived from the word *weala*, by which the Saxons described their predecessors, meaning 'Welsh' or 'foreigners', and the pre-Saxon word Glaze for a river flowing into the Avon on the Moor, indicate some Celtic activity in those areas.

Above all there is the evidence of place-names which speak unmistakably of previous cultivation, an attraction to the new settlers not only because they would have been spared the laborious task of clearing, but because the qualities of a successful site—drainage, soil, shelter and so on—appeal equally to farmers of any period, and here there was evidence of farming having been carried on for perhaps several centuries with success. All round Dartmoor are names such as Yolland or its variants, the 'old land' which the Saxons saw had been cultivated before, even if depopulation had allowed much of it to revert. Chagford with Yelland and Yellam, and probably Yelfords too, South Brent's Yalland, and Yeoland on the south-western side are only a few examples. Whether or not there was actual continuity of occupation, the influence of earlier farming was clearly felt by the new invaders and sometimes even dictated the lay-out of their fields.

Types of Settlement

Here and there throughout the borders of Dartmoor are villages such as one can find almost anywhere in England, some straggling along a road, some concentrated in a nucleus of houses around a green, with a church and a few shops. These, however, are comparatively rare compared with the very large number of single farmsteads or at most groups of two or three scattered over the whole region. As the great majority of these villages and farms were in being by the time of the Norman conquest they represent original forms of settlement dictated by the conditions under which they were founded over a thousand years ago.

The village type was the norm in the lowland zone of England and was adopted in preference to any other by the Saxons wherever possible. On Dartmoor the conditions were such that it was seldom practical for groups to settle together, and so villages such as South Zeal and Chagford are unusual; many parishes have no such examples. While the former is typical of a settlement built along a street, Chagford is entirely different. It has been suggested, partly because so many of these so-called nucleated villages built, like Chagford, around a square were or had been royal property in 1066, that they had been founded as the result of a deliberate policy in the early days when the countryside around them was not always peaceful, so that their inhabitants could protect their stock from marauders and even enjoy a measure of self-defence themselves. There is nothing inherently improbable in such an idea, which was little different from that employed by the builders of the Bronze Age pounds or the later Iron Age hill-forts. Although later building has often partly obscured the original form, it can still often be recognised.

Most of the single or small-group farmsteads, though not necessarily all, were probably founded a little later when individuals or small groups began to tackle the less immediately rewarding land which the first settlers had not attempted. It is impossible to tell if a group of farms lying together represents an original plan or a later family expansion, but as population increased and capital in the form of goods and equipment became more readily available, more single farms were created in some clearing (the names ending in -leigh are evidence of that), the woodland was cut down and the stones were rolled off the land to form fields with the massive hedgebanks and walls which are still such a feature of the area today. There was nothing planned about such settlements; they were slowly formed out of moor and brake and wood, and one lonely, isolated farm would be haphazardly connected to another by a lane whose tortuous course still reflects the long-vanished obstacles that once lay on its path. Anyone who drives in the lanes around Gidleigh and Throwleigh will be fully conscious of the Saxon legacy to the landscape.

By the eleventh century pressure on the land had increased to the point where colonisation of the higher moorland above 1,000ft had begun. Altitude, climate, and a poorer soil must always have put such sites at a disadvantage compared with farms at lower levels, and after a period of occupation they were largely abandoned and indeed remained entirely overlooked until very recently.

Over one hundred abandoned sites are now known, and though very few have so far been scientifically excavated those results have shed a good deal of light on their nature. It has been discovered that beneath the ruined stone-walled houses which first attracted attention are the postholes of earlier wattle and turf huts, built and then rebuilt on almost identical sites on several occasions. The best known example is the Houndtor medieval village where up to ten rebuildings have been noted.

It is remarkable that the Saxon tradition of building in wood was strong enough to overcome the obvious advantages of using stone, which they could have seen was not only readily to hand but also was the material used by the earlier inhabitants; in fact it was not until about 1200 that stone was employed—an innovation which, internal dating apart, can be deduced from Stiniel in Chagford parish being first mentioned in about 1225 as Stenenhalle, the stone hall or house, a description which could only have been used if it were sufficiently unusual to have been worthy of local comment. Thus the succession of wattle and turf houses must have ended about then, and by allowing some twenty years for the life of each—an estimate which remains to be proved—a date of about 1000 is arrived at for the original colonisation.

It is uncertain how far these tenth-century settlements typify the original lower ones whose present farmsteads represent merely the latest of several rebuildings, but three centuries of economic and social development from about 700 and the different climatic conditions of the higher moorland must have had their effect, even if it is difficult to visualise anything more primitive than the huts of the first dwellers at Houndtor.

There seem to be three different types of settlement on the Moor itself. There are the villages of several buildings, the eleven at Houndtor, thirteen at Blackaton and twelve at Challacombe for example (not necessarily all dwelling houses), closely grouped together forming the nucleated type. Then there is an intermediate development exemplified by the numerous abandoned houses and barns in Okehampton Park (there are about thirty-five), some in small groups scattered over a mile of country but obviously interrelated. Lastly there are the isolated farms, singly or in twos or threes with a few ancillary buildings around them. It is well to remember, however, that these numbers refer to the later stone structures and that eventual excavation may show that this final phase of development had somewhat different origins. The settlement at Lydford had a unique history and requires special mention.

In the late ninth century King Alfred constructed a number of *burghs* or fortified positions strategically placed to counter the Danish invasions within his kingdom of Wessex, and a tenth-century list of these (known as the Burghal Hidage) mentions that Lydford was one such town. It was built in a position of great natural defensive strength on a promontory formed by the junction of the deep gorge of the river Lyd on one side and a smaller but steep-sided valley on the other. It is possible that even earlier it was used as a Saxon frontier post to watch for Britons marauding from across the Cornish border—certainly a battle was fought with them at Galford only a few miles away—though no supporting archaeological evidence has so far been forthcoming. It has also been suggested that the dedication of Lydford church to St Petrock (which incidentally it shares with Harford) may be due to there having been an even earlier Celtic settlement, slight confirmation of which has come in the recent discovery of a sherd of early Christian, perhaps fifth-century, date which had later been incorporated into the town's bank defences.

Apart from natural features, the defences consisted of a broad bank of carefully laid layers of turves and branches, later cut back and faced with granite, encircling the town at the edge of the steep valley slopes on two sides and running across the neck of the promontory on the third. At this last point, the weakest in the defences, ditches were cut outside the bank as a further precaution. Excavations have made it clear that the bank was constructed in sections of perhaps twenty feet with different materials used in adjacent lengths, a striking confirmation of the Burghal Hidage document which says that four men were needed for the maintenance and defence of each $5\frac{1}{2}$yd of wall.

Inside the enclosed twenty acres the streets were laid out on a grid pattern, modified by the shape of the site, easily recognisable today. The main entry from the east is still that used by the modern road, and at this point the town bank is very obvious on either side, a survival of a thousand years. Between the streets or lanes the burgage tenements were themselves laid out systematically, the houses seemingly similar to those discovered elsewhere in the district.

Though small, as one of the four Devon *burghs* it was an important centre and even minted its own coins in the tenth and eleventh centuries. This early importance led to its choice as the administrative centre for Dartmoor for several centuries afterwards. The only recorded occasion when its defences were put to the test was in the year 997, when the Danes on one of their periodic seaborne invasions of Devon pillaged and burnt the Benedictine Tavistock Abbey, founded only twenty-three years earlier, and then pushed northwards to attack Lydford. Here they were apparently repulsed and withdrew to their ships.

Field Systems

At Lydford, as at other nucleated villages and some hamlets, the Saxon open-field system existed where each farmer had his land scattered around the common fields in blocks of strips, so that no man had better land than his neighbour and agricultural operations had to be carried out by the mutual agreement of all concerned. With so much grazing available on Dartmoor itself, it is unlikely that the fields were used on the normal Midland system with one of three lying fallow for pasture; there would hardly have been need for more than two always in intensive cultivation, with other parts of the neighbouring rough grazing sometimes being ploughed up for a few years as occasion demanded.

Later on, mostly by the thirteenth or fourteenth century, it was seen that the system was less efficient than where farms were held in severalty, that is to say with each farmer having his own fields; so the strips (by then enlarged by a process of consolidation of adjacent blocks) were enclosed, thus 'fossilising' the system. The land was parcelled out between the farmers concerned in as fair a way as could be devised, so that any single individual's fields were found throughout the area and the access tracks to each tended to follow the previous tracks round the old headlands. This process is well exemplified by the fields just to the north-east of Lydford, where they still tend to be elongated in blocks and where the access track proceeds through them by a series of right-angle bends.

Many other examples have been obliterated by later removal of hedges, but here and there, as around Michelcombe in Holne and Dunstone in Widecombe, the pattern still remains. Chagford has what is for the Dartmoor region and possibly for all Devon a unique survival. A group of fields lying a short distance outside the town are still thrown open for the grazing of certain commoners' stock for three months from the beginning of August, an echo of the 'Lammas lands' where the stubble of the harvested fields was grazed over to augment the common pasture before being ploughed up again.

Although in lowland England the open-field was the normal Saxon system of agriculture, there were large numbers of isolated settlements of single farms where from the very beginning the land was farmed by one family only and where there was never any open-field. This was the more general pattern in the west; each field was enclosed piecemeal from the surrounding woodland or waste until the outermost met with the boundary of an expanding adjacent farm, so that the pattern of isolated dwellings scattered throughout a parish and still so evident around most of Dartmoor's borders has remained largely unaltered from the earliest days of colonisation.

On much of what is today open moorland, apart from the highest and wettest regions, traces of agriculture and fields abound. These Dartmoor field-systems are only now beginning to receive the study they deserve, and much more will have to be investigated before they are perfectly understood and dates are assigned to all of them. Obviously some will be found to have been formed in one century and modified and re-worked perhaps centuries later. However, certain conclusions can be drawn. For example, around many of the abandoned medieval farm-steads a system of fields radiates which must be contemporary with the occupation of the houses from which they were farmed. The fields tend to be an irregular oblong in shape, usually with no sign of having been divided into blocks of strips, even where they surround a small village as at Houndtor. But it must be remembered that we see today what existed at the time of their abandonment in about 1300—occasionally modified in later years perhaps—which may, like the houses themselves, have begun life somewhat differently.

In fact there is some evidence that, in parts, cultivation began with ploughing contourwise along the slope, so probably forming the strips that one would expect. The shape of many fields in use today in the Widecombe valley and elsewhere suggests such an origin, though they have been considerably altered in subsequent ages. Not far from Hound-tor village, on Halshanger Common, and elsewhere, there are traces of terraces as well as the more normal-shaped abandoned fields. Exactly what the relationship is between these two different types and what economic differences gave rise to them are puzzles that remain to be solved. It is rare to be able to detect blocks of strips on open moorland, but two small examples seem to occur near the abandoned Blackslade site and just below the Venford reservoir on Holne Common.

The most obvious strip cultivation is found in the valley of the upper West Webburn in Widecombe and Manaton parishes, particularly on the east side of Challacombe Down where there are the most pronounced banks or 'lynchets'. (A lynchet is a bank formed by ploughing along a slope against a slight artificial barrier, such as an unploughed narrow strip of turf or a line of stones, preventing the soil from sliding down-hill, and also by undercutting such a barrier on the lower side by plough-ing up to it on the next strip below.) Evidently the villagers of Challa-combe used their strips on the steep hillside over a long period of time and so gradually enlarged the lynchets. The ends of the fields thus formed are staggered to enable the ox-ploughs to be taken up to the top levels. On the Hameldon side of the valley a similar but much smaller lay-out can be seen on the lower slopes, and these contour strips of early cultiva-tion are found all round the Moor including, as its name suggests, Lynch Common in Meavy parish.

On the west side of Challacombe there is an area divided into large blocks of one-time strips laid out at right angles to one another. These too must have belonged to the early settlers at Challacombe village, and

Fig 10.   Layout of fields, Blackaton deserted village, Widecombe.

it seems likely that they represent an open field or fields whose strips subsequently became consolidated in fewer and fewer hands until enclosure
of adjacent blocks became unnecessary, some boundary baulks being
left where convenient, particularly to deal with a difference in levels
where the slope of the ground increased.

The Period 1066–1300

To the vast majority of people on the hundreds of farms on and around
Dartmoor, the Norman invasion initially made little or no practical
difference. The conquest was not followed by wholesale displacement or
enslavement as had been the Saxons' way with any surviving Britons;
no battles were fought in the area. A few Saxon landowners who lived
locally on their manors may have found themselves suddenly turned out,
though some remained for a generation or more longer, but to the farming family battling for a living on poor soils and often in harsh climatic
conditions the substitution of one normally absentee manorial lord for
another from a foreign country must have been largely a matter of
indifference. Much more would they have been concerned with the
lord's local representative, his steward or bailiff, and what boon work he
would exact from the peasantry, for the manorial system was already
well established by the year 1066.

Yet within comparatively few years some changes must have been
noted. The Normans expanded the feudal system, bringing it to a higher
standard of administrative efficiency, and throughout the land an attempt
was made to see that every manor played its full economic part. On
Dartmoor the placing of the Saxon hunting-ground under the machinery
of Norman forest laws and the twelfth-century extension of these to all
of Devon must have had considerable effect. The local inhabitants must
inevitably have felt the added burdens put upon them.

The great Domesday survey of 1086 gives some picture of the land
at that time and, with its backward look to 1066, enables a comparison
between the dates to be made. The Saxon chroniclers may have complained bitterly at such a bureaucratic exercise—we do the same when
confronted with similar clerical impositions—but it remains a unique
and valuable record of the period without parallel elsewhere. With a few
exceptions there are two versions of the survey for Devon and therefore
for those manors in the Dartmoor region. Apart from the better-known
Exchequer Domesday there exists in the Exeter Cathedral archives an
earlier version known as the Exeter or Exon Domesday from which the
former was compiled. It gives some fuller details, notably of the num-

bers of livestock on the demesne farms, and is the version used here in discussing facts revealed by the survey.

It is well-known that in Domesday Book Dartmoor is not mentioned by name. (A Pipe-Roll of 1181 has the earliest reference.) It is true that the part of it forming the royal Forest would probably have been omitted, though even this is not quite certain, but the theory that in any case the survey was not concerned with waste land is no longer tenable; in manor after manor the entries imply that large areas of rough grazing existed, and much other information incidental to each manor is given. There are two ways in which the facts can be used : by considering individual entries and by analysing the statistics obtained from the area as a whole. Though one or two problems remain, identifications have fortunately already been made, so that a list of those manors comprising Dartmoor and its immediate borders can be drawn up and will be found, subject to individual interpretation of precisely where the border should be drawn, to number rather over seventy.

Of far greater difficulty is the interpretation of Domesday figures and knowing what exactly is meant to be conveyed by certain statements. Measurements are particularly troublesome as it is not possible to say, for example what relationship the acre of Norman days had to the modern one, making exact comparisons impossible. In spite of this, much can be learned as one or two individual entries will show.

Holne was one of the larger-than-average manors and included all hamlets and farms in the parish except the Stoke farms, which formed a separate manor of their own. Its full entry runs as follows :

> William (of Falaise) has a manor called Holle which Alwin held on the day on which King Edward was alive and dead, and it rendered geld for one hide and a half. This can be ploughed by twelve ploughs. Of this William has in demesne half a hide and one plough, and the villeins have one hide and five ploughs. There William has thirteen villeins, and seven bordars, and eight serfs, and one packhorse, and six head of cattle, and six swine, and fifty-two sheep, and wood one leuga in length and the same in breadth, and pasture one leuga in length and breadth. This is worth sixty shillings, and it was worth as much when William received it.

The first information given is that the manor was held by William of Falaise himself—he had put no under-tenant in—and that Alwin, the abbot of Buckfast, had been the owner at Edward the Confessor's death in 1066 (the Normans would have none of Harold, of course). Next comes its taxation rating, the hide here being in effect a fiscal and not an area measurement, which was higher than that for the average Dartmoor manor. The phrase 'this can be ploughed by twelve ploughs' is the usual one employed and opinions vary as to its exact significance. It may mean that if the manor were fully developed the number of farms which it could support would be twelve, though this seems to take no account of the predominance or otherwise of pastoralism. The figure is over twice the Dartmoor average. After giving the division of the hidage and ploughs between the demesne farm and the villeins, the numbers of villeins (ie the unfree peasant farmers), bordars (small-holders), and slaves who worked the demesne farm are quoted. Roughly speaking there must have been one villein to a farm, though two brothers or father and son may have worked one together and have been counted as two. Perhaps, therefore, there were about thirteen farms apart from the home farm.

The numbers of animals on the latter are given next and included, un-usually, a packhorse, but unlike many other manors no goats. Lastly there are given the areas of woodland, meadow and 'pasture'. The areas of the first and last are the same, but even if it is assumed that a Domesday league was about a mile and a half in length these measurements must be treated with caution and not held to represent actual shapes. The woodland may already have been conveniently consolidated so that it could be given by one set of figures; the pasture representing the rough grazing on the moorland is more likely always to have been in one block; but in either case there is ample room for error. Nevertheless the amount of both must have been substantial, and today they are repre-sented by Holne Woods together with the woodland running up the Dart above New Bridge, and by Holne Common except near the Stoke farms. Its total value had not changed over twenty years.

Marytavy, the Taui of Domesday, was a small manor gelding at only a quarter of Holne's assessment, equally divided between the home and peasant farms. Nigel held it from Juhel of Totnes and there were four ploughlands, but it was underdeveloped as there were only one and a half plough teams on the demesne and one plough amongst the six villeins and two bordars. But there were six slaves, some of whom may have looked after 120 sheep, sixteen cattle and four swine. There was no wood or coppice (there can be very little even today), twelve acres of meadow, and rough grazing half a league by six furlongs. Its value had increased from thirty to forty shillings. The survey here records that Burntown, Warne and Wringworthy in Marytavy parish, which in 1066 had been owned by three English thegns who had been free to go to whichever lord they wished, had since then been collectively added to Marytavy manor.

Okehampton was a large manor with a total of twenty-four plough teams and thirty-one villeins. It also had a mill and a castle, and had evidently just given birth to a borough, for we learn that there were also four burgesses. It is curious that the abandoned dwellings already referred to are in Okehampton Park on the opposite side of the valley to the old town where the church stands. Perhaps the manor and borough co-existed on different sites for a period and eventually ended on the third site where the new town lies today.

Lydford was the only other borough and was held by the king. Within it were twenty-eight burgesses, though forty houses had been destroyed since 1066, probably when a small fort was built on the tip of the promontory within the town. No less than forty-one burgesses dwelt outside the town, some as far away as Fernworthy, just inside the Forest in the valley of the South Teign, an extraordinary arrangement which resulted in their never being considered as among the ancient tenement holders. The borough was still of sufficient importance to render as much service as Barnstaple and Totnes when an expedition was mounted by land or sea.

Turning to the general analysis of all the Dartmoor manors, one is at once struck by their widely varying sizes. There can hardly be said to be a 'normal' one, but a handful were much larger than all the others, and if these are excluded the rest come within closer limits. Thus five had twenty or more ploughlands each (South Tawton had fifty), but almost two-thirds had only four or under and of these no less than twenty-six had two or less. The largest manor would contain a number of villages or hamlets as well as many farms, while at the other end of the scale it could consist of just the demesne, as was the case at Willsworthy. On about twenty-five per cent of the manors there were fewer teams than the number of ploughlands, in some cases markedly fewer; thus Sampford Spiney, where there were eight ploughlands, had only three.

Some population figures can be given. There were 500 villeins recorded and 272 bordars, 223 serfs and 103 others, making a total of about 1,100. But the serfs were probably enumerated individually, whereas the rest represented households, so that the usually adopted multiplication factor of between five and six to calculate total population should be applied to 875 with the serf total then added. This indicates that the population numbered somewhere between 4,500 and 5,500 representing a density of between fifteen and nineteen per square mile, lower than almost all other parts of Devon. Expressed in terms of plough teams, again the moorland edge can be seen to have been comparatively sparsely settled, supporting little more than one per square mile. The total number of farms which were included is impossible to calculate accurately; if each

Page 89 (above) *Pug or clay-kneading mill at Lee Moor, now used as a school: it was also part of the first brickmaking plant to utilise china clay waste as a new material; (below) industrial housing on Dartmoor is a legacy of china clay working in the last century. The cottages at Lee Moor are still occupied*

Page 90 (above) *Water wheels at Cholwich Town china clay pit. They have been demolished since the photograph was taken in 1958;* (below) *the old cleave mill at Belstone where scarlet cloth for the Nizam of Hyderabad's bodyguard was woven*

villein lived on a separate one (and this is uncertain) there would have been about 500, to which must be added some seventy demesne farms.

The demesne livestock may also be totalled. There were about 470 head of cattle, of which about 200 were shared between only five manors, the other manors averaging around four each, while 129 swine were recorded, half of them in a sector between Holne and Cornwood. Goats were surprisingly numerous, 575 on twenty-five farms, no farm, if it had any at all, having less than ten. Seven manors had a packhorse each and Cornwood had three unbroken horses—the only ones recorded. If it is assumed that a full plough team consisted of eight oxen, there must have been about 650 oxen on the demesne and another 1,700 on the villein farms, making them the most numerous animal apart from the sheep, of which 2,600 are recorded on the demesnes alone. South Tawton had 400 (several totals are exact multiples of 100 or 50 : sheep were evidently tiresome to count exactly) and six other manors 100 or more. There is evidence that in the ensuing few centuries in other parts of England the villeins between them had roughly four times as many sheep as were on the demesne farms, so that the total numbers represented here could be as high as 13,000.

It is in the pasture entries that Dartmoor itself is described. In only about a dozen manors is no rough grazing recorded, whereas many have very large entries : South Tawton four leagues by four, Teigncombe three by one, Blachford one and a half by one, Willsworthy two by one and so on round the Moor. There are some curiosities; those manors lying below Hameldown seem to have pasture much smaller in extent than would have been expected, even allowing for difficulties in comparison with modern figures. Spitchwick with its present large common was in 1086 entered as having 100 acres only, as was Walkhampton which some centuries later had no less than 10,000. It is possible that these two apparent deficiencies may be connected with the fact that they were both royal manors and that most of their commons were held to be part of the royal hunting-ground. The size of the South Tawton pasture may be a considerable exaggeration. It is far too large to be represented by the modern common, which would have had to extend deep into the Forest. But it is very striking how, taken as a whole, the entries reveal the presence of the commons around the central hunting-ground, which later on became known as the Commons of Devon.

The final figures from the Domesday survey show that the values since 1066 had increased on thirty-seven manors, a few by as much as three times (though one cannot be sure that land had not been added

F

meanwhile), were the same on another twenty-five and had decreased on five, of which Sourton had dropped from £11 (a high figure) to £7, and the other four were all adjacent on the south side of the Moor, in Ermington Hundred, which had an exceptionally large number of manors with lowered values. Some economic disaster must have struck the area since 1066 from which recovery was not complete at the time the survey was made. The variations in value were very great; five in 1086 were worth £10 or more, with the royal manor of South Tawton once again in the lead with £48, but about one-third were worth 10s or less.

The pattern of farmsteads thinly scattered over the whole area shown by Domesday Book was one which varied only slightly over the next two centuries. The great majority of farms had already been founded, so that the ensuing years were ones of consolidation rather than fresh settlement, though more remote and difficult sites were still being tackled by fresh pioneers hungry for land in an age of increasing population, and some of the waste on existing farms must have been brought into cultivation. The period, particularly the twelfth century, is not well documented, but it is known that new settlements were made in the Forest in the thirteenth.

Lydford remained in royal hands, though temporarily granted out from time to time. In 1195 a stone keep was built there for the custody of the king's prisoners; it cost £74, of which £32 was charged against revenue from the county and the balance against the Cornwall stannaries. Four years later, during the disturbances following Richard I's death, it was stocked with fifteen sides of bacon, ten carcasses of cows, ten horseloads of rye, twenty quarters of oats and a tun of wine, as well as lead, iron and other warlike requisites, but no siege took place. The old fortlet was by now disused, and the timber houses or sheds of about twenty-five feet in length and between eight and twelve feet in width erected within it were then used as granaries. Subsequently they were burnt down, and recent excavation has uncovered much charred grain which, when fully analysed, will enable a good deal to be discovered about the types of corn grown locally. Peas and beans were also found. In 1221 a market was established 'as it anciently used to be', but the importance of the borough diminished with the rise of Okehampton and Tavistock as commercial centres and of Launceston as a strong defensive town. The borough and manor, together with the Forest of Dartmoor, were given to Richard, Earl of Cornwall in 1239. He was afterwards granted a market and fair, but by 1300 the castle or keep was reported to be ruinous, the 'easements of which do not suffice to its sustentation', and there were still only forty-eight burgesses rendering 51s 5¼d—less than had been rendered a century before. It was now a borough in name only.

The other major development in the post-Conquest period was the change from wood to stone for building purposes, round about 1200. The houses so constructed were sometimes of considerable size, up to eighty feet in length and fifteen in breadth. There were entrances opposite each other, with a cross passage, shared by humans and cattle, the latter occupying the lower end of the building and presumably keeping the former warm in winter. With a thatched roof supported by centre-line posts, this was the so-called longhouse in its most primitive form, which survives still, though much altered, on Dartmoor today.

Forest and Commons

For several generations after the coming of the Saxons, Dartmoor remained virtually an unclaimed area. Round the edges, perhaps, some of the large estates took in pieces of moorland, but for the most part it hardly tempted ownership. To those living around it, however, it was a fine summer grazing ground, far bigger than they could ever require, and so came to be used by all those in the shire of Devon—and of Cornwall too until 850—who were willing to drive their cattle and sheep to it for the valuable pasturage it had to offer. This seasonal movement has left its mark on the landscape. All round the Moor the map reveals lanes leading up to it from the more distant parts of Devon, particularly from the north and north-west, along which the animals were driven. Another way can be seen starting in the Berry Pomeroy area—great sheep country by the eleventh century—and going via Ipplepen and Woodland parishes to Ashburton Down and on to the open moorland.

At some time, perhaps in the ninth century, the area became the hunting-ground of the Wessex kings, and with that development common rights may be said to have begun. From the evidence of entries in the Domesday survey it appears that the commons surrounding the central moor began to be appropriated by the manorial lords at about the same time, but grazing went on as before, subject only to a gradually developing code of conduct. The curious exclusion of the inhabitants of Barnstaple and Totnes, both boroughs by 900, from grazing rights on Dartmoor indicates that those rights already existed and, the town's charters not specifically including them, they were held not to enjoy them.

The whole system became more formalised with the Normans' creation of Dartmoor as a royal forest. Nothing at all is known of the Saxon organisation except that there was a local forester named Aethelraed, probably the same man as the Aderet or Adret who held various Dartmoor manors in both 1066 and 1086. And Aluric, an English thegn who held Skerraton at both dates too, may have been a forest official, for in the 1270s the same manor was held by the service of providing the king with three arrows when he hunted on Dartmoor. The Norman forestal system was well-organised and harsh in operation. Beasts of the forest, deer, hare, boar and wolf, were strictly preserved and there were dire penalties for transgressing the laws. A Court of Attachment was convened every forty days which made presentments to the Court of Swainmote, held thrice yearly, whose jurors were normally drawn from the forest freeholders. As the Forest of Dartmoor was not inhabited until the thirteenth century the jurors here must have been those enjoying rights within it. If the indictment brought by the forest officers were proved the freeholders sealed it, but sentence was passed by the Court of Justice Seat which only met every three years.

It is possible that here we have an echo of 'Lydford law', the practice of executing a prisoner and passing sentence afterwards which, although applied to the notorious Stannary Courts of later years, may have had its origin in forest administration. If the Court of Swainmote found a man guilty of an offence it would obviously be administratively inconvenient to keep him for up to nearly three years before passing sentence; temptation to anticipate must have been strong.

During the twelfth century the whole county was afforested, though it is doubtful if the full rigour of the laws could have been enforced over such a large area. Nevertheless it was an edict to discourage development of the countryside, and was sufficient of an imposition to lead later to the commonalty of Devon petitioning King John to remove it, agreeing to pay him a very large sum for the privilege which he granted in 1204. His charter disafforested the county 'up to the metes of the ancient regards of Dartmoor and Exmoor', and granted the men of Devon and their heirs 'the customs within the regards of those Moors as they were accustomed to have' in Henry Is time, the earliest known reference to such rights.

In 1239 the king granted the Forest of Dartmoor and Manor of Lydford to Richard, Earl of Cornwall, and from that date it ceased to be a forest (though the name stuck) and became in law a chase, with manor courts held every three weeks for the three (later four) separate 'quarters' into which it was divided. No records of the old forest courts survive, but from the mid-thirteenth century details of administration begin to be recorded. In 1240, to clarify the boundaries between the Forest and the

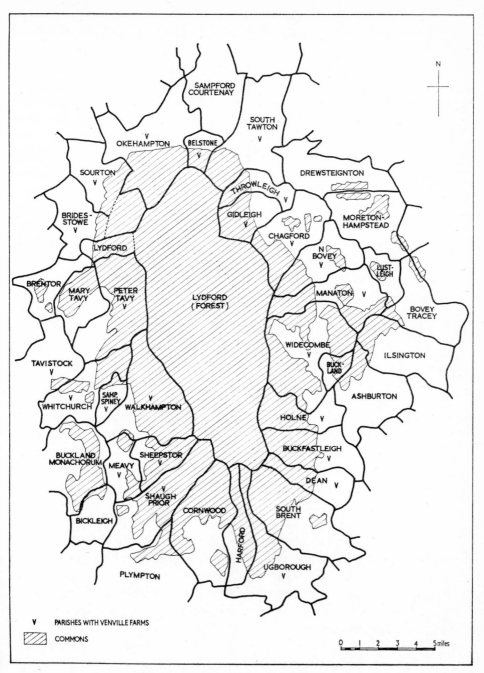

Fig 11. Dartmoor and border parishes.

commons of neighbouring landowners (who had more than once been in dispute as to their rights with the old Forest officials), the Sheriff of Devon in person, accompanied by twelve 'lawful knights of the county' perambulated the Forest and recorded its bounds. Even this did not entirely remove all uncertainty, for the Earls, and later Dukes, of Cornwall always claimed a right to drive cattle from most of the commons surrounding the Forest at certain times of year, and in many cases asserted actual ownership. In spite of the perambulation, places which were clearly outside the Forest and on the surrounding commons are sometimes described in the old records as being 'in the King's Forest', thus adding to a confusion which lingered on to a greater or lesser degree right into modern times.

The founding of the ancient tenements in the Forest began at about the same time. A glance at fig 12 will show how this new colonisation was made along the valleys of the East and West Dart and their tributaries, on land no higher than that where other farms had survived for centuries on the edge of the Moor. It was not in fact unusual to allow some colonisation of a forest or chase; so long as the lord's hunting was not prejudiced it was even an advantage to have freeholders (the tenements were copyhold of inheritance, which was virtually a freehold) who in return for privileges had certain administrative duties to perform. There are two pieces of evidence which point to the tenements' not having been settled earlier. Of the many sites of farms founded from about the eleventh century and abandoned by about 1300, none has been discovered within the Forest, though the territory would seem perfectly suitable. Clearly some policy must have up till then prevented what would surely otherwise have been attempted. The other evidence is more positive; in 1260 the inhabitants of Babeny and Pizwell, just inside the eastern bounds of the Forest, successfully petitioned Bishop Bronescombe to allow them to use Widecombe church for almost all purposes, the journey across the Moor to Lydford being arduous in good weather and very lengthy and difficult in bad. As only two tenements are mentioned, one must suppose that none of the others had then been founded, though most were recorded in the next generation or two and they also used Widecombe church.

In later centuries there were thirty-four or thirty-five such ancient tenements on seventeen different sites, but in a list given in old records of places paying no rent in the mid-fourteenth century after the Black Death, several other names such as Algarslake, Blakefurses and Edithull appear. They were probably farms that never survived and were either merged into others or refounded under different names. The following

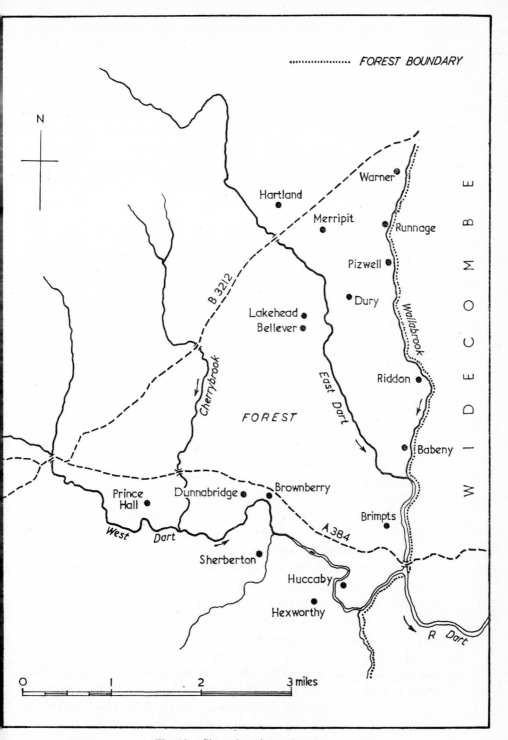

Fig 12. Sites of ancient tenements.

is a list of the names of the later tenements (there being of course often more than one farm in the same place), together with the date of their first mention in records so far discovered.

Babeny	(1260)	Dury	(1344)
Pizwell	(1260)	Merripit	(1344)
Huccaby	(1296)	Lake(head)	(1347–8)
Warner	(1301–2)	Bellever	(1355)
Runnage	(1304–5)	Riddon	(1488)
Dunnabridge	(1305)	Hartiland	(1521)
Brimpts	(1307)	Princehall	(1521)
Sherberton	(1307)	Brownberry	(1563)
Hexworthy	(1317)		

The other class of commoner not yet described was the venville-right holder. The word venville is a corruption of the latin words *fines villarum*, the rents of the vills, as entered in the official accounts. The parishes which lay around the Moor having certain farms enjoying these rights were accordingly said to be 'in venville'. Their distribution has peculiarities; in some parishes such as Ugborough and Chagford almost every holding had them, while in others—Dean and Manaton for example—comparatively few did. There were one or two isolated farms or areas such as Taviton tithing specified as having the rights, yet one or two parishes such as Marytavy and, most strikingly, South Brent and Cornwood were not in venville at all. The distribution must in some way reflect the circumstances prevailing at the time the rights originated, but the reason for it is lost in antiquity. They are first mentioned in 1296 but evidently were old then.

Each of these classes of commoner enjoyed different rights. Least privileged were the householders of the rest of Devon who were classed as 'strangers' or 'foreigners' and were allowed to depasture beasts on the Commons of Devon surrounding the Forest without payment, and upon the Forest only on payment of certain small fees. Next were the venville tenants who paid a certain very small fixed rent to the king or Duchy and were allowed free pasture on the Commons and Forest by day but had to pay extra if they remained in the Forest by night. The numbers they turned out were supposed to be limited to the number their farms would support in winter (the restriction of levancy and couchancy), but extra beasts could be grazed if they paid for them as 'strangers'. They could also take from the Forest all they needed for fuel, building, hedging and so on 'save green oak and venison'. Lastly there were the ancient tenement holders who had free rights in the Forest only and who owed certain services such as forming manor court juries and assisting in cattle drifts. A few other rights appear to have existed, such as that enjoyed by the *carbonarii*, the diggers of peat used for making charcoal for smelting tin-ore.

A record of the numbers of cattle and sheep going into the Forest was carefully made, and indeed the whole machinery for administering Dartmoor was very thorough and in full swing by the thirteenth century. Though conceived in medieval times, it remained virtually unchanged for several centuries.

Notes to this chapter are on pages 288–289.

4

Industry

Frank Booker

DARTMOOR has been industrially exploited for over nine centuries. Tin, copper, iron, lead and arsenic have all been taken from its granite. Moorland sheep have nourished a considerable cloth industry, and its stores of peat and water have provided fuel and power. Its mineral wealth has attracted not only the big capitalist but the lone adventurer toiling with pick and shovel, and each has left his mark on the landscape. Today its traditional industries languish. There is no metal mining and the cloth and corn mills have long ceased working. Peat is not commercially cut any more and there is only an intermittent demand for granite. Dartmoor's contribution to the mid-twentieth century industrial scene is china clay, dug from its ancient granite in ever increasing quantities, which helps to prop up the national revenue with the currency it earns abroad.

The Tin Trade

The mineral on Dartmoor is cassiterite, the dioxide of tin. Tin is the rarest of the base metals.

Tin working is as much a part of Dartmoor as the granite forming the tors, and in historical importance, interest, and fascination no other industrial activity on the Moor compares with it. Tin was worked in Cornwall in the Bronze Age, but the earliest documentary evidence for its extraction on Dartmoor occurs in the Pipe Roll of 1156. Rich deposits of alluvial tin were then being worked at Sheepstor and Brisworthy, not far from the headwaters of the Plym. Who found the tin and how is not known, but the discovery appears to have been made when knowledge of the Cornish tin-bearing grounds seems temporarily to have been lost. From this beginning (in fact the settlement of Brisworthy may well date from this time) tin working assumes three distinct phases, made up of the early medieval tin streaming activity, the Tudor and Elizabethan workings when streaming merged with open cutting and adit mining, and the eighteenth- and nineteenth-century shaft-mining activity when copper, arsenic, lead and iron were also produced.

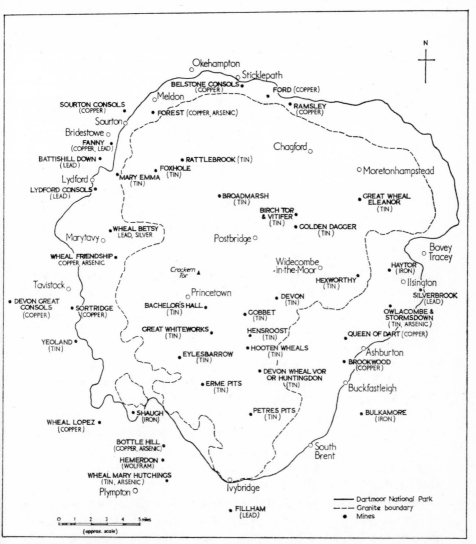

Fig 13. Metal mining in and around Dartmoor. Tin is largely confined within the granite while copper, arsenic, lead and iron have been worked mainly on the fringe.

Tin occurs on Dartmoor (with negligible exceptions it is found nowhere else in Devon) in thin, scattered veins or lodes deep in the granite or sometimes in clay rock. Such lodes are mostly on the southern half of the Moor, but they increase in richness and size as one moves west, becomming more abundant in West Cornwall. The early tin workings on Dartmoor were of stream or alluvial tin, believed in medieval times to have been deposited by 'Noah's Floode', and it was often the custom after severe storms for tinners to go out into the country to see whether tin veins had been exposed. There was a sound instinct behind this belief. In many places, particularly at the heads of valleys (those of the Plym, East Dart and Webburn are good examples), the granite has been denuded and rotted by rain and frost, exposing the heads of the lodes. Floods, particularly during the glacial period, exposed the tin crystals in the lodes, washing them out in the form of large stones, pebbles and sand. As these were carried down and sorted by the water, their heavier specific gravity caused them to sink to the rocky shelves of the valley bottoms where they were deposited in sandwich-like layers of tin, stone, and mud, often up to ten feet or more deep and quite frequently the width of a valley. The heaviest deposits occurred in the broad, shallow valleys. Where a river like the Dart runs much of its way through gorge-like cuttings, a good deal of the tin swept down was probably carried straight out to sea.

To work these valley deposits a method akin to opencast mining was used. The valleys were trenched and excavated, the heavier tin sand being placed on one side for further treatment. We do not know the tin values of those days, but in alluvial work in Malaya the proportion of tin ore found is from under one lb to two or three lbs a cubic yard. Where the metal was difficult to reach, streams or even rivers were diverted to wash it out. Large tin stones were crushed on rocks or ground in a primitive hand-mill. The pulverised ore then underwent a further washing by having a stream of water turned over it to clear away the remaining sand and mud, leaving the darker and heavier tin grains behind. Great ingenuity was displayed in bringing water to the tin-washing sites. The East Dart at Sandy Hole Pass, above Postbridge, and the Teign and Wallabrook near Chagford have been narrowed by embanking to obtain a faster flow of water for tin-washing, while on hillsides crescent or pear-shaped ponds were often dug, into which leats carried rainwater to be stored. Extra labour was often employed solely for the tin 'wash'.

Smelting in this early period consisted of two operations—a rough drawing of the metal in a peat fire where it often melted in harsh, gritty lumps, and a more careful refining at a recognised smelting centre. At this last refining the metal in Devon was weighed against a heavier standard pound of 18oz, to compensate for a tax of 2s 6d paid on the first smelting and for wastage and carriage costs to the second refining centre, usually a market town.

Stream tin smelted in this way was extremely pure, and when cast into ingots of 195lb (the average weight in Devon) was transported by pack-horse throughout the length and breadth of the country. A good deal found its way into Europe and the Near East, for at this period, before Cornish tin production had been resumed or the tin deposits of Bohemia discovered, Dartmoor was probably the richest source of tin in Europe. In 1156, when Dartmoor tin is first heard of, the production was about 60 tons, but between 1171–89 it was about 343 tons a year, most of which was taken between the Plym and the Dart.

Tin has always had widespread uses in the civilised world and had a social importance equal to gold. Mixing it with copper to make bronze was a discovery comparable in importance to that of gunpowder. Tools and weapons could be given a sharper cutting edge and lasted longer. With lead it was made up into solder bars, the principal stock-in-trade of travelling tinkers, and it was used with copper in bell casting, the proportion of tin varying with the size and tone of the bell. In the form of pewter it has a long history of use for domestic purposes and ceremonial occasions.

It was and still is much used as a decorative metal for bracelets, brooches, beads and costume jewellery. It was also often used to counterfeit gold and silver. A genuine silver article will tarnish with age, but tin can retain its lustre indefinitely. Monkish chroniclers mixed tin with saffron to simulate gold in illuminated manuscripts. The coffins of prominent people were often made of tin; notable examples are the tombs of some of the Habsburgs in Vienna, which are carried out wholly in tin. The metal type from which papers and books are printed is made from an alloy containing tin, and it is also used in organ pipes to lighten the tone.

Salts of tin were used to prepare dyes important to the wool trade, and the metal entered into the making of brass cannon and firearms in the fifteenth and early sixteenth centuries. In 1195 more than 254 thousandweight of Dartmoor tin (a thousandweight was 1,200lb) were shipped to La Rochelle for Richard the Lion Heart to adulterate the coinage with which he paid his troops. The actual production was probably greater than the records of the time show, for despite strict taxation and stringent laws considerable quantities were smuggled out of the country. Apart

from Cornish ports like Fowey, tin was shipped from Plymouth and also
from Dartmouth, which took the metal produced from the Ashburton
stannary district. Both Ashburton and Dartmouth were at times staple
(or depot) towns for tin, as also was Exeter, through which passed much
of the tin from the north-eastern corner of the Moor.

Very early in the thirteenth century the refining process was improved by the introduction of the blowing house (each one of which
had to be registered), making only one smelting necessary. At the time
this was a technical innovation of great importance, and the blowing
house, with few alterations, remained the sole means of smelting tin ore
until its gradual supersession in the eighteenth century by the reverberatory
furnace, which was more suitable for smelting lode tin. Blowing houses
on Dartmoor present a number of problems. Some may also have been
crushing mills and at least one, at Gobbet (Swincombe), may have been
a crushing and grinding mill as well as a smelting house. Generally they
were rectangular structures of unmortared moorstone, with walls frequently $2\frac{1}{2}$ft or more thick and having, probably, a turf or thatch roof
which was periodically burnt to catch the tin particles driven into it by
the blast from the bellows. The molten metal in the furnace ran out
from a hole in the bottom into a moorstone trough or float from which
it was ladled into stone moulds, a process in which the smelter, a skilled
and fairly well-paid worker, was often badly scalded. The fuel was charcoal (about two tons was needed to smelt a ton of metal) urged by a
bellows worked by an overshot water wheel about 9ft in diameter which,
Hansford Worth calculated, developed about ·66hp. Typical sites for
blowing houses are against a bank or tongue of land jutting into a stream,
and some forty-three are known on Dartmoor; not a great number when
compared with the extent of tin-working. The oldest known smelting
house on Dartmoor was the so-called 'Furnum Regis' or King's Oven,
which stood above the Warren House Inn and is known only because
it appeared on the map of the 1240 Perambulation of Dartmoor. Its remains were robbed in the eighteenth century for wall building. No blowing house exists in its entirety, but the ruins of one above Merrivale
Bridge on the Walkham gives a fair idea of what they looked like and
how they were positioned. A mould stone lies close to its entrance and a
well-defined wheel pit can be traced. Tradition has always linked the
Jews with the tin trade, and blowing houses have been called 'Jew's
Houses', but the association of Jews with the early tin industry in the
west has never been established satisfactorily. If they played any part,
and this is neither impossible nor improbable, it was almost certainly as
buyers or merchants at ports and markets and never as tin workers.

Jews were active traders in England from the Conquest until they were banished by Edward I in 1290.

Tin streaming in the southern valleys of Dartmoor must have been so intense in the twelfth century that the most accessible deposits had probably been worked out by the beginning of the thirteenth century. This is when Cornwall, where tin working had been resumed, took a lead in production it has never since lost. By 1243 output on Dartmoor had fallen to 40 tons of refined tin, and by the end of the century, when Cornwall was producing 300 tons, the average on Dartmoor had fallen to 33 tons a year. Throughout the thirteenth and fourteenth centuries the Devon production remained at about one-tenth of the Cornish and an eighth of what it had been in the boom days of the twelfth century. The search for new deposits ranged widely. The Plym valley beds seem to have been the first to have been worked out, for the Tavistock stannary district which embraced it ceased to be the leading producer after 1381. Chagford, in the north-eastern quarter of the Moor, becomes the chief source from 1385 until the middle of the fifteenth century, after which the Ashburton Stannary accounted for nearly 40 per cent of the output. A field above Ashburton was reputed to be so rich in tin that a bullock lying down covered its worth in the metal.

Stream working probably continued extensively throughout the fifteenth and sixteenth centuries. It is possible to guess this from the number of Acts of Parliament passed to try and stop the choking of harbours, particularly the mouths of the Plym and Dart, by the enormous quantities of sand and gravel washed into them by the tin workings. But it also seems probable that increasing amounts of the metal were obtained on Dartmoor towards the end of the sixteenth century from open cuttings like Greenwell Gert and Shady Combe near Clearbrook, Fox Tor Gert near Cater's Beam, and Chew Gulley near the Vitifer mines. Works like these were traced up from the stream works by 'shoading', or digging pits at intervals until the source of the lode was found, after which the tin was excavated from the top or 'back' of the lode. Shoads are isolated stones of tin ore, and the art of tracing them back to the parent lode is a skill largely lost today.

From methods such as this, shallow adit mining, by which levels were driven into the sides of the valleys to reach the metal and drain the workings at the same time, would be a logical extension, and it is probable that these methods played a part in the minor boom in tin production occurring on Dartmoor in the fifteenth and early sixteenth centuries. In a table sufficiently well based to be within a possibility of an error of half of one per cent, Hansford Worth estimated that 23,749 tons of tin were dug from Dartmoor between 1400 and 1650 and of this about 14,600 tons was produced in the sixteenth century with a peak of 252 tons in 1524. In that year the price of tin was 4d a pound, making the gross value realised by the trade £9,408, a substantial sum at the then value of money. From these peaks the output rapidly declined until the Civil War brought production temporarily to an end.

At least it would appear so if one accepts Lewis's figures in *The Stannaries*, for between 1643 and 1673 he records no production from Devon or Cornwall, although the coinage dues remain substantial. A faint ray of light is shed on these 'lost years' by the Plymouth Port Books in the Public Record Office. They show 410cwt exported to London from Plymouth between July and December 1649, 2,852cwt in the twelve months from December 1650 and 1,678cwt between October and June 1657–58. In 1688 Plymouth imported 4,593cwt coastwise from all the Cornish ports. Whether the earlier figures include some proportion of Dartmoor tin it is impossible to say, although it is not improbable, for in the first half of the seventeenth century Plymouth appears to have been the chief tin exporting port in the south-west, losing this position in the second half to Falmouth and Penzance.

Disease, war and politics all had a bearing on tin working and partly explain the fluctuations in output. On the evidence of the Stannary returns the Black Death, which depopulated many settlements, almost brought a cessation of working; so did the Wars of the Roses and the Civil War, which profoundly disturbed an industry always sensitive to political conditions because of its association with the Crown. Moreover the labour force was never constant. Most Dartmoor tinners in medieval times appear to have been artisans or small husbandmen who may sometimes have worked in voluntary partnerships or groups eking out their livelihood by going occasionally in search of tin ore. In the thirteenth century there were never more than 200 or 450 of them, producing between 25 and 45 tons a year. An estimate in Edward IIIs time put the stannary population of Devon at a little over 1,000, of whom about 20, 'all of the poorer sort', actually lived on the Moor.

Tinners were proverbially among the 'poorer sort'. The wretched state of the Cornish tinner, an easy prey of merchants, living in hovel-like surroundings and with little alternative employment, is vividly described by Carew. Raleigh, who as Lord Warden of the Stannaries tried to better their lot, described them as ten thousand of the roughest and most mutinous men in England.

Although it is misleading to equate conditions on Dartmoor too exactly with Cornwall, where the tinners' plight was exacerbated by the

Page 107 (above) *Devonshire farm fireplace;* (below) *scalding the milk on a Dartmoor farm*

Page 108 (above) *After work on a Dartmoor farm;* (below) *Lake Farm, Poundsgate, 1909*

almost total lack of alternative employment, there is no reason to think that in terms of real wages the Dartmoor tinner was any better off. According to Westcote, quoting in 1630 something that had been written thirty years earlier, the Devon tinner was a labourer having the coarsest fare and diet and frequently drinking from his hand or shovel for want of a cup. This is a picture of extreme poverty which suggests that, as the industry progressed from medieval times and the metal became harder to get, the tinners' lot got worse. In the Devon coinage rolls from the fourteenth to the early sixteenth century, when the industry was one of steady growth, the names of landed gentry jostle with those of bakers, tanners and fullers in what seems essentially to have been a small man's trade, but the picture gradually changes as the merchant and the capitalist adventurer came more and more to the fore. According to Hansford Worth the average wage of the poorer class of tinner in the latter half of the sixteenth century was 2s a week with a limit of £4 10s a year, the latter a fixed wage for a yearly contract which would have made it difficult for a man to have earned more by outside employment. In 1667 he was getting 14s or 15s a month and by 1728 8d a day or £6 a year. Even in the boom years of the nineteenth century he remained a figure of poverty with wages of little more than 50s a month. He was just slightly better off than that other skilled worker, the farm labourer, for as late as 1878 a Launceston labourer celebrating his golden wedding could be praised for keeping off the poor rate although his wages had never exceeded 11s a week.

Curiously, in medieval times tinners were often regarded as men of leisure through the holidays they took for feasts and saints' days and in connection with special seasonal customs. In Cornwall this could amount to nearly a third of the year; it is unlikely that things were much different on Dartmoor.

Tin working was an intensely conservative industry and techniques in dressing the metal advanced slowly. The advent of stamps or 'knacking mills' late in the seventeenth century enabled the ore to be crushed when wet; for the earlier hand-worked mills it had to be dried before crushing. Carew, in 1602, describing practices which had probably long been common in Devon and Cornwall, mentions how crushed ore was at one time sprinkled on turf clods over which water was allowed to trickle, and then was poured into a wooden bowl rocked by a tinner to and fro in his arms to separate the impurities. The stamping mill, which on Dartmoor was a frame in which two or three logs of iron-shod timber (usually ash logs) were erected and lifted up and down in sequence by wooden pegs or cams attached to a shaft turned by a water wheel, not

G

only enabled the tin gravels to be pulverised more finely but assisted the process of separating the ore from the sand. The crushed ore, after it had been 'stamped', was washed out through a 'pass' or grate at the bottom of the mill and then guided by water into rectangular ground frames. From these it was thrown up by shovels against sloping boards which allowed the metal to be roughly graded. Further processes such as buddling, trambling, sezing (sieving) and kieveing (where the tin was put in a tub and shaken or beaten by men and boys until the heavier tin sand had settled in the middle—a practice still carried out in Camborne as late as 1950) were all varieties of a procedure for grading the metal more and more finely by utilising its heavier specific gravity.

Sometimes the coarser slimes left from the grading processes were placed on one side in a heap and sold, the buyer making his profit by re-stamping them and selling the tin obtained. At Geevor mine in 1967 a heap of low-grade tin residue treated in a somewhat similar way realised over £41,000. With the first crude attempts in the 1670s of calcining lode tin in a kiln to burn off arsenical and iron impurities, and the introduction later in the nineteenth century of the round buddle frame with a revolving sprinkler arm to replace the older rectangular frame, the operations for dressing tin assumed a form not vitally different from those carried out today with more sophisticated apparatus.

Similarly, methods of getting tin ore were becoming more costly and complex. By the late eighteenth century shaft mining had become increasingly the pattern on Dartmoor as production from stream and open cutting works dwindled to a point where it was almost non-existent. Even in 1670 it was reckoned that the annual output from Dartmoor did not exceed ten tons, although open excavations like the so-called Erme Pits, a series of ancient workings above the source of the Erme, were still yielding tin. According to Crossing a particular kind of ore called zill tin was being taken from these workings in 1672. The year 1706 produced an isolated peak of fifty-five tons, but a few years later only ten tinners could be found in the whole of the Tavistock stannary, while for six years between 1734 and 1740 no tin at all was produced. By 1797, when the Rev John Swete was touring Dartmoor, he could note that the Warren and Fox Tor mines, together with the Bachelor's Hall mine near Princetown (discovered about 1794 during the digging of the Devonport leat and employing 16 men), 'comprised the whole of what was now worked on Dartmoor'.

The Dartmoor stannary was now of scarcely any importance. From 1750 outputs of tin ceased to be listed separately in the yearly Stannary returns, the first time this had happened since the twelfth century. Cheap tin from the Far East seriously competed with the British product and the outbreak of war with France further unsettled the trade. Yet the revival, when it came in the nineteenth century, had its origin in these depressed years. It stemmed in part from the introduction in South Wales in 1730 of tin plate manufacture, a process given a new stimulus in the Napoleonic wars by the production in a Bermondsy factory in 1812 of a tin plate canister for preserving food. From this gradually grew the tinned food industry which today absorbs more than a third of the world's tin production. Again in 1829 Isaac Babbitt patented a tin bearing which, by allowing machinery to run much faster, paved the way for mass production processes and spelled the end of cottage industries. As industrial demand rose so did the price of tin. Between 1780 and 1814 it increased from £69 to £156 a ton, and under this stimulus workings long dormant on Dartmoor began to be looked at again. Typical of their type was a Dartmoor mine, which in 1798 had a shaft twenty-four fathoms deep and employed thirty men 'most of whom lived on the farms and outskirts of the moor'. Tin from it was carted eighteen miles to the Tamar for smelting, and coal for the smith's forge was brought back in return. Mines like this demanded capital for shaft sinking and preliminary exploration, and this was provided by a speculator or a group of shareholders who installed a manager to watch their interests and hire labour. By 1808 the lone bucket and shovel prospector had so far disappeared from the scene that only one tin streamer could be found at work in the whole of Devon.

Hansford Worth notes (*Dartmoor* p 23) how tinners working in deposits of small boulders and large pebbles often proceeded by means of parallel trenches. The large stones were used to build a rough wall on the verge of the trench and smaller ones were thrown behind to be retained by the wall. A series of parallel ridges or walls was thus formed which can be well seen at Drizzlecombe Burrows and in the lower part of Langcombe Valley, on the Plym.

But lode mining was never as rich as the palmy days of medieval streaming. Throughout the nineteenth-century revival the average yearly yield of tin on Dartmoor was probably less than 45 tons. Because of foreign competition the price sometimes dropped to between £55 and £50 a ton, which must have been less than the cost of production. Moreover the nineteenth-century revival revealed little new tin ground, for many of the hundred or so mines or trials one can trace from this time were really underground extensions of the old tin streaming and open cutting works. This can be seen clearly at Eylesbarrow, on the eastern flank of Sheepstor, where the nineteenth-century workings merge with the debris left by the medieval tin streamers in the Plym valley—debris which was also worked over in 1824 by the short-lived Wheal Bedford mine. Similarly the Vitifer, Birch Tor (where the miners underground were constantly drenched with water from the higher workings), and Golden Dagger mines east of Postbridge carry on from the earlier workings in the valley of the West Webburn. The Golden Dagger mine was worked by an adit driven westwards into the hill, the levels being connected to the surface by shafts. With neighbouring setts these workings formed in the nineteenth century the largest group of tin mines on Dartmoor, and present today a spectacular area of tinners' scenery. At Hexworthy, where the Hensroost and Hooten Wheals workings form a similar but smaller complex, the nineteenth-century shafts were sunk into the earlier workings.

Only Vitifer went to any depth (seventy-seven fathoms), and almost all were worked by water wheels, many deriving their power from leats which had served the earlier tinners. At Eylesbarrow can still be seen the lines of granite stones put up to carry the flat rods worked by its wheels, some still bearing the stains of the lubricant used over 100 years ago on the pulley axles. The Vitifer mines were served by an 8-mile leat, and the Taw powered a 60ft wheel, working flat rods, which drained the Belstone mine. At nearby Ramsley a 50ft pumping wheel raised water to work a 33ft wheel for crushing ore, while Great Week mine near Chagford was installing a 40ft wheel as late as the 1880s for pumping. In contrast Hexworthy, which ceased production in 1914, strode into the twentieth century with a flourish, channelling its ancient leats in 1906 to drive a turbine which generated electricity for lighting and working the mine. Because of the abundance of its 'run off' streams and the configuration of the land, the use of water power for working mines probably lingered longer on Dartmoor than anywhere else in the west of England. In perfect order the efficiency of a water wheel was about 65 per cent, but with the conditions prevailing on Dartmoor it is doubtful if any of these wheels achieved much more than 35 per cent.

Tin was not the only metal sought on Dartmoor in the nineteenth century. Wheal Betsy, among the foothills near Marytavy, had been an important lead mine in the 1790s and continued to produce notable amounts of lead and silver well into the following century. Lead was also mined around Bridestowe, a village regarded in 1850 as 'neat and improving'. The tin at the Birch Tor and Vitifer mines was associated with specular iron, but its unsuitability for paint manufacture made it of more nuisance than value. Iron (the more valuable magnetic ore) was taken extensively from a mine at Haytor whose workings, unknown probably to thousands of visitors, come within a few hundred yards of the Rock Inn in Haytor Vale. Iron has been found and worked near South Brent, while the dump of an isolated ferro-ceramic mine can be found in the woods at Shaugh.

More spectacular was the pursuit of copper, the glamour metal of the mid-nineteenth century, which was produced in considerable quantities in mines on the Moor's fringe. The best-known and richest was the Devon Friendship mine at Marytavy, at work before 1796 and which, when it stopped in 1925, had a longer history of continuous working than any other mine in Devon and Cornwall. Besides copper, tin, arsenic, tungsten, iron and lead were all taken from it. To the north the Belstone and Ramsley mines, near Sticklepath, produced fair amounts of copper and arsenic (waste from Ramsley's dumps is still a potent weed killer on garden paths), while a handful of mines bordering the Moor near Ashburton and Buckfastleigh produced enough copper to raise extravagant hopes of the south-eastern fringe of the Moor becoming a second Tavistock mining district. Near Sigford, where the granite gives way to shales, are the heavily-worked sites of the Owlacombe and Stormsdown mines, which tap the picturesquely named Great North, North Beam, and South Beam lodes. Worked for tin in the seventeenth century, they became a profitable source of arsenic until the first world war.

The flirtation with copper, a comparatively serious one, for some 70,000 tons of copper ore were taken from mines fringing Dartmoor, was, however, a transient incident in the mining story of an area which has been one of the historic sources of tin in Europe. The skills were not dissimilar, for the copper miner, as a boy, had been a tin worker inheriting traditions handed down by ancestors who had worked up to their knees in water to get tin. The last tin to be produced in any quantity on Dartmoor came from the dumps of the Birch Tor and Vitifer mines in 1939, and when this was taken away for smelting in South Wales an almost continuous record of tin working on Dartmoor stretching back to the twelfth century came to an end.

How much tin Dartmoor produced we are unlikely ever to know. Not only are the records inadequate, but it is not always clear whether they refer to black tin (which is the pulverised ore) or white tin (the smelted metal). In 1778 Price noted that good stream tin in Cornwall produced 14cwt of metal from 20cwt of ore, which is a high yield of about 70 per cent. With lode tin a yield of between 30 and 40lb of cassiterite per ton would be considered good. Few, if any, of the Dartmoor lodes were as rich as this, but vague and incomplete records make comparisons difficult. Much clearer is the evidence in 'stream works of immense magnitude and excavations so prodigious' of the toil which went to its getting. Out of 250 square miles of Dartmoor granite, something like 130 bear evidence of tin working. Around the source of the East Dart the Moor has been permanently lowered by stream works, and below the Warren House Inn, which thrived on the custom of the Vitifer mines, the scenery has been radically altered by centuries of tin working, leaving scars which are now of challenging interest rather than eyesores.

The economic importance of the industry to Dartmoor is still incompletely understood. Almost every village and settlement had some interest in tin working and mining, and when it ceased many of them suffered a sharp decline in population. For at least 900 years it provided a source of work, embodying almost every type of labour from individual and communal working to the semi-forced labour of the stannaries and the hired and piece-rate working of the nineteenth and twentieth centuries. Many of the valleys on the southern fringe of the Moor were first opened up and populated through the search for tin, and the present B3212, crossing the moor from east to north-west, probably originated as a tinner's highway. Parish guilds, certainly those of Widecombe, Holne, Chagford and Buckland, invested funds in tin or received gifts of the metal. But in the final count it was the Crown, with its monopoly, which made the real fortune. Many others had comfortable rewards, not a few picked up a useful living, and some found their independence under the protection of the Stannaries. But for the great majority the Dartmoor tin trade was a means of ekeing out a subsistence.

There is still lode tin on the Moor and tin gravels in the streams, but the great beds of alluvial ore, so pure that the tin from it often ran in a quicksilver stream when heated in a humble peat fire, have vanished for ever.

The Stannaries

The titular office of Lord Warden of the Stannaries of Cornwall and Devon is one of the few reminders today of the ancient and once powerful stannary organisation which controlled and taxed the tin industry as a source of revenue for the Crown.

It is not clear when the Devon tinners separated from those of Cornwall or why. A stannary court was in existence in the reign of Athelstan (AD 950) when dues had to be paid to the sovereign on all tin mined, but some form of stannary organisation was in existence before this date.

Because it was found mainly on Duchy lands, tin in medieval England

was regarded as a royal metal in which the Crown had a proprietary
interest. To emphasise this the King occasionally did some trading in
tin on his own account, buying up the metal through his collectors at one
price and selling it at another. Richard I twice did this, and in 1197
cleared £352 on his deal. In 1367 the Black Prince, as Duke of Cornwall, bought up all the tin at 20s a cwt and sold it to the merchants at
26s 8d. But these royal sallies were unpopular among both merchants
and tinners, and generally the collection of the royal revenues from tin
was left to stannary officials. At their head was the Lord Warden, who
stood in direct relationship between the tinners and the King or the
Prince of Wales as Duke of Cornwall.

All Dartmoor was a stannary area, and for the purposes of
tin production was virtually a self-governing state within the State.
As a stannary it had its own laws and customs, its own courts
and gaol, and it bestowed upon all working tinners rights and
privileges which placed them above the common law. Unless he
killed or injured somebody, or stole their land, a tinner was exempt
from all jurisdiction other than that of the stannary courts. He could
at any time leave the employment of his feudal lord, to whom he was
bound for fees and service, to go and dig for tin anywhere he chose,
and the manorial lord was without any power to compel him to return.
The only privilege the latter possessed was the right to a small toll on any
tin taken from his land. This ancient and important right of 'bounding',
or searching for tin on any land, was confirmed and firmly anchored in
a charter granted in 1201 by John and retained in its main essentials in
the 1305 charter of Edward I, which with few exceptions remained the
basis of the constitution of the stannaries until they were abolished in the
nineteenth century.

No worker was more favoured than the medieval tinner. He enjoyed
exemption from all normal 'tallages, aids, tolls' and customary dues at
ports, fairs and markets within the county, a concession which the Devon
tinners construed and eventually got recognised as exempting them from
all ordinary national taxes. They were free of all forms of jury service
unless summoned by their warden, and in times of war had the right
to be mustered in their own militia under the command of the Lord
Warden. In the Armada crisis, says Dr A. L. Rowse, there were frequent
complaints that many Devon men escaped their duty altogether on the
plea of belonging to their stannary.

Such privileges, cutting right across the laws and social conventions
of the time, were actively resented. Landowners complained that tinners
often blackmailed them with the threat of digging on their land, and the

stannary bailiffs retorted that many landowners falsely represented themselves as tinners to escape taxes. In 1314 the 'poor men of the county of
Devon' complained that tinners were destroying good farm land as well
as houses at the rate of 300 acres a year—a complaint that has an up-
to-date ring. In 1320 ten different remonstrances were presented against
them in Parliament. There were further grievances in 1347, and in 1376
two petitions were introduced into Parliament praying for a more rigor-
ous definition of stannary privileges. 'Had the financial interest of the
Crown been less involved', says Professor Finberg in his history of the
Tavistock stannary, 'the tinners might have appealed in vain to established custom and a succession of royal charters. As it was the Crown
upheld them against every attack.'

Most if not all the tinners' privileges were based on the plea of ancient
custom, and some form of stannary organisation through which tinners
enjoyed certain rights by paying taxes on tin to the Crown seems to have
existed from early times. The effective history of the Dartmoor stannary
begins in 1198 when William de Wrotham, a Westminster civil servant,
was sent down to reorganise the trade and put it on a sound fiscal basis
for the Crown. The Dartmoor tinners were by now separated from those
of Cornwall, with their own common seal and parliament and their
own legislature.

The special interest of William de Wrotham's appointment lies not
only in the light it sheds on the working of the stannaries, but in the
recognition of the growing value of the Dartmoor tin workings at a time
when the national exchequer was nearly empty. Along with the threat
of war with France, there had been the cost of the Third Crusade and
the burden of the fine of 150,000 marks (a mark was 66½p) demanded
for the ransom of Richard I, who had been seized by a jealous rival and
imprisoned in Austria. Although never paid in full, the initial instalments towards this ransom had been such a drain on the national purse
'that all the chalices of England and a fourth part of the revenue of
the realm went into the possession of foreigners to secure the King's
liberation, which was a ruin and irreparable loss to England.' (C. A.
Campbell's *The Crusades* (1935).) The tin mining districts were thus laid
under tribute to help replenish an almost empty exchequer.

Almost the first act of the new Lord Warden was to put a further
tax on the industry. To the existing toll of 30s a cwt which had to be
paid when the tin was first smelted, he added a further tax of one mark
on each thousandweight at the second smelting. Within a year this had
produced £600, quadrupling the revenue from the stannaries, and
although production immediately began to decline, it was still sufficiently

remunerative fourteen years later to bring in £799, or nearly £300 more than the combined revenues of the Duchy without the stannaries. At various times in Devon the industry bore other stannary tolls such as 'black rent', a tax of 2d on every digger of tin ore, later replaced by 'white rent', a toll on those who brought the ore to the smelter and took away the finished product, smelters being prohibited from 'blowing' their own metal. Profits also arose from hearings at the courts and from fines on uncoined tin.

Early in the fourteenth century most of these taxes were swept away to be replaced by the coinage dues—far and away the greatest source of revenue the stannaries afforded. In Devon this was fixed at 1s $6\frac{3}{4}$d per cwt of 120lb, and Tavistock, Chagford and Ashburton, all market centres, were designated as coinage towns for its collection. Plympton was added in 1328 because a powerful lobby persuaded the sheriff of Devon that it was nearer the sea and easier for merchants to get at. The boundaries of the coinage towns met at Crockern Tor, chosen because it was the centre of the Dartmoor stannary area. Tavistock covered the western part of the moor from a line drawn from Barnstaple through Crockern Tor to Plymouth, Ashburton the south-eastern and Chagford the north-eastern quarter of the moor. The Plympton stannary was a small wedge of land adjoining Plymouth on the west and bounded on the east by a line from Crockern Tor through 'Modbury steeple' to Burgh Island.

A compound of lively pageantry and strict control attended the collection of the coinage duty. The pageantry came from the attendance from 'London and southern ports of intending purchasers, country chapmen, London dealers, pewterers' agents and a sprinkling of Italian and Florentine traders'. The strict control was emphasised by the actual ceremony of weighing and coining the tin. The King's weights were brought to a roped-off space in the public market place, inspected by the controller, and then solemnly unsealed. Each block of tin, which had previously been stamped with the mark of its owner, was then brought forward and placed on the scales. After the weight had been shouted out the assay master struck off a small piece or 'coign' from the corner to test its quality. This was probably a quick gravity test. Lead was commonly used to adulterate tin. If it was satisfactory the royal arms or those of the Duchy of Cornwall were struck on it, and a bill was made out showing the weight charged against each tinner and the amount due from him. Only then could it be sold.

The key note of this ceremony was the publicity afforded by the weighing. The probity of the King's weights was plain for all to see, and no buyer of coined metal is known to have complained of receiving 'corrupt or deceitful tin', a risk he ran in buying unstamped or smuggled tin. In the earliest extant coinage roll of the Devon stannaries, dated 1301, the duty paid was £69 17s 1d. At the same time in Cornwall it was £1,532 4s 1d making a total of £1,602 1s 2d. In that year there were eight coinages each at Chagford and Ashburton, and five at Tavistock. The last Devon coinage to appear in the rolls was in 1747, when it produced only 8s 1d against £8,255 from Cornwall. The highest single yield from the Dartmoor stannary was £368 in 1524 against a total in Cornwall of £2,403.

The administration of the stannaries—and few medieval industries were more efficiently managed—derived from their parliaments and district courts. In Devon the earliest known sitting of the Great Court or Parliament on Crockern Tor is 1494. They were convoked by the warden who summoned the ninety-six representatives (twenty-four from each district) to meet at this bleak spot at 8am. At these meetings the customs of the tin works were declared, the laws and rules of the trade laid down and petitions heard. The sittings were irregular. At least ten are known between 1494 and 1703—a supposed sitting in 1749 is less sure.

The task of administering the laws and rules promulgated by the Great Court fell to the district courts, of which there was one for each stannary district in Devon. Presided over by a steward who sat as the warden's representative, with a jury of tinners, they punished with impartial rigour not only their own officials for misdemeanours or slackness, but offenders against the statutes, persons claiming who were not genuine tinners stannary privileges encroaching on their jurisdiction, and suits or cases by landowners alleging assault by tinners.

No one, civil or ecclesiastical, was immune, as Richard Strode, the MP for Plympton, found out when he sought to promote a Bill prohibiting unrestrained digging by tinners, a privilege which had been specifically reaffirmed at the Devon tinner's Parliament sitting at Crockern Tor in 1512. Strode, himself a tinner, complained that tinners' waste was endangering ports and harbours. He was presented in his absence before each of the four stannary courts and fined a total of £160. On refusing to pay he was thrown into Lydford gaol, where he had to bribe the gaoler to prevent himself being confined in irons and fed on bread and water. His release was secured, not as a member of the Westminster Parliament, but on the ground of his former employment as a collector of government dues. The King and Parliament had always retained the right to overrule stannary laws and charters, but it was not often done, and it is significant that Strode thought it necessary to protect himself and his family from further stannary action by getting the Westminster

Parliament to pass a statute granting him and his associates immunity from future interference. In this statute probably lies the germ of the principle of parliamentary privilege.

Although the Crockern Tor Parliament in 1532 considered special measures to counteract the effect of tinner's waste, stannary action in this matter seems to have been tardy. Leland, some years afterwards, stated that not only was the mouth of the Plym badly silted up and Plympton Priory endangered, but Dartmouth harbour was imperilled through tinners' waste being swept down the Dart.

The Dartmoor stannary had another hundred years of active life after Strode's case, but by the middle of the seventeenth century its importance had begun to wane with the decline of the industry that had brought it into being. The Crown was getting less dependent on tin for revenue; the calling of the tinners' parliaments grew less and, by the Commonwealth, many of their privileges, especially immunity from taxation, had been lost. Lydford gaol, built as a stannary prison in 1195, was a dilapidated ruin in 1650. Chagford, Ashburton and Tavistock began to lose their stannary importance and Plympton was seldom heard of. The last tin coinage in Devon was at the little Tamarside port of Morwellham in 1838, the year in which the coinage dues, then bringing in about £12,000 annually from the whole of the Duchy, were abolished and a compensation awarded to the Crown in their place. Nearly sixty years later (1896) the stannary courts themselves were abolished and their jurisdiction was transferred to the humbler portals of the county court.

Mining communities enjoying separate laws and customs have existed in other parts of England, but the stannaries stand apart because of their importance to the Crown as a source of revenue. Tinners could defy the common law because they knew the King could always be counted upon to block all attempts threatening, even remotely, to cause mining to slacken. The Dartmoor stannary was no pale copy of its Cornish neighbour. It had a vigorous and independent life of its own, and the arbitrary harshness of its administration (one litigant feelingly complained of the 'quyke spede' of the Tavistock stannary court), backed by the terrors of the Lydford dungeon, was a frequent cause of complaint.

The stannary organisation (and in this Devon and Cornwall were alike) had all the aspects of an industrial corporation and many of the features of a modern totalitarian state, while in the actions of the tinners themselves there are many reminders of present-day industrial practices. Strikes and go-slow tactics for better prices and for the enforcement of privileges (particularly exemption from taxation) were weapons well-known to them. The action of the Crockern Tor parliament in 1494 in prohibiting anybody owning estate worth more than £10 a year from becoming a tinner has the stamp of the closed shop of the trade unions. It is not clear whether this prohibition was ever strictly enforced. Probably it was not. But monopoly can inhibit progress. Better methods of working, treating and dressing tin came mainly as the power of the stannaries declined and the spur of competition was felt. The stannary organisation made little contribution to the techniques of tin working on Dartmoor.

Wool and Cloth

Dartmoor's tumbling streams have not been the monopoly of the tinners. They were led by leats and launders to work fulling, corn, paper, leather and even gunpowder mills. The fulling or 'tucking' mills, as they were known in Devon, involved Dartmoor in the wool trade, and they are of particular interest for they partially mechanised weaving skills developed in cottage crafts and utilised the wool of Dartmoor sheep.

Wool is woven deeply into Devon's historic economy. As an industry it was largely contemporary with the tin trade, and in towns like Tavistock, Ashburton and Chagford retained its importance after the stannaries had declined. Cloth incorporating Dartmoor wool was milled or 'fulled' in the towns and settlements of the moor's perimeter, but the carding and spinning of the raw wool, and often its weaving, was an industry of the cottage and lonely farmstead. For its beginnings the Dartmoor wool trade owed much to the Cistercians who, settling at Buckfast in the twelfth century, pastured their sheep on Holne, Buckfast and Brent moors and built up a considerable wool exchange with Florentine merchants. Profit from wool sales was also a valuable part of the economy of Tavistock Abbey, a Benedictine house. By the end of the fourteenth century, however, England had developed a thriving and expanding home cloth trade, and to help it Edward III prohibited the export of English wool. The development of the tucking mill in the thirteenth and early fourteenth centuries brought clothmaking out of the towns and into those areas where wool was produced and where there was water power to work the mills.

After wool had been carded and spun it had to be scoured to cleanse it of superfluous oil or grease. On Dartmoor this was often done by dipping it in baskets into streams, and at Ashburton the grease and scum washed out was collected into pits as a highly prized fertiliser. The process was also carried out in the tucking mill with soap or fullers earth or, as was more usual in the West Country, with stale urine as a scouring agent. The cloth, particularly that made from the short Dartmoor wool, was then pounded with heavy wooden hammers driven off a water wheel, rather in the manner of the tinners' stamps. This pounding or milling process promoted thickening or felting, after which the cloth was stretched on racks or tenters and partly dried. The surface could then be raised by teazle heads and cropped and sheared to make a nap.

Moretonhampstead had a tucking mill before the end of the thirteenth century, and a tradition of clothmaking began there lasting into the eighteenth. A tucking mill was probably established at Ashburton about the same time, and a century-and-a-half later there were fifteen mills in and around Tavistock engaged in cloth manufacture. Some of these may well have been rudimentary, perhaps merely buildings housing tubs for scouring wool, but they formed the nucleus of a clothmaking industry which by the eighteenth century had made Tavistock a considerable serge-making centre. Sticklepath, Bridestowe, Belstone and Dean Prior all had tucking mills in the seventeenth century, and so did Widecombe which had a thriving cloth industry well into the eighteenth century, embracing not only spinners and weavers but quite prosperous clothiers. Another important centre was South Brent, where in 1691 the tucking mill had an adjoining close with four dozen cloth racks where the cloth was stretched after it had been milled. Here, too, was a water-powered teazle mill.

Joyce Youings in *Devon and Cornwall Notes and Queries*, Vol. 30, Part 3, refers to the purchase by a Florentine merchant of wool from Buckfast Abbey in about 1340. The price ranged from 7 to 12 marks a sack of 364lb, well below the price paid for better quality wool from Ford Abbey, which fetched 15 marks or £10 a sack. The merchant was connected with the great banking firm of the Bardi. An Act of Edward III forbade the export of English wool except by alien merchants.

Medieval Dartmoor wool was coarse, short and spiky; that taken by the Tavistock mills off the western quarter of the moor was of 'such grossness and stubbornness' that it had to be worked up with lambs' wool and flock (a practice prohibited in the manufacture of most other woollen cloths) to make it saleable under the name of 'Tavistocks', a light, coarse serge. In 1463 the inhabitants of Roborough, Lifton and Tavistock Hundreds were allowed by Act of Parliament to use flock wool in the manufacture of Tavistocks. This was extended in 1534 to the manufacture of 'plains', a similar variety of cloth made in South Devon. Laura Nicholls in her thesis *The Trading Community of Totnes and Dartmouth* says that much of the wool for the cloth made in that area

came from Dartmoor. But by the end of the seventeenth century Dartmoor and Devon sheep had been sufficiently improved to produce a
dense, medium-length fleece, furnishing a tolerable middle-grade wool,
and this, with a mixture of Irish wool imported through Barnstaple and
Bideford, provided much of the wool for coarse serge making around
Dartmoor. In 1791 it was estimated that out of a sheep population in
Devon of almost 700,000, nearly 80,000 were 'summered' on Dartmoor
proper.

The wool trade had peaks and slumps but in its best years, in the
fourteenth and sixteenth centuries, it rivalled the tin trade in importance,
and the accounts of the wardens of the Guild of St Michael in Chagford show a steadier income being derived from wool sales than from
their shares in tin workings. The pattern gradually established around
and on Dartmoor saw Tavistock and the area to the north and north-
east becoming a centre of coarse cloth manufacture, using a large percentage of Dartmoor wool, while the middle Dartside towns of Ashburton
and Buckfastleigh, which served as 'catchment' areas for the fleeces
from the moor's southern slopes and valleys, became mainly spinning
centres.

This pattern was preserved well into the nineteenth century. In 1838
around Tavistock there were over a hundred looms weaving cloth. Along
the Taw between Okehampton and Sticklepath, where there was a re-
surgence of the trade in the early 1800s, there were 500, among them
the Old Cleave or Willmott's mill at Belstone, which had earlier turned
out scarlet cloth for the Nizam of Hyderabad's bodyguard. In Ashburton,
Buckfastleigh and Buckfast something like a third of the population was
employed on over 1,300 looms. In 1816 William Stephens, a Bicking-
ton spinning operator, had given an added impetus to the industry by
patenting a spring-levered spinning frame employing a larger bobbin,
which cut out wastage caused by the thread breaking and speeded up
spinning. On the strength of this patent Stephens was taken into partnership by his employer, John Couch of Buckfastleigh. To Ashburton, which
incorporates in its arms a teazle, the fuller's emblem, the wool trade
had been worth £100,000 a year, and its merchants went to Widecombe, Rattery and South Brent among other places to buy carded and
spun wool from the cottagers. Mixing Dartmoor wool with the long-
woolled fleeces of the valley sheep, Ashburton turned increasingly to
serge manufacture in the last century and in the late 1860s was supplying
scarlet army serge to India. It equipped the German army with blankets
for the 1870 war with France, turned out fine dress lengths for ladies'
costumes, made horse cloths and light serge coverings for cartridge cases.

By 1914, when the German army was looking elsewhere for its supplies, orders for puttees and coarse cheap cloth for British army uniforms kept the district, and particularly Buckfastleigh, busy. Buckfastleigh used much Dartmoor wool for its blanket and serge combing mills, and produced navy serge and blankets until well into the present century.

Blanket and serge manufacture spilled over into Chagford in 1800 when John Berry, finding labour scarce in Ashburton, moved there to employ over 1,200 weavers finishing 700 serges a week. Chagford was on the old wool packhorse route between North Devon and Ashburton and spun for itself a modest living from the wool trade. The industry declined here in the 1860s, as it had before this date along the northern fringes of the Moor, killed off by the more ready availability of cheap cotton goods, the loss of the East India Company market, and the better organised Yorkshire woollen trade. By the end of the nineteenth century Moretonhampstead, Okehampton and Widecombe had forgotten about wool, and Tavistock only just recalled it in a combing mill which finally ceased working in 1960. Only around Buckfastleigh and further down the Dart valley at Harberton did the industry retain some importance with a blanket and coat tweed manufacture. Today the trade lingers only at Buckfast, where a quantity of Dartmoor wool is taken for yarn spinning, and in the tweed and blanket manufacture at Dartington Hall.

Like the tin trade, clothmaking on and around Dartmoor was an industry springing from the area's natural resources. The sheep, the water, the wool, and even the moss to dye it, all come off the Moor, and in the so-called Tavistock serges it produced its own distinctive coarse cloth. If in scale its relationship to the Devon wool trade as a whole was small, it was a highly characteristic one and, unlike the tin industry with which it rubbed shoulders at different times, it still has some significance, for wool from the black-faced Scotch sheep which now run on Dartmoor finds a ready export outlet in Italy, where it is used for mattress filling.

Edge Tool and Corn Mills

Water-operated mills are highly adaptable structures and on and around Dartmoor they served many purposes. The cloth mill at Belstone ground corn before it made scarlet serge for Hyderabad and then reverted to grist milling. At Horrabridge the Phoenix mill, which has stood on the same site for two centuries, began as a corn mill, became successively a leather dressing, paper, and woollen mill, and ended by reverting to corn grinding. It has since been badly damaged by fire. Chagford made its own electricity (it was one of the first towns in Devon to do so) by adapting a corn mill water wheel to drive a generating plant; at Ashburton another corn mill was similarly utilised.

Once a water wheel was in position, a train of gears could be attached to it for serving a variety of processes, as happened at Sticklepath. Here a mill originally making cloth in one section and grinding corn in another turned over early in the last century to making edge tools, becoming a combined saw mill and foundry. Forging was carried out by massive trip hammers worked off a wheel, and a simple coupling to the wheel also operated shears for cutting iron bars. Another wheel drove a fan feeding air to five hearths and two furnaces, and a third a grinding wheel on which tools were sharpened and polished. With its attached saw mill the foundry turned out over thirty types of agricultural tools, six varieties of shovels, turfing irons for peat cutting, and specialised delving tools and scoops for the china clay industry. Carts and wheel barrows were made, ready-cut boat knees supplied to boat yards, gates and hurdles to sheep-farmers, while housewives from the villages around called in to have their smoothing irons polished up on the emery wheel. Its owners imported special laminated steel from Sheffield for their edge tools and kept a stall in Okehampton market selling not only their own wares but acting as agents for American tools.

In the 1930s this foundry was still employing twenty-five men, and an old employee could recall that in one day five men turned out 400 swan-neck hoes from cutting the steel bars to the final polished and varnished product. All this was in a Dartmoor border village of less than 500 inhabitants. The south wall of this foundry, battered by a century of wind and rain, fell down in 1960, compelling the foundry's closure, but it is now being restored with much of its original and unique machinery. Another edge tool mill at Steps Bridge, Dunsford, adapted from a former flour mill, still works.

The flour mills, where the miller ground grain for flour and bread, are now chiefly remembered only in names like 'Mill Corner' or 'Mill Lane', but the miller played an important and far from humble part in the industrial economy of the Moor and its towns and villages, supplying flour for bread, cattle feed, and malt for the small town brewing-houses and inns. Corn mills were not only found in the big perimeter towns of Okehampton, Tavistock and Ashburton, but at Moretonhampstead, South Brent, Meavy, Widecombe, Petertavy (which had two), Shaugh Prior and Walkhampton. Chagford had four within its parish boundary. In the smaller settlements they catered for immediate local needs—three

Page 125 (above) *Jordan, Ponsworthy;* (below) *Tor Farm, Leusdon*

Page 126 (above) *Cutting turf ties of peat on Dartmoor in 1912;* (below) *general view of Babeny farmland*

bushels of flour here and two cwt of barley there—and seldom operated more than two pairs of grinding stones. But Two Bridges, an important cattle centre in the last century, had in 1858 a mill operating three pairs of French burr stones, with an attached bolting mill for sieving and cleansing grain, along with a sack hoist all worked off a sixteen-foot water wheel. Such a mill could turn out sixty sacks of flour a week. Corn milling survived at Chagford until 1917, and even later at Walkhampton and Horrabridge. None work now; they were victims of the big steam roller mills with their higher and faster rates of extraction which began to appear in centres like Plymouth, Exeter and Brixham by the middle of the last century, making cheaper, whiter, and more palatable if less wholesome flour.

Leather, Paper and Gunpowder

Similarly it was the concentration of industry in the big perimeter towns which killed the moorland tanning and paper mills. As with the fulling and textile processes, tanning and leather dressing on Dartmoor before the days of the railway was closely linked with a local product— the calf and ox hides of Dartmoor cattle. They provided, too, the raw material for the cordwainer and saddler, while serge makers frequently carried on the business of dressing sheepskins (fellmongering) to provide an outlet for their capital during fluctuations in the cloth trade. Plymouth was the big tanning centre, but Okehampton, Moretonhampstead and Tavistock had tanyards, and so did Sticklepath, where the tannery had adjoining premises used for candle making. The tanners worked closely with the oak bark rippers, whose trade stained their hands and clothes red. Bark was taken from young coppice oaks when the sap was rising, a vertical cut being made down the length of the tree to peel it off. After 'ripping' the bark was stacked for a year and then steeped in vats in the tanyards before it was placed in alternate layers between the tanned hides to impart suppleness and colour to the leather. When the Horrabridge leather mill was taken over in 1850 by Hamlyns, the Buckfastleigh wool factors, the inventory records the taking over of a stock of bark in the mill. Oak bark ripping is still occasionally carried out on the eastern and southern slopes of the moor.

Papermaking, for which the clear moorland water was greatly esteemed, was more haphazard in distribution, reaching its fullest development along the Moor's edge. The product of the smaller mills was a stiff, thick pasteboard or wrapping paper made mostly from coarse rags, but peat fibres were used for the same sort of paper in a short-

H

lived mill at Princetown in the middle of the last century, and paper from Dartmoor peat was manufactured in a mill at Gunnislake, largely destroyed by fire in the 1860s. Paper was made at Shaugh Bridge from 1760 to 1832, where the beating irons were worked by a water wheel driven off the Plym. There were town paper mills at Moretonhampstead for nearly a century until 1826; at one time they made pasteboard for packing bales of serge. Paper was also made at Buckfastleigh, Lee Mill (where the mill was burnt in 1908), South Brent and Horrabridge. It is still made at Ivybridge, where for over two centuries the Erme has been utilised for manufacturing high quality hand-processed paper. There were originally two mills here; the lower mill, now the site of a printing works, and the higher mill near the railway viaduct where the Wiggins Teape group, in a much modified building known as Stowford Mills, produce paper for bank and government use. It was in this mill, established in 1786 and bought and enlarged by John Allen of Plymouth in the middle of the last century, that a remarkably high-grade writing paper was being made in 1858 with a surface prepared from boiled buffalo skins, Plymouth Millbay white soap, soda and alum. A ten hp water wheel drove a 'machine which charged the paper with electricity to assist the glazing process'.

The making of gunpowder on Dartmoor arose from the demand for 'rock' powder in the granite and slate quarries. This was carried out for nearly fifty years at Cherrybrook, between Two Bridges and Postbridge, a remote spot sheltered by trees to minimise the effects of frequent explosions, one of which in 1857 caused £500 worth of damage. The industry was established in 1844 by a Plymouth alderman, George Frean, using methods similar to those in the Royal gunpowder mills at Faversham, Kent, where powder was made for the Army and Navy. Charcoal (of which 100lb was needed to make a ton of gunpowder), saltpetre and sulphur were mixed, the quantities varying with the type of charge required, but normally in the proportion of 75 parts of saltpetre to 15 of charcoal and 10 of sulphur. The powder was ground by being placed in a trough on a circular stone bed in which heavy wheel stones turned, driven by centrally-placed water wheels turned by water from a leat taken off the East Dart. The gunpowder was tested by detonating small pieces of granite clitter or by firing an iron ball from a military-type mortar, the quality being classified according to the distance the ball travelled. Packed in barrels made on the site, it had the advantage of dislodging stone more cleanly than dynamite, which tended to shatter it. 'Rock powder' is still used for special tasks in the Merrivale quarry, but dynamite, invented in 1867, rapidly superseded it and the Dartmoor powder mills, which employed about 100 men, closed in the 1890s. A farm now occupies the site, but the testing mortar and outlines of the buildings remain and so does the leat, now long dry.

Peat Working

Peat took the place of coal on Dartmoor. A charter of Henry III granting the right to take peat from the Moor referred to it as coal, and in the eighteenth century the people who cut and sold it were known as colliers. The tang of a 'yaffle o' peat' caught up in a blazing faggot of crackling furze was once a characteristic smell on Dartmoor, but one seldom encountered today. Yet peat cutting for domestic and industrial fuel and its carbonisation in mounds to make a hard, clean, grey charcoal for smelting was an almost continuous industry on Dartmoor from the time of John until George IV. Peat charcoal has the same calorific value as good English coal, 100lb of dried peat yielding about 36lb of charcoal. For smelting it was purer than coal and infinitely lighter to carry, but it was consumed very rapidly and for this reason wood charcoal, which was denser and burned with a more even and steady heat, was preferred.

The right of taking peat was a tinner's privilege; it was transported to Cornwall and was used in some Dartmoor mines, notably Wheal Betsy, near Tavistock, for which peat was cut around Walkham Head, although the main peat-cutting areas on Dartmoor have been north of the Tavistock-Moretonhampstead road. Apart from its industrial use, peat was the domestic fuel for almost everyone living on Dartmoor and the peat stack was a familiar object near many moorland dwellings. In the eighteenth century large amounts were transported to the South Hams for this purpose and dried peat turves were hawked at a shilling a dozen in towns and villages. The Rev John Swete at the end of the eighteenth century watched a man cutting slabs of 'fat, bitumous turf' two inches thick and trudging six miles into Tavistock to sell twenty of them for two shillings. It was often bought by poor people in pennyworths and two pennyworths.

The peat cutter worked with three special tools—a triangular shovel called a budding iron for cutting; a long knife for trimming heather roots; and a turf iron, a semi-circular tool with one of its horns or prongs turned at right angles to help lever out the turf after it had been cut by the shovel. Peat-cutting grounds were known as ties, and a farmer could keep himself supplied from one tie for twenty years. Peat used for the domestic hearth came from the top 'smouldery layers' of turf and was known as 'vag'. The darker, richer bog peat for industrial use, which burned with a clean white ash, was taken from deeper levels. Peat slabs were generally 20in long, 7in wide and 2in thick and a good peat-cutter, with little more to sustain him than a hunk of raw bacon for his midday meal, could cut 1,440 slabs in half a day.

Naphtha, petrol, tar oil and acetic acid can be distilled from peat, and the possibility of doing this on a large scale on Dartmoor has bewitched a number of speculators. The earliest and most successful attempt was in 1844, when £19,000 was spent on establishing a peat distillation works at Bachelor's Hall. This was later moved over into the then empty Princetown Prison which was lit with gas and candles made in the plant, while mothballs were also manufactured. Naphtha is a volatile oil, burning with a bright flare, and candles made from it were in great demand by miners. The peat came from beds at Holming Beam and Greena Ball, connected to Princetown by a horse tramway, at the back of the Devil's Elbow Inn, which was earlier known as the Railway Tavern. The rapidly expanding coal gas industry killed this project, as it did the South Brent peat and peat charcoal works set up in 1846 at Shipley Bridge. Here use was made of the peat beds at Redlake to manufacture not only naphtha but a 'dense, cheap coal' for smelting mineral ores, especially the rich iron ore then being taken in considerable amount from a mine on Furzeham Common, Brixham. This venture failed in 1850 and the tramway laid down to carry the peat was taken over by the Redlake Clay works, whose ruined buildings are now intermingled with those of the naphtha plant.

Thirty years later the lure of naphtha attracted speculators to the massive peat beds at the source of the Rattlebrook, between Great Links Tor and Hare Tor. The West of England Compressed Peat Company, mostly Exeter men, sought to exploit a process invented by John Howard of Topsham to eliminate water from the peat by hydraulic compression. This venture, started in 1878, lasted little more than two years, but in 1901 another company took over the site, setting up plant to carbonise peat by subjecting it to great pressure and heat. The combustion rate proved too rapid for economical use and the venture failed. But the spell of the Rattlebrook beds was still potent. A German chemist in the intervening years was said to have perfected a plant to extract alcohol from them, but died without revealing his formula. This claim, scouted by many, was sufficiently believed in for a company to lease 360 acres at Rattlebrook in 1937 and announce a plan to produce crude oils, petrol, gas and charcoal from a plant on the site and to sell the peat petrol in pumps by the roadside. Another speculator offered to join them and build a hydro at Rattlebrook to give patients peat baths if the long-disused peat railway connecting the beds with the LSWR system at Bride-stowe could be reconstructed to passenger standards. The war ended this scheme although some peat-cutting on the site was resumed in 1946. The same beds were prospected again in 1955 by a Torquay firm when peat for agricultural purposes was taken from them. Some of this was used in the 1956 Royal Show for bedding flowers and shrubs in the display pavilion. But transport costs killed this venture after two years, and since then the Rattlebrook peat beds have remained in peace and isolation.

The large heather-humus content and acidity of much Dartmoor peat, together with its remoteness and the lack of labour to cut it, prevents its wider use at a time when over 50,000 tons a year are being taken for horticultural use from peat beds near Glastonbury. Exploitation at that rate would be disastrous on Dartmoor. But if the peat-cutter is no longer seen on Dartmoor, he has left his mark as surely as the tinner, seaming the ground with pits and trenches often twenty feet deep. Small pieces of carbonised peat lie scattered over a large area, particularly around Okement Hill, Hangingstone Hill, Wild Tor and Quintin's Man, where the moor has been lowered several feet through centuries of peat-cutting.

Quarries

Quarry workings pock-mark Dartmoor. Some are little more than the merest paring of the granite for road and farm use, others have involved the near destruction of tors, while workings such as the Haytor quarries are substantial excavations of several acres. Some 400 varieties of granite and allied stone are known on Dartmoor, but the quarried Dartmoor granite is coarse-grained, hard, and blue-grey. It is fairly resistant to corrosion, as Nelson's Column in Trafalgar Square shows. The granite for this came from Foggin Tor, near Princetown. Granite is also capable of being richly carved, as can be seen in many churches.

Granite-working on Dartmoor has rivalled mining in economic importance, but quarrying in the sense understood today is little more than 150 years old. Before this the ancient forest and commons laws allowed only the taking of surface granite (moorstone) free of charge in the form of boulders or clitters. Undressed moorstone was used by Bronze Age men; in its dressed forms, split by wedges, it has been worked up into gateposts, feeding troughs, cheese and cider presses, and has provided grindstones and rollers for domestic hand corn mills. Dressed with axes, it has formed the quoins and buttresses of Devon churches, and shaped

Dartmoor boulders have been included in many of the larger moorland farmhouses. Evidence of stone-cutting from granite clitter can be found on areas like Soussons common.

Probably the earliest granite to be quarried on Dartmoor was at Haytor, where quarries were opened in the first twenty years of the last century by George Templer of Stover. The granite here is notably hard (some say the hardest on Dartmoor, but this is a matter of fierce dispute among quarrymen) and was used in the rebuilding of London Bridge in 1825, the stone being carried over a specially-laid tramway of granite rails and blocks (see chapter seven) and shipped in coastal schooners from Teignmouth. It was also used for the British Museum, and the Exeter war memorial was made of Haytor granite in 1919, though the quarries have not actively worked since the latter half of the last century.

The most striking memorial to the durability of Dartmoor granite, however, is probably the prison at Princetown, built with granite taken from Walkhampton Common in 1804–6. These workings were developed into five large quarries around Foggin and King Tors, by Sir Thomas Tyrwhitt, the prison's builder, who was also a Lord Warden of the Stannaries and one of the best-known of the early nineteenth-century industrial pioneers on Dartmoor. He laid a horse tramway, opened in 1823, from the quarries to Plymouth, and this carried stone used for kerbing pavements and channels for street drains. Huge blocks went over the tramway to build up the breakwater at the entrance to the Sound. Later in the century it was used in the defences around Plymouth, and granite corbels for repairing London Bridge were also fashioned here in the late 1890s; about a dozen surplus corbels can still be seen lying in the turf by the abandoned railway siding. These quarries ceased working in 1937, but the deserted and abandoned site, with its remains of inclines, sidings and giant blocks of half-dressed stone is full of fascination. Granite has been quarried at Blackingstone, near Moretonhampstead, from the Dewerstone at Shaugh, and near Ivybridge for the building of the Great Western viaducts over the Erme and on either side of Cornwood. From Trowlesworthy, near Sheepstor, came a distinctive red granite, unlike any other in the West of England, and which took on a high polish for columnar and monumental work.

The demand for granite created the little industrial settlement of Merrivale near Princetown, which grew up around the quarry opened there in 1876. The massive spoil heaps today look down over the tin streamers' blowing houses by the Walkham and dominate the skyline as one climbs the road to Tavistock around the shoulders of Staple Tor. Although the terraces of workmen's cottages have been demolished, this quarry still works—the only one on Dartmoor proper to do so. Stone from it was used in a New Scotland Yard building in the 1950s. It cleaned and repaired the granite blocks of old London Bridge, shipping over 200 tons of them to Arizona in 1970 for re-erection. Granite clitter and moorstone boulders lie strewn over the moorland at Merrivale, and at Staple Tor the clitter was worked in the 1870s to make granite setts or pitches to pave streets.

One highly distinctive felsite stone is no longer quarried. This is Roborough Stone, derived from a granite elvan crossing Roborough Down; it was one of the prized medieval building stones of south-west Devon. It has a warm, buff appearance, and was a favourite stone for dressing and carved work. It can be seen in the two arcades of the fifteenth-century church at Tamerton Foliot. Most of the quarries from which it was taken on Roborough Down have now been filled in.

Surprisingly, ice has also been manufactured on Dartmoor. This was for a short period in the 1870s, when spring water from Sourton Tors was trapped and frozen in stone tanks for the Plymouth fish trade. It was difficult to keep the ice from melting in transit and this largely led to the abandonment of the enterprise.

China Clay

The industrial world of today levies tribute on Dartmoor through the china clay industry. More than two million tons of china clay a year is now produced, of which 76 per cent is exported. Foreign currency earnings are £15 million a year. Nearly 450,000 tons of high-grade china clay were dug from the south western corner of Dartmoor in 1967, or nearly a quarter of the total amount produced in the United Kingdom, and the production figure grows each year.

Dartmoor's 'clay corner' is a dusty, spectacular world of staring pits, towering sandhills, underground pipe lines and streams which run white with the clay effluent. Water pervades almost the whole process of clay working. Hoses (known as monitors) delivering 1,500 gallons a minute wash the clay out of the pit sides from which, after the mica waste has settled, it is piped or pumped to the de-watering and refining tanks. When it has settled to the consistency of putty it is passed through filter presses which reduce the water content of the clay by a further thirty per cent, the water being pumped back to reservoirs for further use. From the presses it passes on to the 'drys'—steam-heated kilns, which at Marsh Mills and Cornwood, reduce to a period of eight hours or less a drying process which once took as many weeks.

In its massiveness and grouping, the china clay industry stands today squarely in the twentieth century, yet in many ways the ancient tin industry it has superseded peers over its shoulder. The same granite from which the tin lodes sprang is the source of china clay, which is the decomposed felspar of the granite, rotted to a soft white powdery substance. Clay and tin working—as in the deposits at Redlake above Ivybridge—often occur in the same area. Terms like 'stope' and 'captain' (a pit foreman) come from the world of the metal miner, while the washing and processing of the clay not only recall the trunking, settling and slime pits of the tinner, but the sand waste brings the same river and estuary pollution problems. Even more striking is the economic parallel, for the importance of china clay as a currency earner places it in much the same relation to the country's economy as the medieval tin industry stood to the exchequer of the Plantagenet kings. China clay is now the country's second largest bulk export and one of its quickest currency earners. It can be in its natural state in the pit on Monday, and by Saturday refined and in a boat on the way to America.

No boring or pit has yet 'bottomed' the china clay deposits on the Moor. Clay is known to be in the Plym valley up to the head of the river. There are indications of it in the whole area between the Erme and the Avon, and these have been worked at Redlake and Leftlake, around the Erme's eastern tributaries. The old-style disused 'dry' by the A38 at Cantrell above Ivybridge (now used by a tractor firm) is a relic of this working, which ceased about 1932. Clay was also dug on Brent Moor above Shipley Bridge in the last century, and settling pits and traces of a tramway still remain. Their remoteness from roads and the variable nature of the clay made these workings uneconomic.

The industry today is concentrated around Lee Moor and Heddon Down, about nine miles from Plymouth, where six pits out of nearly a dozen which have been worked are in production, the others being held in reserve or used as reservoirs. The Dartmoor china clay industry is essentially the creation of William Phillips, a Sunderland engineer, who in 1833, for £75 a year, acquired the tenancy of the Lee Moor pit which had been started in 1830. The clay was early recognised as of exceptional quality and came to be widely used in the pottery established by Thomas Minton in 1796, and in the Great Exhibition of 1851 a sample of Lee Moor clay was singled out for special mention by the judges—the only clay to be so mentioned.

By the time Phillips died, in debt and discredited, in 1861, he had established the Lee Moor working as one of the most advanced and extensive in Devon and Cornwall. The now-abandoned railway (see Chap-

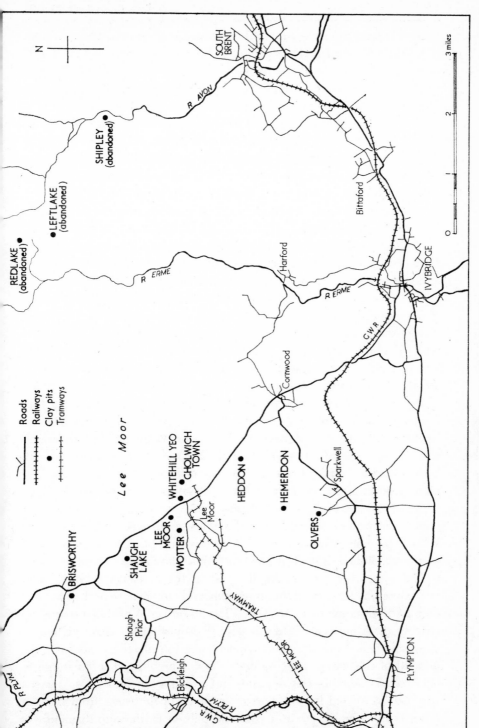

Fig 14. Main china clay pits of Dartmoor.

ter seven) built to link the pit with deep water wharves at Plymouth, the leat from the Plym at Drizzlecombe, cut to bring water to the pit and later extended to serve the Bottle Hill tin mine at Plympton, and the deep drainage adit, driven for half a mile under the Lee Moor pit, are traces of his handiwork which can still be seen and, with the exception of the railway, are still in use. The adit, taking nine years to build by gangs employed continuously day and night, drained the pit to 120ft. With the sand it brought out, Phillips pioneered the making of bricks and sanitary ware from china clay waste. He created the settlement of Lee Moor (building Boringdon and Sunderland cottages, which are still inhabited) for the hundred hands he employed, and established a mechanics' institute for their leisure hours.

Phillips's ambitions outran his capital, and on his death the Lee Moor porcelain works, as they were called, were put up for tender. The annual production was then 4,500 tons, on which Lord Morley, the landowner, received dues of 4s a ton, as well as a toll on the bricks and tiles produced. The works passed to the Martin family of St Austell (bricks stamped with their name are still scattered around Lee Moor) who went on to develop the adjacent Whitehill Yeo and Cholwich Town pits. During the remainder of the century other companies explored the granite mass surrounding Hemerdon Ball, while pits were also opened at Wigford Down, Shaugh Moor and Wotter. In 1919, under a regrouping plan which established the pattern of ownership as it is known today, English China Clays took over the Lee Moor, Whitehill Yeo, and Cholwich Town pits which, with the Shaugh Lake and Heddon Down pit, both owned by Watts, Blake and Bearne of Newton Abbot, are the five main producing pits in the area today. Another pit at Brisworthy is independently operated. It is the only one without a prominent waste dump, the proprietor selling off the waste as it accumulates. The old Wotter pit with its adjoining and picturesque 'dry', now ruined and partly demolished, is used by English China Clays as a reservoir.

The Lee Moor pit, among the first in the industry to be seriously mechanised, is now one of the largest china clay pits in the world, over 300ft deep and extending over 100 acres. The adjoining Whitehill Yeo pit, exploiting the same bed of clay, is only slightly smaller. About eight tons of waste come from the production of one ton of china clay, and the disposal of this waste is the industry's major problem. The huge dumps often cover valuable clay ground, but attempts to find a use for the sand are hampered by transport costs. Some of the waste from the Lee Moor dump (the silicate in it is second only in hardness to diamonds) is utilised in a plant capable of making thirty million silicate bricks a year in a variety of colour finishes for building, agriculture and engineering. They are twice as hard as the conventional clay brick. More is used for prefabricated building structures but none of these processes account for more than three per cent of the waste thrown up.

On the other hand, no single Dartmoor product has ever had a wider use than china clay, for it can be tailored to a variety of requirements. The plastics, paint and pharmaceutical industries use it extensively as a filler and reinforcing agent. It adds to the finish of textiles, and in Spain and Portugal is even used for clarifying wines. Its largest single use—about seventy per cent—is in the paper industry as a filler for imparting a smooth surface. Every newspaper published in Britain may be said to contain a tiny particle of Dartmoor. In addition, a special type of calcining clay is produced at Lee Moor for electrical insulation and crucibles in the chemical industry. Finally there is its historic use in the ceramics industry for earthenware and fine porcelain, for which the Lee Moor clay was early noted. Fine English bone china contains 28 per cent china clay and 47 per cent bone ash, the use of ground animal bones distinguishing English porcelain from Continental, which can contain as much as 75 per cent china clay with felspar used as a flux.

China clay production has altered the skyline of Dartmoor between Shaugh Prior and Heddon Down, where the lower part of the moor between Shell Top and Penn Beacon is being slowly excavated away, bringing the industry into fierce conflict with the preservationists. In an area largely unexplored and unrecorded by the industrial archaeologist, giant earth-moving machines, in their search for new clay areas, are fast pushing aside the relics of earlier workings of an industry which until recently still had primitive open air drys and used water wheels for some of its processes. Vanishing, too, are the old-type drying sheds which used the underground heating principle of the Roman hypocaust, while even the time-honoured method of separating the clay waste by water, which filled the landscape with lakes, leats and launders, is giving place to a method of electronic separation in steel tanks.

Finally there is Lee Moor itself, which for its size probably exports more than any other village in England. Without the china clay industry it would not exist, for nearly 90 per cent of its 500 inhabitants are employed by the industry. When it began there in the 1830s the sole building was a hut, and the only sign of industry a granite and dunstone quarry 'worked largely for pavement purposes'. Twenty years later a contemporary account records that the workings, because of their situation 'in the midst of wild moorland constantly arrest notice of that enterprise which has converted a barren wilderness into a region of profitable and prosperous industry and peopled the wild wastes with an hardy, active and intelligent population'.

Lee Moor, in reality, is a Cornish industrial outpost on Dartmoor, largely peopled by the descendents of migrating Cornish clay workers until today, when the Treviscoe male voice choir comes from the heart of the Cornish clay area to sing in Lee Moor, there are probably more Cornishmen among the listeners than in the choir. But more than anything else Lee Moor is pervaded by the frugal, austere atmosphere of the Methodism which has nurtured the settlement for over a century and is as inseparable from the neighbourhood as the clay pits themselves. Even the present Methodist chapel enshrines an older industrial tradition, for it incorporates part of the old pug mill which Phillips built for his brickworks. English China Clays, who now own the chapel, perpetuate the tradition by making themselves responsible for its exterior upkeep, charging a peppercorn rent of only 2s a year—perhaps the cheapest chapel rent in Britain. Even the burial ground emphasises the common links, for only the Methodist half of it is used, the Anglicans (who are served by a mission hall adjoining the chapel) choosing to share their last rest with the Methodists. There is no inn, no cinema, and although the motor-car has diminished the old feeling of remoteness, a severe snowstorm can still isolate Lee Moor from the urban sophistication of Plymouth.

The china clay industry is the latest and most successful of a long line of industries which have sought to find wealth in and amid the age-old granite of Dartmoor. It is unlikely to be the last. Mineral prospectors are increasingly busy and search is now being made for uranium 'to start possible mining operations'. Around the old Vitifer mine the alluvials and lode outcrops near Birch Tor are known to carry a black tin content of between 4lb and 11lb a ton. Granite still abounds in immeasurable quantities. The problem of the future is to reconcile the still great industrial potentialities of 'the last great wilderness' with the demands of more and more people who seek its solitude for rest and recreation.

Notes to this chapter are on pages 289–292.

5

Farming

Michael Havinden and Freda Wilkinson

FARMING IS the most important occupation on Dartmoor today, as it has been for centuries. The farms within the forest known as the ancient tenements have been reduced from thirty-five to fourteen separate farms, but the area of some of them has been increased by enclosures from the moor, known as 'newtakes,' made mainly in the nineteenth century; and about a dozen entirely new farms, which were created between about 1780 and 1870, have continued in existence. The Moor is also used as a common grazing ground, not only by the moorland farmers but by the large number of venville farms situated around the borders, which depend to a considerable extent upon it for their viability.

The Moor is thus farmed by three different groups: the first two are moorland farmers in the full sense, being settled on the moor, and the third are border farmers, with their main land in enclosed fields just off the Moor but enjoying rights of common grazing. In the northern part of the Moor these rights arc at present reduced by the artillery ranges.

The ancient tenements are now much larger than formerly, ranging in size from about 800 acres to 72, with an average size of about 400 acres, but only two of the original settlements have completely disappeared (see Figure 15). These are Brownberry, whose lands have been absorbed by Sherberton, and Lake in Bellever. Brownberry farmhouse was already a ruin in 1893 when Robert Burnard described it in the third volume of his *Dartmoor Pictorial Records,* and Lake was leased with the rest of Bellever to the Forestry Commission. Much of the best land in Bellever is under trees but one farm and two forestry smallholdings have survived.

The farms created by the Victorian 'improvers' are generally larger than the ancient tenements, ranging from nearly 1,700 acres to 225, but they lie on more exposed parts of the Moor, and are less fertile. Some of their enclosed fields, containing hundreds of acres, are not fields in any meaningful sense, but enclosed pieces of rough moorland. Their walls, however, keep out the livestock grazing on the commons. The farms in the Forest, with only a few exceptions, are rented from the Duchy of Cornwall, either on yearly or longer leases, but even these farms have tended to

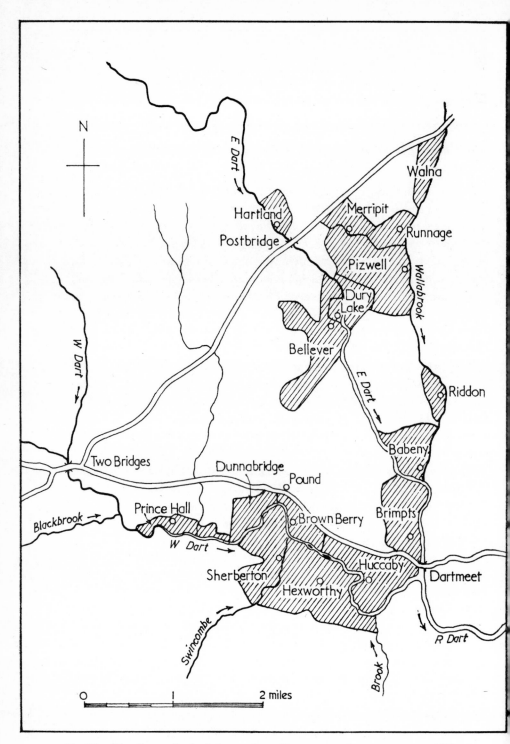

Fig 15. The diagonally shaded area shows Dartmoor ancient tenements, c 1750.

remain in the same hands for long periods of time, often passing from generation to generation.

Before looking more closely at the history of the Dartmoor farms and their ancient common rights, something must be said of the special conditions imposed by the Moor on its farmers. First, the altitude, the frequent rain and mist, and the rugged, stony, and acid nature of the soil rule out cereal growing except in a few favoured valleys. The economic core of the Dartmoor farm, as of all hill farms, is its livestock—cattle, sheep and ponies. A farmer at the moor's edge may milk a dairy herd of Friesians but also keep a flock of Scotch Blackfaced sheep on the open common above his farm. He may even rent from the Duchy one of the large nineteenth-century 'newtakes' of rough grazing in the Forest, miles from his home farm, and stock it with hill sheep and, in the summer, with Galloway beef cattle.

The more traditional Dartmoor farmer, in one of the sheltered valleys that penetrate deep into the Moor, may keep the same strain of dual-purpose South Devon cattle that his grandfather kept, selling great three-year-old steers half-fat to graziers at the Ashburton cattle fairs. His wife may scald cream from the cows to sell at the kitchen door or the local tea-rooms. His Whitefaced Dartmoor sheep (the improved or greyfaced Dartmoor sheep are rarely seen on the Moor itself) will graze the common from shearing-time in June till tupping time in October, and may spend most of the winter 'down-country' on bought keep of swedes and grass. A score of Dartmoor mares, a riding pony or two, a sow and her litter, and some poultry may complete the stocking of such a farm.

Above the 1,000-ft contour there are some farms where only the hill breeds of sheep and cattle are kept and little cultivation is carried out, beyond a certain acreage for hay. The small part-time holdings, once common even on the higher parts of the Moor, that helped support the families of the tin-miners, quarrymen, prison employees and so on, have now almost disappeared. Their land has been amalgamated with larger holdings and their houses have been destroyed or bought up for holiday cottages. The income of any of these moorland farms may be supplemented by boarding summer visitors, by pony trekking, dealing in livestock, or in some cases by a private income or pension. The profit margin on the single-suckling hill beef herds such as the Galloways depends almost entirely on the hill cow and calf subsidies, and to a lesser extent this applies to the flocks of hill sheep.

In a country as well-stocked as Devon is with sheep and beef, there is usually little demand by the down-country grazier for the rather 'wild

and woolly' store animal straight off the high Moor. Of course, once
fattened for the butcher, they make top quality meat but, except where
the breeder is able to 'finish' such animals on his own land, he does not
usually get a fair share of the final value of the animal. This is one
of the reasons why Dartmoor farmers often have some 'accommodation'
land down in lowland Devon.

The farmer who keeps the native breeds of South Devon cattle and
Whitefaced Dartmoor or Devon Closewool sheep has few marketing problems. They are more docile and productive than the Scotch breeds and
are the more popular for having been bred on poor land, so they are in
good demand for either breeding or feeding. But they cost more than
the Scotch breeds to keep, both in food and labour, and make less use
of the natural moorland grazings and more demands on the well-culti-
vated enclosed land.

Grazing

Most of the cultivated land is under grass, reseeded perhaps once in
ten or fifteen years after a crop or two of swedes or kale used for winter
feeding of livestock. As much as possible of this better grass-land is cut
for hay, also for winter fodder. Great reliance is placed on the rough
grazings of the newtakes or the open moor. In the summer this grazing
frees the better land for winter fodder production; in the winter it supplements such fodder.

Due to the high rainfall and the moisture-holding properties of the
peaty soil, the moors can still provide grazing in dry summers when many
of the 'down-country' pastures are brown and bare. Many livestock have
always been brought to the Moor in summer from down country farms
to be 'agisted' on the newtakes, or by the 'moormen' who rent the quarters of the open Forest from the Duchy.

Most of the moorland grasses are relatively unproductive, but they
will grow without assistance from man on the thin acid peat and provide
plenty of summer keep where the better cultivated species would not
grow. Two of the commonest are *molinia caerulea* or flying bent, locally
called sedge grass, and *nardus stricta* or mat grass. *Molinia* is a tall,
flat-bladed grass growing in tussocks. From early May, when it sends up
long green spikes through the heather, till July, when it flowers, it is
relished by stock and provides a useful feed for ewes, cows and mares in
milk. After flowering it loses all food value and turns yellow. *Nardus*
grows in needle-like tufts and is not liked by cattle and sheep. Ponies,
with their opposing incisors, can, however, nip out the green centre of

Page 143 (above) *Bellever clapper bridge over the East Dart, on the line of the Lich Way;* (below) *the medieval cross on Down Ridge near Horse Ford was restored after rediscovery in 1884, and is one of a series of crosses between Buckfastleigh and the west side of the moor*

Page 144 (left) *Windy Post, in Whitchurch parish, on the old line of the track across the moor from Tavistock; (below) direction stone at Cross Furzes, west of Buckfastleigh; B is for Brent, A for Ashburton, and there is a T on another face for Tavistock*

the tufts and discard the dead outer parts, which litter the ground where ponies have been grazing. In this way the ponies help to keep this practically worthless grass in check.

The heather and furze are more useful food plants than the casual observer might think. Being deep-rooted, they can take up minerals and trace elements from the subsoil that the grazing animal cannot get from the grasses. The heather-cropping Scotch Blackfaced sheep rarely suffers from the pine or 'moor-sick', a deficiency disease caused by lack of the trace-element cobalt in the Dartmoor topsoil. Other breeds of sheep, that confine themselves to the grasses, can be decimated by this disease unless given cobalt artificially or shifted to grazing off the Moor for a few weeks every year. Lack of trace-elements and minerals can also cause unthriftiness in cattle, and for this reason the experienced Dartmoor stockman likes to turn his cattle out to browse heather by day in the winter.

Furze or gorse is a plant rich in nutrients, a fact recognised by hill farmers for many centuries. In many hill areas it was the practice to cut and bruise the young growth of furze for the cattle throughout the winter and early spring for, like heather, the furze is an evergreen shrub. In the winter Dartmoor ponies can be seen bruising it with their hooves before eating it. These shrubs can generally be reached even after several inches of snow have buried all other plant life and no grazing is available in the fields.

The early spring is the leanest period for the Scotch sheep and ponies which winter on the open moor. There is very little grass about till late May and the animals have tired of the tough browsing. Most of them are heavy with young and are making milk. At this time they tend to go to the marshy portions of their grazing areas, where the bog cotton grass shoots early and is rich in protein. Hunger may then drive them too close to the green 'eye' of a mire and they may get 'stugged' or bogged. This risk is greater with cattle than with the moor-wise ponies and Scotch sheep.

The least valuable plant on the Moor is the bracken fern. It used to be cut extensively to be dried and used as bedding for the cattle in winter. Now this is only done by a few farmers in places where tractor-drawn mowing machines and trailers can be used, and this may help to account for its spread in recent years. It is poisonous to animals if eaten in large quantities and smothers the herbage wherever it grows strongly. Unfortunately it flourishes on the best moorland soils, where the free-draining, friable, brown earth would support good pasture. It will not grow in water-logged soil or in the thin peat. Traces of ancient cultivation can

I

usually be found in fern-covered areas of the now open moorland. As the old saying runs—'plough heather, find copper; plough furze, find silver; plough fern and find gold'.

Different portions of the moorland grazings are burnt over or 'swaled' every few years to prune down the old woody growth of heather and furze and encourage the production of young, more digestible shoots.

Management

The management of the flocks and herds on these moorland grazings follows the same system as that in similar hill and mountain areas of Britain, as close to nature as possible. The Galloway cows run with the bull usually throughout July and August so that they calve the following April and May when the grass is coming. As the bulls may not be turned out on common land, all the cows must be kept in the newtakes or other enclosed pasture at this time. The majority of herds are bred pure but quite a number use Hereford bulls to produce a heavier white-faced calf for sale, and some farmers use the White Shorthorn bull on their black Galloways to breed the 'blue-grey' beef animal. The calving average throughout the moorland herds is probably about 60–70 per cent each year. Most of the calves are weaned at about 6–7 months old and are either sold at the local suckled calf sales in October or November or reared on hay and oats and 'in-bye' grazing during their first winter. The breeding herd usually remains on the rough grazing throughout the winter, unhoused but fed with straw, rough hay, and sometimes with concentrated supplements. Not being accustomed to much handling, these Galloway cattle are often nervous of people, and when the cows have young calves at foot they should be given a wide berth, especially by walkers accompanied by dogs. Like deer, they often leave their very young calves lying in the heather for hours while they range the grazing. Young calves so found should not be disturbed.

The Scotch Blackfaced rams, after being passed as suitable by the Ministry of Agriculture, may be turned out on the common grazing with their ewes in November. Sometimes the ewes are brought in to enclosed pasture to run with the rams, and this better pasture at tupping time may result in a larger proportion of doubles (twin lambs) in the following spring. Many farmers do not welcome doubles as the ewes cannot rear them well on the hill. The Blackfaced ewes fend for themselves during the winter unless deep frozen snow or the dreaded 'ammil' (glazed frost) makes it impossible for them to get at the heather and furze. They are then usually fed sufficient hay or corn or concentrated food to tide them over till the thaw. Depending on circumstances such as the density of stocking and the lateness or earliness of the spring, it is often necessary to supplement the natural food supply around lambing time. Many farmers bring their hill ewes into their fields just before lambing, to feed on swedes or an early bite of cultivated grass.

The smaller 'inbye' flocks of Closewool or Dartmoor ewes are often brought into yards and sheds by night until their lambs are several weeks old to protect them from the foxes. This is not usually possible with the large flocks of hill sheep and many of their lambs are taken by foxes in their first three weeks of life. After the lambing is finished and the moor is green again, all the hill sheep except the rams go back to the moor or newtakes. They are shorn when weather and haymaking and the condition of the wool permits, in July or August. A few weeks later most flocks are gathered again, to be dipped against the blow-fly, ticks and other parasites. Many farmers also give their sheep a winter dip containing oil, in November or December, to make their fleeces better able to shed the winter rains. After any of these 'gathers' the sheep or their lambs may be 'drenched' (dosed) against intestinal worms, or given trace-elements or injections to immunise them against certain diseases. Fortunately many of the diseases prevalent among sheep kept on rich lowland pasture, such as pulpy kidney and braxy, are almost unknown in sheep kept on the natural moorland grazings. The lambs are usually weaned in the late autumn and sold as stores or reared through their first winter in enclosed land. The old 'broken-mouthed' ewes—those that are beginning to lose their teeth—are culled out at the same time and sent to market. In some cases wether lambs are kept on and sold fat as 'two-tooth' wethers at eighteen months.

The ponies lead the most natural life of all the moorland stock. Most visitors seems to think they are completely wild animals, not belonging to anyone. In fact they all have owners. The stallions run out on the Moor with the mares throughout the year and most foals are born in April, May and June. The native pony is so well adjusted to its environment that a mare, though usually very thin in the early spring, will rear a good foal and become fat and shining herself by late summer. In late September and early October the pony 'drifts' or roundups take place, and most of the colt foals—known as horse suckers—are sold at one of the local pony fairs. Some of the filly foals or mare suckers also go for sale (they make at least twice as much money as their brothers). The rest are retained to join the breeding herd after being branded and probably ear-marked with the owner's marks. The ponies rarely get supplementary feed in the winter unless there is prolonged or hard frozen snow, and fortunately they hardly ever suffer from disease. They even seem to have come to terms with their parasites over the centuries, although redworm can be a cause of malnutrition in over-grazed areas.

All types of livestock grazing the open Moor have identification marks. The sheep have various coloured 'keel' marks on their wool, the cattle have ear tags, and all may have pieces cut out of their ears. These ear-marks have sometimes belonged to the same farm for centuries and in seventeenth-century court rolls such terms as 'top cut' and 'square half-penny' appear. The same descriptions are used today.

The Ancient Tenements

The rapid increase of population which took place in the thirteenth century drove more and more farmers into remote upland areas like Dartmoor in search of new land, and the number and size of the ancient tenements increased fairly rapidly after 1300. For instance a document dated 1300, describing the manor of Lydford, stated that in addition to the 48 burgesses in the borough of Lydford, there was a village in the forest (presumably meaning the ancient tenements) with 25 villeins hold-ing 12 ferlings of land. A list of the tenants of Dartmoor made in 1345 shows that the number of tenants had increased to 44, and their ferlings to 23.[1] In forty-five years the tenant population and the land under cultivation had almost doubled, although it is possible that some of these new tenants lived in nearby villages like Widecombe and merely held small pieces of land in the ancient tenements. In addition to their ferl-ings the tenants in 1345 also had other pieces of land amounting to about 320 acres in all.

If at first sight the terminology is confusing, the use of the archaic term ferling is fortunate, for not only is it possible to find out the approximate size of a ferling, but we are given a clue to the system of farming em-ployed by these early settlers on Dartmoor.

Many ancient documents describe ferlings and it was a common term for land measurement in Devon. The word is related to *furlong*—the long furrow (of 220yd) which the medieval ploughman drove with his ox-team. Since medieval cereal cultivation was almost invariably carried out under the system of strips of different ownership or tenancy, lying scattered and intermixed in a large open common field, the use of the term ferling in this context raises the question of whether such a system of cultivation, so reminiscent of the Midlands, could possibly have existed on Dartmoor. Until fairly recently such a suggestion would have been regarded as ridiculous, for all authorities were agreed that the open field

system had never existed in Devon; but since the publication of H. P.
R. Finberg's essay, 'The open field in Devon', *Devonshire Studies* (1952),
evidence of former open fields has been turning up all over the county,
and the existence of small open fields in the Dartmoor valleys no longer
seems improbable.

With this background, the information in ancient documents becomes
more meaningful. A document of 1566, which is specially relevant, is a
survey or description of Lord Dynham's estate in the moorland border
parish of Ilsington, which includes Haytor. The survey describes the farms
of various tenants in Ilsington. Of particular interest are the five who
occupied farms in the hamlet just south of Haytor Down, which consisted of the settlements of Oldatown, Smallacombe and Middlecott.
These five tenants all enjoyed rights of common grazing on the considerable area of adjoining moorland called Haytor Down ('Idetordowne' in
the survey), and their farms and farming systems must have been very
similar to those of the ancient tenements.

The interest lies in the fact that their lands are described as ferlings
and then it is explained exactly what these ferlings consisted of. This makes
it clear that the remains of common arable fields still existed in 1566.
Hugh Dyggen held three ferlings containing $130\frac{1}{2}$ acres which consisted
of a farmstead in Smallacombe, various closes, and 'divers parcels of land
lying together about the landscore next Idetordowne containing in all
60 acres'. Agnes Orchard, widow, held one ferling amounting to 32 acres,
which consisted of a farmstead at Oldatown, two little closes of one acre
apiece and 'divers parcels of land called *Les Shotes* lying in common about
the bounds called *Les Landscores* with the lands of William [this seems to
be a mistake for Hugh] Dyggen . . . containing in all 30 acres'. That this
was a reference to a common field is confirmed by an entry from another
Dynham manor at Woodhuish in Brixham parish where some lands are
described as lying 'by *land score* in twoe common fields'. The phrase
landscore meant strips lying intermixed in a common field. However, by
1566 these common fields were only remnants of larger ones, as is shown
by the description of Elizabeth Bruseigh's land. It was described as four
ferlings (containing $128\frac{1}{4}$ acres in all—or about 32 acres per ferling), but
her arable land was all enclosed. Besides a farmhouse, outbuildings and garden, she had nine enclosed fields ranging in size from 1 to 12 acres and comprising $59\frac{1}{2}$ acres in all; 2 acres of woodland; 2 acres of meadow (which
were not described as enclosed and so were probably lots in a common
meadow) and 60 acres of 'waste land on the Downe'. The implication is
that this also was unenclosed and it is a puzzling entry. It could mean the
right to cultivate 60 acres of the common moor in any one year, but not

necessarily the same area each year. The implications of this will be considered in more detail below.

Finally there is an extraordinary entry in the Ilsington survey which states that William Prowse has a holding with a garden and 'one ferling of land containing by estimation 30 acres, but he does not know where they are because they lie among the lords' lands and the lands of George Fourde, esq. They are therefore placed here confusedly'.[2]

It is thus clear that a ferling could include many different types and qualities of land, but the evidence is reasonably consistent about its size. It was usually approximately thirty acres and was thus analogous to the virgate or yardland holding so widespread in the open-field villages of the Midlands until the enclosures of the eighteenth century. It was in fact the standard size of farm considered adequate for the support of one family, and could vary in acreage depending on the quality of the soil.

That the average size of the Dartmoor ferlings was about 32 acres is suggested by a document of 1305 in which the royal officials who were collecting the Dartmoor rents at that time recorded a new rent from 3 'ferlings of land containing 96 acres at Donnebruge [Dunnabridge] in the waste of the King'. This gives an average of 32 acres per ferling, but the document also shows that a man did not necessarily need to farm a whole ferling to make a living, for the 3 ferlings in Dunnabridge were let to 5 tenants who held 19⅖ acres each.[3] However, some of them may also have held other land near by. These five tenants were probably the founders of Dunnabridge.

Thus the documents of 1305 and 1566 agree about the size of ferlings, but the survey of 1566 is not too clear about their nature. Evidently all kinds of land could be included—enclosures, strips in arable common fields, lots in common meadows, pieces of open moor, and even land which was so intermixed that its tenant did not know where it was. It seems likely therefore that the Ilsington ferlings of 1566 are the remnants of some very ancient communal system of farming. This system bore certain resemblances to the well-known Midland system, yet obviously the small pastoral hamlets on Dartmoor were fundamentally different from the large Midland villages with their extensive open arable fields often amounting to 1,000 acres or more.

As suggested by Professor Finberg in his essay on Devon open fields, the medieval systems of farming in Devon were probably variants of the ancient system of semi-communal farming which used to be widespread in Scotland, Wales, Ireland and probably Cornwall.[4] It was variously called the infield-outfield, run-rig or Celtic system, but perhaps it should have been called the pastoral-hill system, since it is more likely to have been influenced by geographical conditions than by cultural characteristics.

The essential features of this system have been well described by James Anderson in his report on Aberdeenshire farming in 1794. He noted that the settlements were usually hamlets containing from two to eight farming families who were co-tenants of the hamlet, which was called a 'farm'. He described the system as follows :

> Throughout the whole district the general practice that has prevailed from time immemorial is to divide the arable lands of each farm into two parts . . . Infield and Outfield. The in-field, as the name implies, is that portion of ground which is nearest to the farmstead, and usually consists of about one-fifth part of the whole arable ground in the farm. This is kept in perpetual tillage; and the invariable system of management was . . . to have it divided into three equal parts to be cropped thus : First Bear [barley], with all the dung made by the beasts housed on the farm laid upon it.
>
> Second and third, oats . . . That part of the farm called out-field is divided into two unequal portions. The smallest, usually about one-third part, is called *folds*, provincially *falds*; the other larger portion is denominated *faughs*. The fold ground usually consists of ten divisions, one of which each year is brought into 'tillage' from grass. With this intent it is surrounded with a wall of sod the last year it is to remain in grass, which forms a temporary inclosure that is employed as a penn for confining cattle during the night time and for two or three hours each day at noon. It thus gets a tolerably full dunging, after which it is plowed up for oats during the winter. In the same manner it is plowed successively for *oats* for four or five years, or as long as it will carry any crop worth replacing. It is then abandoned for five or six years, during which time it gets by degrees a sward of poor grass, when it is again subjected to the same rotation.
>
> The *faughs* never receive manure of any sort; and they are cropped in exactly the same manner as the folds, with this difference, that instead of being folded upon, they are broke up from grass by what they call rib-plowing about midsummer; one part of the sward being turned by the plow upon the surface of an equal portion that is not raised, so as to be covered by the furrow. This operation on grass land is called *faughing*, from when the division of the farm takes its name. It is allowed to lie in this state until autumn, when it is plowed all over . . . and is sown with oats in the spring. It produces a poor crop and three or four succeeding crops still poorer and poorer; till at last they are forced to abandon it by the plow after it will scarcely return the seed.[5]

Although the division of the outfield into *folds* and *faughs* may have been a special Scottish refinement, this description probably accords well with the ancient system of Dartmoor farming. The evidence of documents and of the land itself suggests that some such method was employed, and the faughing was similar to the 'skirting' process which was the first phase in the old south-western practice known as Devonshiring or Denshiring (ie paring and burning of old turf before ploughing). The early surveys, and the surviving farmhouses in some cases (for instance Pizwell and Babeny) indicate that most of the ancient tenements were once hamlets, supporting from three to five families each.

Old maps tell the same story. The map of Hexworthy, made in 1838 in connection with tithe collection, shows that there were then five farmers whose fields were scattered throughout the hamlet. Although the fields were enclosed, the shape of those nearest the homesteads—long narrow strips, sometimes terraced—suggests that they may have been the remains of a former unenclosed infield. They were surrounded by larger, rectangular fields, which may originally have been sections on an intermittently cultivated outfield. This pattern is found in most of the ancient tenements, and almost invariably the open moor beyond the enclosures is scarred with long ridges and furrows, the remains of ancient cultivation. These remnants are too widely scattered to have been permanent fields which were later abandoned, although this probably happened in some cases. They are more likely to be the remains of outfield cultivation of the type described by James Anderson in Aberdeen.[6]

In order to encourage tenants to settle in the remote interior of Dartmoor, the Duchy of Cornwall, which had been granted the Forest of Dartmoor and Manor of Lydford in 1239, was prepared to grant leases on easy terms. Their basis was what was called a copyhold of inheritance— there was a copy of the lease in the court roll of the Manor of Lydford and the tenants' heirs had the right to succeed on the payment of a 're-lief' (usually the best cow or ox). These tenancies soon became known as 'customary freeholds' and were so described in later Duchy documents. The tenants could bequeath the farms in their wills, or sell the succession, and eventually, in the nineteenth century, the Duchy bought out most of the tenants as if they had been genuine freeholders.

Although the annual rents payable to the Duchy were very low (about $\frac{1}{2}$d an acre) the tenants were also bound by certain feudal obligations. They had to attend the sittings of the manorial court at Lydford several times a year and to grind their corn at the Duchy's mill at Babeny (built in 1303 and now demolished), but their most important duty was attendance at the four annual 'drifts', when the livestock placed on the moor by the commoners from all over Devon were rounded up and claimed by their owners on payment of the customary fees. Strays were driven to Lydford to be auctioned.

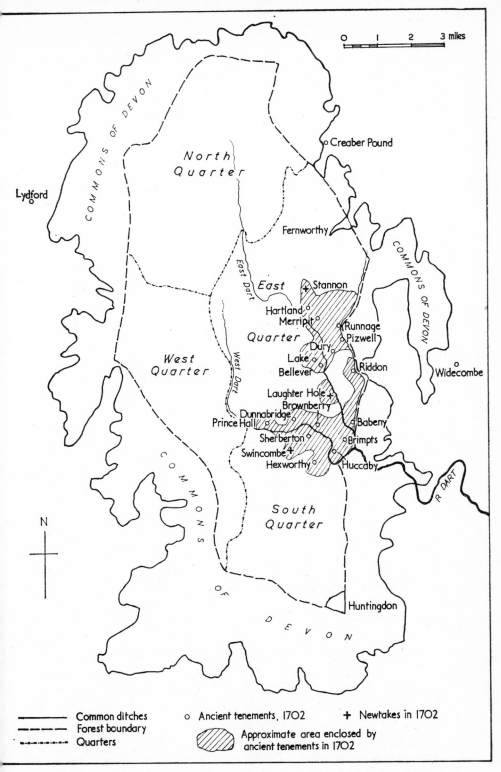

Fig 16. Ancient tenements and new enclosures in the early eighteenth century.

At a Court of Survey of the Manor of Lydford held at Okehampton in 1608 the jurors declared that the tenants were obliged to assist the foresters in making one winter and three summer drifts a year in the east, south and west quarters of the Moor (see fig 16).[7] The north quarter was driven to Creaber pound in Gidleigh parish, near Chagford, and its drifts were not the responsibility of the holders of the ancient tenements. A few years later, in 1627, a Widecombe man, Robert Hanna-ford, giving evidence in the Court of Exchequer, said that the tenants of the ancient tenements

> have been accustomed time out of mind to make three several drifts yearly for cattle and one for horses depasturing upon the said Forest to Dynabridge [Dunnabridge] pound, and are to attend there two or three days and nights for the watering and depasturing of the said cattle near the pound and to drive such as are not owned to Lydford for estrays, and every of the said tenants is to have upon the bringing of the cattle and horses to Dynabridge pound a halfpenny loaf and that such as make default of such service do forfeit 6s 8d.[8]

Newtakes and the Duchy

The ancient infield-outfield system of farming on Dartmoor gradually gave place to more modern methods. Various factors contributed to this. As regional specialisation in agriculture developed from the sixteenth century onwards, and grain surpluses were produced in the 'down country', farmers became less dependent on growing their own corn on the outfield (at low yields) and turned increasingly to livestock and livestock products. Then there was the ancient forest custom of the newtakes—which allowed the occupants of the ancient tenements to reclaim and enclose eight acres of moor each time a new tenant entered a farm. For this they paid a nominal rent of 1½d an acre to the Duchy of Cornwall. Increasingly these newtakes encroached upon the outfield and converted it to pasture.

The custom of newtakes was probably old in 1345, since the lands measured in acres, which the tenants held in addition to their ferlings, seem to have derived from this custom. In that year there were about 320 acres of such land held by 36 tenants in sizes ranging from 31 acres to 1 acre, with an average size of about 10. Thus the typical Dartmoor farmer in the mid-fourteenth century held about 40 acres—consisting of his ferling (about 30 acres) and about 10 acres of newtakes, in addition to his common grazing rights on the open Moor.[9]

The custom of allowing newtakes was open to abuse and the records of the Duchy of Cornwall reveal that this abuse was also ancient. In the survey of 1608 only 22 newtakes were listed, yielding an annual rent

of 6s 4d, but a memorandum added to the survey noted that 'at the
time of making the above Rentall there was [sic] many more than is
therein mentioned'. Moreover the size of the newtakes was consistently
understated. For instance the largest newtake, held by Robert French,
was described as 7 acres and a half penny land. For this he paid 8½d a
year. Yet in a paper drawn up in 1621 to advise the Prince's Council on
the better management of Dartmoor and entitled 'Certain objections concerning the Forest of Dartmoor and the Manor of Lidford', it was stated
that a newtaker would often claim 5 acres, and pay 5d to the Duchy, but
would take 20 to 30 acres, calling it Forest Measure.[10] There are also
many later references to this abuse, the idea apparently being that the
tenants regarded themselves as entitled to eight acres of good new land
on inheritance, and that this gave them the right to enclose large
quantities of inferior land in the process. This was doubtless special plead-
ing in most cases.

The author of the 1621 paper urged that all newtakes should be surveyed because they had lately been illegally made and no rents had
been paid for them; this should be 'timely redeemed'. He also urged that
further newtakes should be stopped because the takers exhaust the ground
in tillage before they 'lay it out again'. This passage is puzzling because
it suggests that the newtake was not a permanent enclosure but merely
an outfield cultivation which would later revert to common pasture.
Perhaps newtakes had originally taken this form, but it seems quite in-
appropriate to the conditions of 1621, when newtakes were walled enclosures. The abuse flourished because the Duchy seldom administered
the Forest itself, but usually let it to tenants. These tenants often held
leases for limited periods, and so had no special interest in the details of
administration. Their officials winked at excessive enclosures.

The report of 1621 was probably made in connection with the coming
of age of a new Prince of Wales—Prince Charles (later Charles I) who
was born in 1600. It is a useful source for the general condition of Dartmoor at the time and for its rôle in Devon farming as well as for the
disadvantages to the Duchy of the previous haphazard management. The
Duchy had lost interest in the Moor because of the decline in the number of deer available for hunting. By 1621 these were estimated at only
50, and they were probably still declining. The soil was hardly suitable
for extensive agricultural improvements (as nineteenth-century enthusiasts
later found to their cost) and timber—that other standby of estate improvers—was also lacking. The only trees growing on the Moor were a
few stunted oaks, the most notable of which were in 'Welshman Wood'
(Wistman's Wood).

As a result administration had become lax and neighbouring land-owners had acquired portions of the moor, particularly on the Commons of Devon outside the Forest boundary, where rights of ownership were vague. Nicholas Slanning had appropriated 10,000 acres around Walk-hampton and Sheepstor during the ninth year of Elizabeth I's reign (be-tween 17 Nov. 1567 and 17 Nov. 1568). He had been ordered by a court of law to restore it to the Duchy; this, the author of the paper comments, 'were fitt to be looked into for I suppose the Intrusion continues Not-withstanding the Recovery. I have likewise heard of the like Recovery against the Abbot of Buckfast in the time of King Henry VIII'. He went on to advocate that the claims of all the landowners round the Moor should be reviewed because they classed parts of the Commons of Devon as their own soil and thus reduced the profits of the Prince's drifts (the rents paid for pasturing livestock on the moor).

In its struggle against neighbouring landowners the Duchy was engaging in a popular cause, since the whole of Devon except Barnstaple and Totnes claimed summer common on the Moor on the payment of certain customary dues. The heart of the problem of Duchy administra-tion of common grazing lay in the reduction of the value of these dues by the inflation of the sixteenth century to such an extent that they were hardly worth collecting; hence the Duchy became half-hearted in its efforts to protect common rights against powerful encroachers. The 1621 paper stated that the customary dues for summer grazing were $1\frac{1}{2}$d for oxen, cows or young cattle, 2d for colts and $7\frac{1}{2}$d for 20 sheep. They also paid 5d for the right to cut turf for fuel. These charges had once represented real values, but no longer did so. They were the main source of the Prince's income from the Forest, combined with the rents of the venville tenants and the perquisites from the Forest Court at Lydford (both of these had also been greatly devalued by inflation). As a result the Prince's income from all sources on Dartmoor in 1620 had been £25 6s 8d compared with £110 which Sir Philip Courtney had paid as annual rent for the Forest in the reign of Henry VI (Courtney rented the Forest at various times between 1425 and 1451, but did not always pay as much as £110).[11] Even so, considering that Courtney must have made a profit over and above his rent, the income from Dartmoor had fallen by more than three-quarters regardless of any changes in the value of money. Yet the pound in 1620 was worth only about one-third of its value in 1450, which reveals the extent of the fall of Dartmoor's value to the Duchy.

As a result of the decline in the value of the customary dues, their collection had largely lapsed, and under the heading of 'Things needing Reformation' the 1621 paper suggested that the foresters should keep a record of all stock placed on the Moor and should collect the fees. They should also prevent the venville men from overstocking the commons, especially with sheep. He also urged a rise in the fines imposed at Lydford Court for breaking the Forest rules. The tenants claimed that no fine could be more than 3d, with the result that the worst offenders were 'secured by payment 3d' !

Despite the good intentions of 1621, administration of the Moor does not seem to have improved, particularly in relation to newtakes, which continued unabated, though not yet on the massive scale that they were to assume after 1780. After the failure of various ambitious schemes to enclose the whole of Dartmoor, the tenants' right to make newtakes was abolished and the attempts at wholesale 'improvement' were gradually abandoned. However, before this happened the large new farms mentioned at the beginning of this chapter came into existence and were regularised by leases from the Duchy, although the legality of their creation has always been in doubt.

About the middle of the nineteenth century the Duchy gave up holding the drifts and leased the quarters of the Moor to moormen, usually holders of the ancient tenements. Since then the moormen have continued to take in the commoners' cattle in the summer and to collect the dues themselves, paying a rent to the Duchy.

The development of Dartmoor farming can perhaps be more clearly understood by examining the details of a single farm than by generalisation, and one of the oldest of the ancient tenements, Babeny, will serve as a good example.

Babeny Farm: a case study

Babeny lies at the junction of the East Dart and the Wallabrook. These two rivers divide the Forest from Spitchwick Manor in this part of the Moor. The farmstead's buildings are scattered in three groups around what is still known as 'the Green'. These buildings are almost certainly on the sites of the three original holdings or ancient tenements which have now been amalgamated into one. The shippon (cowshed) end of one of the old longhouses is still used as a cowshed, but beyond the central passage, now used as a bull's house, the old kitchen, with its large hearth and baking oven, is roofless and half ruined. This dwelling or 'livier' was last occupied in about 1880. The present dwellinghouse was built on the site of another old house at about the same date, and part of the 'lime ash' floor of the old 'livier' extends into the garden. The new

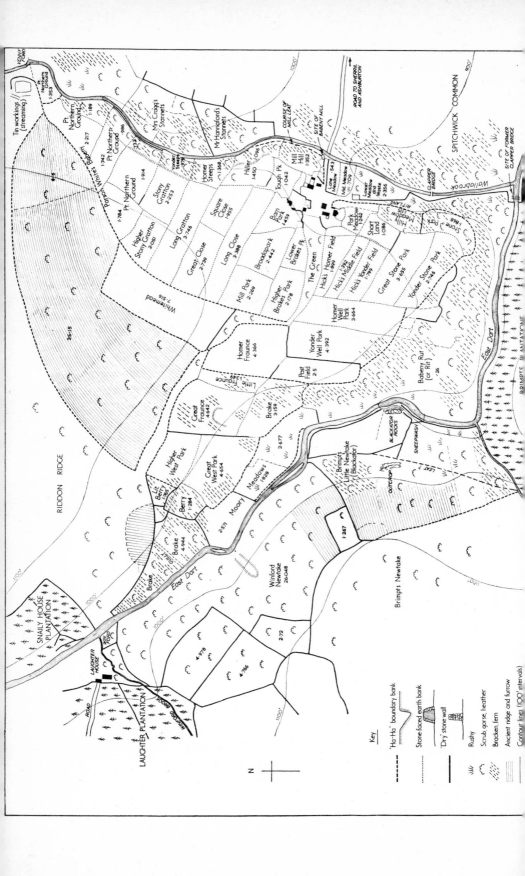

shippon was built near the new house at about the turn of the century. Two of the old corn barns remain, with their central threshing floors. One had a threshing machine powered by horses installed in the early part of this century. This has now gone and the barns are used for storing hay or housing bullocks. There is an interesting old ash-house built into a bank amongst one group of buildings. It is round with a corbelled stone roof covered with turf, and it harbours the rare and beautiful light-reflecting moss *(Schistostega osmundacea)*. Above the present dwelling house is the 'kennel plat', with traces of the granite kennels where a gentleman owner of the eighteenth century kept a small pack of fox-hounds. A millstone serves as a doorstep to one of the buildings—a relic of the ancient watermill, the ruins of which lie beside the Wallabrook and close to the entrance gate. The hanging post of this gate was once a bearing stone from the mill.

The only new buildings are a small pole hay shed and an open-fronted general purpose building near the house. This was erected in 1960, and hundreds of tons of bedrock granite and growan had first to be blasted and bulldozed out to make a level site of about 65 by 20ft. This is no larger than the average Dartmoor longhouse. It is an illustration of the difficulties that must have been overcome by the earlier builders and of the reasons for building long, narrow houses along the contour and rebuilding, if necessary, on the same sites. The excavated material has now formed two sizeable terraces on the slope below this group of buildings. During excavation a hidden spring of water was released and diverted, another problem that must often have been encountered by the old builders.

The bridge over the Wallabrook outside the farm gate was built in about 1905. Before that there was only a ford across the brook, and foot travellers used the little clapper bridge a couple of hundred yards down stream. A path also leads downstream from this foot clapper, between the Wallabrook and the boundary wall, to the remains of a larger pack-horse clapper bridge which once spanned the East Dart, just above the junction of the two rivers. On the other side of the Dart the path turned downstream towards Brimpts, still bounded by a stone wall on the inland side. Now the Dart can only be crossed by the stepping stones at low water.

This larger bridge was probably built by the tenants of the Forest to enable them to carry their corn to be ground at Babeny Mills. In 1303 there was 4s rent due to the Crown for the mill 'newly constructed in Dartmoor at Babeny—which mill was constructed by the King's tenants at their own costs except the timber, which they had in the King's

Opposite: Fig 17. Babeny Farm.

wood'.[12] A modern farmer may be surprised at corn-growing on ground above the 1,000-ft contour and with rainfall approaching 70in a year, but witnesses in a tithe dispute concerning these farms in 1627 said 'The farthest parts of the parish of Lydford, near the wild wastes, are good land, inhabited by rich inhabitants and tilled with oats and rye, and, with manurancé, tilled with barley'.[13] Admittedly they were witnesses for the parson who was anxious for his tithes, but at that time, if corn was not grown at home, the husbandmen and their families went short of bread. After black rye bread went out of favour these farmers grew wheat, which was grown and harvested at Babeny within living memory. The difficulties are illustrated by a local memory of extra hands being called in at Runnage to knock snow off standing wheat in November.

Babeny Farm today contains about 80 acres of arable land, about 70 acres of rough pasture too steep and rocky or too marshy to cultivate, and the 40-acre Winford Newtake, on the west bank of the East Dart. This newtake contains about 14 acres of cultivable land which shows signs of having been ploughed and limed within the last century and is enclosed by low stone walls, and a further 3 or 4 acres lying in ridge and furrow showing earlier cultivation. It was probably the 'Wendford' mentioned in 1358 in a list of tenements for which no rent had been paid.

The ancient dwelling was probably near where the Wendford Brook joins the East Dart. It may well have been a tinner's holding, because there is a very old adit hole near the river, halfway along the newtake, which belongs to no recorded mine but which might be the origin of the name of the lost holding of Edithull, also mentioned in the fourteenth century.

Even earlier settlers may have made the tiny cultivation terraces at the top of the rough ground called Babeny Rit, east of the right-angled bend in the Dart. They lie in one of the most sheltered and fertile parts of the farm, but have survived because the area is too steep to be cultivated other than by hand. They could date back to Celtic settlement. The Wallabrook, which joins the Dart below them, is said to mean the brook of the *Weallas*, the remnants of the Britons who had settlements along its banks when the Saxons came.

Blackator newtake, on the west bank of the Dart opposite Babeny Rit, belonged to Brimpts farm but since March 1970 has been rented as part of Babeny Farm. About 8 of its 25 acres lie in ancient ridge and furrow, and against the river there are about 4 acres of very old meadow—Blackator mead—which was once watered by a leat from a spring near the top south-west corner of the newtake. Just south of the cliff, near the

Page 161 (above) *Two Bridges in 1797, from a painting by John Swete. The new turn-pike bridge is on the right, the Saracen's Head Inn on the opposite bank; (below) Post-bridge in the mid-nineteenth century. The clapper and turnpike bridges are shown; to the west are the blacksmith's shop, the turnpike house and gate and the Greyhound Inn*

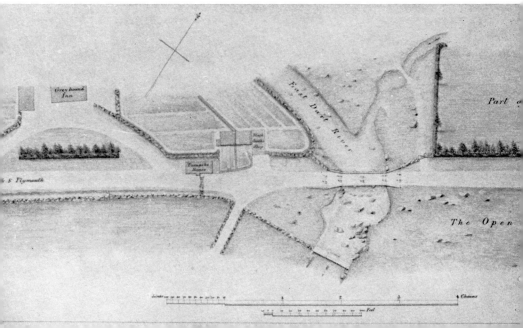

Page 162 (above) *Sir Thomas Tyrwhitt's wharf on Roborough Down, Yelverton, in 1828, with the granite-railed siding leading to it;* (below) *the granite-railed siding leading to Tyrwhitt's Wharf on Roborough Down at Yelverton in about 1912*

river bank known as Blackator Rocks, there are the remains of pens leading to a sheep wash in a wide shallow stretch of the river. All these remnants of an ancient farming economy appear to be several hundred years
old.

At the northern end of the farm is Vennyford, on the Wallabrook,
where an ancient driftway from Spitchwick Common to Riddon Ridge
divides Babeny from Riddon, the next ancient tenement on the Wallabrook (see Fig 15, p 140). A wall and gate between the two farms
prevents trespass by stock between the common and the Forest, an exception to the generalisation that there are no physical barriers between
the Forest of Dartmoor and the surrounding commons. This is no modern
barrier. In 1586 it was presented at the Court of Augmentations at Lydford that the tenants of Babeny and Riddon had allowed Beniford Yeat
(Veniford gate) and the fences adjoining it to become ruinous.[14] The
presentment was repeated till 1590 when they were warned that if the
gate and fence were not repaired before the next court they would be
fined forty shillings. The next recorded complaint was in the reign of
Elizabeth II! In 1955 the lord of the manor of Spitchwick complained
that Veniford gate was again ruinous, allowing stock from the Forest of
Dartmoor to stray on to Spitchwick Common. The gate and fence are
now in good repair.

From a point near Vennyford an old boundary ditch and bank, now
in ruins, runs westward to link with the western end of Babeny farm,
enclosing $41\frac{3}{4}$ acres of old arable land covered in ridge and furrow. This
land has now gone back to open common and has not been let with the
farm for at least 130 years, though it is marked as part of Babeny in
the earlier maps. This area, together with the 80 acres of arable which
was enclosed, would have been enough for three of the typical peasant
holdings each to have a 32 acre ferling of ploughable land plus an acre
or two of meadow and some rough pasture. There would also have been a
further 26 acres which could have been occupied by the miller, and
possibly also by a part-time tinner, at the western end of the farm. The
main hedge dividing this end of the farm from the rest looks as if it was
at one time a boundary bank and ditch. There were in fact five holdings
assessed for poor rate at Babeny in 1702 and 1740, though that does not
necessarily mean there were five homesteads, since some may have been
pieces of land owned or rented by farmers whose main homestead was
elsewhere.

By 1810 there were only four holdings assessed, one being Babeny Rit
newtake. The owners were the Reverend Lane for one tenement and
Sir John Rodgers for two more, in contrast to the eighteenth-century

K

owners who were local men and women with such Dartmoor yeoman names as Hext, French, Nosworthy and Hodge.

By 1838 there were three holdings. One was the ten acres at the northern end, 'White's Babeny or Northern ground', owned by the Rev John White; the second of thirty-nine acres was mainly in one block on the northern side of the driftway that divides the farm, rented by William Hamlyn White from the Rev Samuel Lane; and the largest, which now included the Rit and lay south and west of the central driftway, was owned and occupied by Thomas Irish.

By that time only the small watered meadows of the two main tenements were still intermingled, the larger holding having Mill Hill meadow on the other side of Babeny, and the smaller holding having the centre one of the three little Wallabrook meadows on the southern side and the middle Moory meadow against the Dart. Meadowland was always the most valuable and scarce under the old farming systems. The meadows provided an early bite of grass to shorten the winter, but they could only be made in sheltered, fertile land below a spring of water to irrigate them throughout the winter. Now nitrogenous fertilisers encourage early grass on temporary leys, and the old watered meadows, which needed a great deal of hand labour to maintain them, have reverted to rough pasture.

The consolidation of the arable lands of each holding into ring-fenced blocks took place earlier at Babeny than on some of the other ancient tenements such as Hexworthy. Babeny, like most of the ancient tenements on the East Dart and Wallabrook, is enclosed with 'cornditches', the bank and ditch type of boundary, made like a ha-ha, to conform with the forest law that no land holder within a forest or its purlieus might 'forestall the king's deer with either dead hay or quick' (fences or hedges) from regaining the forest. The cornditches made it difficult for the deer to break in to the cornlands, having a deep wide ditch on the forest side, with a vertical stone-faced bank on its inner side. This bank was little if any higher than the level of the field on the inside. Thus if a deer did manage to jump in, there was no impediment to its jumping out again. Stone walls, fences or hedges were only permitted after the full rigour of forest law had been relaxed.

For centuries these cornditches enclosed the large common arable fields of the whole hamlet, in which each peasant had his individual strips, being only divided into the outfield and the infield as previously described. The hedgebanks dividing these blocks into individual 'parks' came later as the strips were consolidated. It is interesting to note that at Babeny there are several instances of three adjoining fields all having variations of the same name—such as Stony Gratton, Higher Stony Gratton and Long Gratton—and having a combined acreage of eight acres or thereabouts. It seems possible that these were originally one of the eight-acre newtakes enclosed from the outfield. The sub-tenants, who would have had to join forces to reclaim such an area, would each have had a share in the newtake, which would account for the later sub-division. The Northern Ground and Whitemead were probably the last portions to be so enclosed at Babeny. Whitemead is an interesting name, appearing, with slight variations, at Hexworthy, Huccaby, Laughter Hole and Pizwell. The Whitemeads were always on the extreme edge of cultivation, and probably the name means the metes (boundary) of the cornlands, which were often known as the white lands.

Today the farm supports a small pedigree herd of South Devon cattle, a larger herd of Galloway cows producing crossbred calves for sale, a flock of Scotch Blackfaced sheep, and a small flock of Cheviots. Ponies are also bred, both Dartmoor and part-bred Arabians. The arable land is mostly under grass leys, sown after pioneer crops of swedes and thousand-head kale and left about ten years before being ploughed again. As much as possible of this grassland is cut for hay, but a proportion of the winter fodder has to be bought.

Farming Methods, Old and New

Wheat used to be grown regularly on Dartmoor, as previously noted. This is the more remarkable since the only manures available were dung, compost, ashes and lime. Guano from Peru was not used until the latter half of the nineteenth century. Practically all the work, after the ploughing and harrowing with oxen or horses, was done by hand.

When an old ley was to be broken for tillage, the turf was first pared off by the plough, which was fitted with a broad 'velling' or 'skirting' share and set to turn a furrow of 12in to 18in wide but only 2in deep, leaving a 'comb' of about 3in width of unturned turf between each furrow. This 'comb' anchored the thin slice of turf to the ground on one side, so that the subsequent harrowing tore it up and finally reduced it to small pieces of dry roots known as 'beat', which were then gathered into heaps with hand rakes and burned.

The resulting ashes were mixed with quicklime, hedgerow mould and road scrapings or other fresh soil. When the lime was slaked all would be spread over the surface of the ground. The field was then ploughed in ridges, 16 to 20 furrows wide, and the seed-corn was broadcast along the ridges. Oats were usually the first crop on Dartmoor. The seed was then harrowed in along the ridge, the furrows between the ridges were shovelled out by hand, and the earth was spread evenly over the ridges.

During the summer the corn would be weeded by hand with thistle spudders or dock irons. The harvesting was also done by hand. Wheat was reaped with a reaping hook with a smooth edge which replaced the sickle with its saw-toothed edge in the nineteenth century. The sheaves were bound with a few straws twisted into a knot and set up in stooks, before being made into small round ricks or taken home to the barn by wain, sledge or packhorse. Oats and barley were generally mown with a scythe and sometimes bound into sheaves, sometimes saved loose like hay. Common turnips might follow wheat in the rotation, or peas might be sown. These would require another dressing of lime, and were harvested and threshed like corn.

In the late eighteenth century the eastern edge of Dartmoor became famous for potato production. The area round Chagford and Moreton-hampstead enjoyed a monopoly because farmers in southern and western Devon were forbidden by their leases to grow potatoes except for their own use. Consequently Plymouth and Tavistock came to rely on the Chagford region for potatoes which were carried across the Moor by packhorses and sold at a potato market at Two Bridges.[15] This market was marked on Benjamin Donn's map of Devon as early as 1765.

Dartmoor farmers frequently grew potatoes in 'lazy-beds', which were described by Charles Vancouver in 1808 as follows :

> the ground is ploughed some time in the preceding winter, and after-wards seared into beds of three feet and a half in width, with an interval of about 18 or 20 inches. The manure is spread upon these beds, and the setts placed regularly upon it at the distance of about seven or eight inches square : the earth is dug from out the interval, which thus be-comes a trench, and is cast as evenly as possible on both hands, cover-ing the nearer tops of the adjoining beds.[16]

When the plants began to show they were covered two or three times more to protect them from frosts and to smother weeds. The system was known as a 'lazy-bed' because the potatoes were not planted in fully cultivated soil but merely laid upon the ploughed earth. The subsequent trenching operations, however, could hardly be recommended for lazy men. The true Highland lazy-bed was also used on Dartmoor within living memory. For this the ground was not ploughed at all, the dung and potatoes being laid on the undisturbed turf and the earth dug from the trenches or water-furrows thrown over them.

Barley was widely grown, but was of poor quality. Vancouver noted

that Widecombe barley was a much inferior sample to that produced in
the country below, and presumably the same applied to the wheat. Barley
was usually the final corn crop in a cereal rotation, being under-sown
with a seed mixture of 6lb of red clover, 2lb of White Dutch clover and
2 bushels of eaver (Devon rye-grass) per acre, which formed a pasture
lasting for seven to ten years.

Cattle

In the last century, the cattle were almost certainly the 'Widecombe
type' of South Devons. Very rarely was any other kind seen before 1939.
The South Devon breed, or the South Hams as it used to be called, is
little known outside Devon. It is the largest breed of cattle native to
Britain, bulls and fully mature steers often attaining a ton in weight. The
cows give a reasonable quantity of milk, probably averaging 700 gallons
in a lactation, though the best will average 1,000. (These yields are
modern ones, with concentrate feeding; in earlier times, with only grazing in the summer, supplemented by bulk fodders in the winter, they
are likely to have been considerably less). The milk is of excellent quality,
rivalling Channel Island milk. Two gallons will give a pound of butter
or over two pounds of cheese. South Devons are very good con-
verters of roughage, and are dark chestnut in colour, often lighter about
the eyes and muzzle and inside the legs, but without any white mark-
ings.

The 'Widecombe type' probably had some North Devon blood in it,
as a darker bullock was favoured, a little shorter in the leg and shorter
in the ear and face than the true South Hams. These points are thought
to denote greater hardiness, a bullock with a yellow coat and a big
'papery' ear being considered likely to be a bit 'naish' (nice) for the rigours
of Dartmoor. However, even a pedigree South Devon, reared on the
Moor, will 'do' better than most other breeds, having a large belly to
deal with coarse fare and a thick, rather curly, winter coat. They were
the ideal animals for the traditional mixed farm. Milk was not sold in any
quantity, but nearly every farmer's wife scalded cream and made butter
for sale, so quality was much more important than quantity. The steers,
the old cows, and any unwanted calves would always be sold for better
prices than those of any other breed because of their size and fleshing
qualities. They were also strong and docile for the plough.

The origins of the South Devon breed are obscure, but they are almost
identical with the French Limousin breed, and as the province of Limousin in central France was an English possession from 1152 till 1369, there

is no reason why the two breeds should not at that time have been one. The south Devon ports, except in times of war, have always carried on trade with France and probably some of the great landowners and monastic houses in south Devon had connections in that part of France, which might well have led to an interchange of cattle.

During the last thirty years there has been a drift away from the breed, as dual-purpose cattle have lost their popularity all over the country in favour of pure dairy breeds, particularly the Friesian. This is because liquid milk has been more profitable than butter, cream, or beef. Where dairy farming is impracticable, the pure beef breeds have been preferred. Just as in earlier times wheat and barley were grown by most farmers, even though the soil and climate were unsuitable, because the cost of transport would have made it uneconomical to buy grain, so now economic factors make milk production the best way for a small farmer to make a reasonable living, even though it is not a system of farming very suitable to Dartmoor. So Friesian, Guernsey, Jersey and all sorts of 'sparky' dairy breeds have recently made their appearance.

However, there are now signs of a revival in the fortunes of the South Devon, for though milk prices still favour quantity rather than quality, the beef industry is turning away from the small early-maturing breeds to the ones with the biggest weight-for-age gains that will not run away to fat before reaching ten hundredweight. Hence the import of French Charollais cattle. In various beefing trials the South Devon has usually equalled or slightly excelled the Charollais, whose only advantage has been its big carthorse-like rump, caused by an hereditary 'double-muscling' characteristic. This sometimes turns up in the South Devon breed but has never been bred for because it is inclined to lead to calving difficulties.

The Ashburton cattle fairs, in March, June, August and November, have always been the market for South Devon cattle from Dartmoor and the 2½-year-old steers sell well, often to graziers as far away as Northumberland, who find that these strong moorland animals will 'go away and do' anywhere.

Dartmoor farmers have always supplemented the feed for their livestock by purchasing extra keep off the Moor in the 'down country'. This would usually be grass keep for cattle in the summer, and turnip keep (with a run back on grass) for sheep in the winter. This practice still continues. There are keep sales in the spring and autumn, where farmers, having previously inspected the lots they are interested in, bid at auction for the keep. There is great competition for the best, which often makes very high prices. Its value will depend on such things as the healthiness of the land (particularly its freedom from such diseases as red water and liver fluke), and on its feeding qualities. Perhaps even more important is the integrity and experience of the person who has charge of the stock; if he does not see when a bullock is going sick, but only notices it when it is half dead, a lot of the owner's money can be lost. A stock farmer whose animals have done well on a certain place will generally try to get that keep again every year, very often buying it privately. Grass keep has been sold in this way in Devon for centuries, and was recorded in the Tavistock Abbey accounts as early as 1342.[17] It is particularly useful for Dartmoor farmers, as the down-country grazing may be a month or six weeks earlier in the spring than the moorland grazing, and the change saves animals, particularly sheep, from suffering the 'pine' caused by cobalt deficiency in the moorland grasses.

The cattle on the high moors of the Forest during the summer were very largely either the 'Scotch' cattle (Galloways and Highlanders) that were being kept by some of the forest farmers towards the end of the nineteenth century, or the store cattle belonging to down country farmers that were sent up to be agisted by the moormen. Farmers from Torbay and the Totnes and Newton Abbot areas would drive their cattle to Denbury Green from where they would all be herded by the mounted men and boys, each with his dog, who were employed by Mr Coaker of Runnage, the moorman of the East Quarter.

The long red ribbon of bullocks wound along the lanes to Dartmoor, approaching Widecombe by Cockingford Hill and spilling out over Wind Tor Down like a red tide, crowding through the lanes again past Langworthy, Hatchwell and Blackaton and finally reaching Runnage, near Postbridge, where they would be parted into smaller herds to go to the various lairs and newtakes.

Sheep

The modern breed of Dartmoor sheep are a grey-faced, long-wooled type, and are not the original old Dartmoor breed, which are white-faced and smaller. Despite their name, the grey-faced Dartmoors are almost never seen on the high moor even in the summer, but are largely confined to the moorland border parishes.

The true Dartmoor white-faced sheep continue on the Moor, though, as noted earlier, they have been displaced to some extent by northern mountain sheep like the Scotch Blackface and Cheviot, whose breeding ewes can spend the winter on the Moor. The Dartmoor white-faced ewes are brought in for the winter, though the wethers (castrated rams) used to remain on the Moor. Although producing good long wool, the Dartmoor white-faces were known throughout England in the past for their excellent mutton.

They probably formed the most important part of the Dartmoor farm in the nineteenth century. Traditionally wool and mutton paid the rent, which was always an expensive item, while dairy produce and steers covered the wages (often only seven shillings a week per man) and other miscellaneous expenses.

The importance of sheep was well brought out by Charles Vancouver in 1808, when he wrote that

> on the commons belonging to the parish of Widdecombe . . . in the month of October last, there were estimated by gentlemen residing in the neighbourhood, to be no less than 14,000 sheep, besides the usual proportion of horned cattle . . . from the number of sheep annually summered on Dartmoor and Exmoor forests, the ewes and lambs of which are always brought down into the country on the approach of winter, it will readily be supposed, that a large proportion of sheep stock is always found to occupy the surrounding districts in the winter season. The greater part of these flocks however, being wethers, and chiefly preserved for their wool, are left on the forests during winter . . . the caw or rot [liver fluke disease] has never yet been traced to have originated with sheep constantly depasturing . . . these forests, the usual consideration paid to those who rent the different quarters of the Forest of Dartmoor directly from His Royal Highness the Prince of Wales is 3s per score, annually; a sum considered sufficient to exempt them from all liability of having their sheep impounded or taken up as estrays. The number of sheep thus summered and kept the year round upon Dartmoor, the depasturable parts of which, in a dry summer, is one of the best sheepwalks in the kingdom, is not easy to ascertain; but if any inference can be drawn from the returns made from Widdecombe and Buckland in the Moor, their numbers must necessarily be very considerable indeed. A dry summer is always the most favourable for these sheep-walks. These afforded, in the months of August and September last [1808], flocks more numerous and in much higher condition, than has ever been observed by the Surveyor in any other part of England, when such have not been aided by access to the enclosures or artificial food.[18]

Oxen and Horses

The nineteenth century saw another change in the agriculture of Dartmoor which was in large part due to the replacement of oxen by labour horses as the main source of tractive power. The ox was the power unit of peasant or subsistance farming. It was bred from the milking cow and destined finally for sale to the butcher. It was cheaper to feed than a cart horse, and its gear, little more than a yoke and a wooden plough, could be made mainly from hedgerow timber by the peasant owner. With them and a few hand tools—his shovel and mattock, his 'prang' (pitchfork) and 'eaval' (dung fork), his axe and scythe and hook, he could till and husband his few acres.

Horses were more expensive to breed and feed than oxen but were faster and more versatile, qualities which had to be exploited to the full if they were to be worth keeping. This meant buying harrows and rollers to speed the cultivation that was formerly done by hand hacking and by pounding of the clods. Then reaping and mowing machinery had to be bought which horses were fast enough to draw and which enabled the extra fodder they required to be harvested more quickly. The old method of ploughing in narrow bouts of ridge and furrow had to be given up, because the corrugations thus formed precluded the use of wheeled machinery. This, incidentally, brought to an end the cultivation of the 'moory' soils of shallow peat—the old outfields that lay wet and sour unless ridged up between water furrows. With the wheeled carts and traps that horses could draw, and the parallel improvement in the country roads, communications became easier. Produce could be taken to market every week, and new methods, seen over some other man's hedges further afield, could be adopted. Less manpower was employed for field and barn work, so threshing machines were hired or installed.

All this meant that a great deal of money had to be found, and fortunately the mid-nineteenth century was a prosperous era for farmers, with an expanding market in the new manufacturing towns and as yet little food imported. So most of the work was directed to producing crops and animal products for sale, and less to the making of every commodity necessary to the household. It was cheaper to buy soap and even bread than to spend time making it, and tallow candles gave way to oil lamps. Farming became more intensive as root crops were introduced, and purchased manures like Chilean guano were applied.

Ponies

Working horses were not the only ones to contribute to the economy of the Dartmoor farm. The famous Dartmoor pony also played (and still plays) his part. In the nineteenth century ponies were in great demand all over the country for the coal pits, and for drawing small traps, governess carts and costers' carts, as well as for children to ride. The Dartmoors, like all the British breeds of ponies, are the descendants of the original feral Celtic ponies that have bred and fended for themselves in the forests and waste lands since prehistoric times. Ponies of this type drew the light British war chariots that charged the first invading Roman legions. They were the foundation stock that, crossed with foreign horses imported by kings and noblemen—the great battle horses of medieval Europe, and the Spanish, Barb, and Arab 'hot-bloods' of the Stuart era—produced the many different types of horse formerly used in Britain. In general the horses of earlier times were what we would call large ponies. The Dartmoor pony is above all the product of its environment. Having to find its own food all the year round, in rough country and rough weather, natural selection preserves it as a small animal (under 12.2 hands), hardy and clever. Other breed characteristics like colour or shape of head are matters of breeding fashion, with the exception of small, thick ears which, as with sheep and cattle, are indicative of hardihood.

The older writers who mention Dartmoor ponies all confirm that they lived on the Moor, without hand feeding, all the year round. This was probably an easier life than it is now that the Forest has a larger proportion of enclosed newtakes and gates and grids which curtail the free range, but it is still a fact that the true Dartmoor pony is the only domestic animal that can breed and fatten simultaneously on the open moor. A Galloway cow suckling a calf, or a Scotch ewe with a lamb, will maintain her condition and rear her young, but a mare pony, thin as a rake in the spring, will usually rear her sucker and be fat and shining herself by the fall of the year. This may well have been the case with prehistoric breeds of cattle and sheep who were not given much winter fodder but were completely adapted to their environment by the stern moulding of natural selection by the survival of the fittest. Natural selection however, though it evolves a stock which costs the owner little to breed, does not produce the animals most fitted to man's purposes. So the pony breeders have always used selected mares from the reservoir of feral ponies to take into better keep and put to larger, faster, or more beautiful stallions, to breed more valuable colts. Years ago one saw bunches of mares sold at Princetown Fair for an enhanced price because they were said to have been running with a cart colt.

That would not be a selling point now, but in those days the resulting utility cobs could have made good working animals. For many years Shetland pony stallions were used to produce the little thick 'stuggy' ponies wanted for the Northern coalmines. These had the added advantage that they and their offspring were as moor-hardy as the Dartmoor pony itself.

Many ponies on the Moor are now being 'graded up' by their owners towards full registration in the Stud Book, not so much to compete with

the show ponies but because registration certificates are often now necessary before ponies can be exported for breeding and riding.

Fortunately a few genuine moorland breeders kept to their original
hardy registered strains, stallions of which can still be used to run on
the moor. The export trade is a profitable one. Ten to fifteen years ago
shiploads of mares were bought on Dartmoor by Canadian dealers for what
were then excellent prices, and shipped across to Canada for breeding children's small riding ponies, there being no native stocks of small ponies in the
Americas. They had to be small, 11.2 hands or under. So Shetland stallions came into vogue again, since the average pure-bred Dartmoor
is between 11.2 and 12 hands. This traffic ended fairly suddenly, to the
chagrin of those who had started breeding for it a little too late. During
the last four or five years however, the European countries have discovered in their tots a passion for ponies, and shiploads of mares and
fillies have been sent from Dartmoor to Denmark, Holland, Belgium and
other parts of Europe. These foreign dealers are now a welcome and
familiar sight at the annual pony fairs at Ashburton, Tavistock, and
Chagford. Whether Europe will reach saturation point before Dartmoor
is denuded of breeding stocking is a matter of conjecture, but it is a
welcome trade to those who can remember when, before and during the
last war, ninety per cent of the ponies sold at the fairs went for a matter
of shillings to the horse-butchers. Now ponies are the best-paying livestock to breed on the moor. They do not have to be supported by subsidies
and they help the export drive.

Rabbits

Rabbits were introduced into Britain in the twelfth century, and several
warrens were set up on Dartmoor, away from the farms, where they
could be bred for profit. Trowlesworthy Warren dates back to 1272;
higher up the Plym there is Ditsworthy Warren, and other well-known
warrens are those of Huntingdon and Headland. Because the ground made
burrowing difficult, long banks of stone covered with soil and turf were
made to serve as artificial buries. Sometimes special enclosures were
made, with one or two narrow entrances into which the rabbits would
go to feed at night. Then the narrow gaps in the wall would be netted
and the rabbits made to bolt and so be caught. Some of these enclosures,
which were worked into modern times, had dog kennels made in the
walls and the dogs would be used to drive the rabbits into long nets set
up at night. In these enclosures it is also possible to find vermin traps,
with funnel-like approaches made of stone, at the end of which the stoat

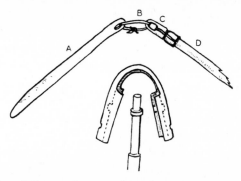

Fig 18. 'Drashel' or flail as made and used on Dartmoor farms. A: flail; B: leather thong fastened with wooden pin; C: 'keepall' of bent ash or horn enabling flail to revolve around D: handstave. Inset: keepall unbound showing how ridge on hand-stave fits into groove inside keepall.

or weasel would spring a slate which would drop and imprison it. Rabbits did much damage both to crops and hedges on the Moor, though often providing a large part of the income, until their numbers were decimated by myxomatosis in 1954. This brought an end to the traditional Boxing Day shoot and the ferreting that was a pastime of many Dartmoor men.

The Dartmoor Farmhouse

Many of the present Dartmoor farmsteads are of sixteenth- and seventeenth-century date. They consist, typically, of a longhouse and a corn-barn. Both buildings have a central passage-way, usually with opposing outer doors. In the barn this passage-way was the threshing floor where the corn—oats, barley and rye, or, after the mid-eighteenth century, oats, barley and wheat, were threshed on wet winter days with hand 'drashels'

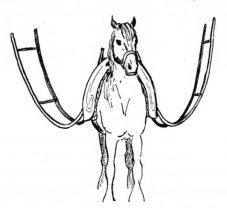

Fig 19. Pack saddle with crooks.

(flails). The threshing-floor was boarded over sleeper beams to give some spring to help the threshers. The through draught helped to blow the 'doust' (chaff) from the grain, though the winnowing proper was done later, originally on some breezy hilltop 'wimstraw' by the womenfolk with sieves, the grain being shaken and tossed over a 'wim-sheet'. The through passage, which often had large double doors, gave access originally to the packhorses which carried the sheaves in from the harvest field in 'crooks' fixed to their pack saddles. The sheaves were stacked in mows on each side of the threshing-floor. This floor was also used in June to shear the sheep on, shorn sheep being penned on one side of the barn, those awaiting shearing on the other.

The wool, the main cash crop of earlier days, was stored in the 'wool chamber' in the upper floor of the dwelling house or 'livier'. This small room, well plastered against damp and rats, was generally above the porch, and had a trap-door in its floor so that the fleeces could be passed up without having to be taken through the kitchen and up the winding stairs.

The livier was in the higher end of the long house, separated from the shippon (cow-shed) by a central passage, but with communicating doors so that the housewife, who generally milked and looked after the cows and calves, had no need to go out of doors to tend them. In the earlier long houses there was sometimes no other way into the shippon, so that the human and bovine inhabitants of the long house used the same front door, turning to the right or left inside to their respective quarters. Later most had a separate doorway from the yard into the shippon for the cows to use.

The tradition of having an outer door at each end of the passage may have persisted from medieval times, when the housewife herself threshed out the day's or week's allowance of bread-corn there—hence 'threshold'.

She ground it in a stone quern and, this being even more laborious if the grain had a high moisture content, she first crisped it over heat. What are thought to be corn-drying kilns made for this purpose have been found in deserted long houses and corn barns on Dartmoor.

The medieval housewife had her hearthstone set in her kitchen floor, with no chimney other than perhaps a wattle and daub funnel leading to a hole in the roof. Against the hearthstone was her tiny, box-like oven, made of slabs of moorstone, where she baked her bread after raking out the hot ashes with which she had heated it. But by the mid-seventeenth century every farm kitchen had its great open hearth and chimney, generally against the passage wall.

Most hearths have a stone 'furze-oven' built into one of the sides. These were heated with a blazing faggot of dried furze, the ashes were scraped out, and bread, cakes and pasties were baked inside, behind an oven door. Where there was no oven, baking was done on the hearth, either in a baking 'kettle'—a cauldron inverted on a large iron plate set in the embers—or a 'camp kettle'—a type of cauldron with a lid that hung from the chimney crook. These kettles were covered over with smouldering 'vags', the dried slabs of heathery turf that were one of the main sources of fuel on Dartmoor until the last war. Near every farm and cottage back-

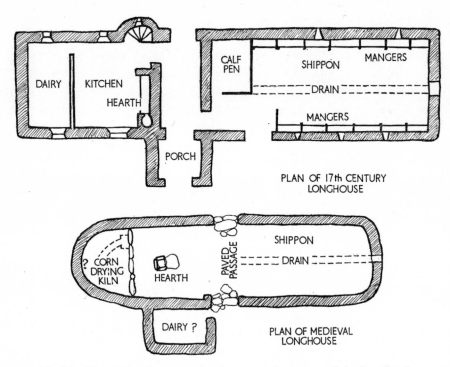

Fig 20.   Plans of longhouses: (*above*) seventeenth century; (*below*) medieval.

door was the 'vaghouse' where the fuel was stored. In the border parishes the 'ood-rick' of faggots cut from the hedges stood near, on the high moor the thatched 'turf-rick' of peats took its place.

An important function of the hearth was for scalding the cream. This method of separating cream for butter-making has been the accepted one in the West Country since records began, when churns were unknown in Devon. The milk was left in large shallow pans or 'steans' in the cool dairy at the far end of the house for twenty-four hours till the cream had risen. The pans were then placed carefully over a gentle heat inside a larger pan of water. This was brought to simmering point, and when the cream began to crinkle, without being allowed to boil, it was taken back to the dairy to cool. The cold scalded cream could be lifted off the surface of the milk with a skimmer, and, by stirring with the hand, made into butter.

The sale of butter on market day, together with scalded (clotted) cream and sometimes eggs or poultry, provided the housewife with enough cash to pay for any bought food and household goods, and often paid the wages of any labour hired by the farm.

The dairy also housed the salting 'standards' or tubs in which the bacon was dry-salted after pig-killing day. Once salted, the hams and cuts of bacon were hung from the beams in the kitchen ceiling until required.

Today, farmhouse production of Devonshire cream continues, aided by the mechanical separator, to the disgust of the purists. The old type of Dartmoor farmhouse, in which dwelling and shippon were all part of the same building, has also been altered out of all recognition. The sanitary laws of the 1920s banished the cows to a separate building, and the former shippons on dozens of Dartmoor farms have been converted into extra rooms in the farmhouse, often to accommodate summer visitors.

The shippon was always at the lower end of the house to facilitate drainage. It commonly housed between 8 and 14 head of cattle, usually with a small pen for the calves in one corner. The gutter for the dung and urine ran down between the standings to a drain at the far end. Above this was a large hole through which dung and soiled bedding could

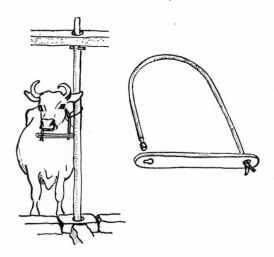

Fig 21. Stall post and tethering yoke.

be thrown out. The mangers were at floor-level, separated from the standings by a raised stone curb. At intervals of about 4ft a hole about 4in in diameter was made in the curb to take the lower end of the wooden stall-post to which each cow was secured. The upper ends of these posts were first pushed up into holes through a beam above and then rammed down and secured by a peg or nail through the post just below the beam. This meant that they could be easily removed and renewed when broken.

Fifty years ago the Dartmoor farmer never bought anything if he could make it himself from what lay around him, so instead af using neck chains or even rope tethers to tie his cows he made 'tethering-yokes' from hedge wood. He cut a springy 'nuthalse' (hazel) stick about a yard long, with a small fork at one end. Near the other end he pared out a notch. This formed the bow. He made a base with a flat piece of wood about 14in long, drilling a hole near one end wide enough to pass the bow-stick through. Near the other end he cut a 'key-hole'. The bow was held in the first hole by its fork, then bent over and the other end put through the wide part of the key-hole. As the thinner, notched section entered it sprang into the narrow outer end of the 'key-hole' and was held there by its own tension. To tie up the cow, the bow was passed over her neck and through the ring on the stall-post before the end was locked in the key-hole.

Above the shippon was the 'tallet' or hayloft, from which hay could be thrown down to the cows through holes left above the mangers. Most tallets originally had 'braith' floors of loose hedge poles and brushwood laid over the beams. About a week's supply of hay was brought in from the field hayricks in trusses by packhorse and hauled up through a space between the beams just inside the shippon door.

Later, when two-wheeled 'wains' came to the district, tallet doors were usually put into the gable-end so that the hay could be pitched in direct from the cart.

Though the long house and the barn were the main buildings, most Dartmoor farms in the course of the centuries added one or two 'young-bullock's houses', sometimes as a lean-to; a stable for the 'labour-horses' which took the place of the plough-oxen in the nineteenth century; a pig's 'loose' (Anglo-Saxon 'hlos') with troughs hollowed out of moorstone; and an 'ash house'. This last was important, as the wood and turf ashes were an essential manure but lost their value if leached by rain.

The ash house was the only building not thatched with combed straw 'reed'. The warm ashes might have held sparks which could fly up and set fire to thatch, so the ash houses usually had corbelled stone roofs. They were generally round and sometimes built into a bank and turfed

Page 179 (above) *The north portal to Leigham tunnel on the Plymouth & Dartmoor railway;* (below) *bridge at the foot of Cann Wood incline on the Lee Moor tramway*

Page 180 (above) *Bridge over the Plym at Marsh Mills for the Cann quarry railway;* (below) *South Devon & Tavistock railway: Plymbridge halt today*

over, but the best had an aperture high in the wall where the ashes could
be thrown in, and a shuttered opening at ground level from which they
could be shovelled out. In some cases perches were put in as a roost for
the farmyard fowls, the mixture of ash and poultry droppings making a
rich, easily-handled manure.

Fig 22.   Dartmoor ash-house.

Nothing was wasted. The drainings from dung heaps and shippon
were caught in gutters into which the nearest spring of water was diverted
to irrigate the meadow that almost always lay just below the farmyard.
A meadow watered like this during the winter could provide lush spring
grazing for cows or ewes at least a month before the dry pastures had
started chinking.

Notes to this chapter are on page 292.

L

6

Roads and Tracks

Robert Groves

IF WE scan a map of Devonshire we see that Dartmoor stands out clearly, not only because of its height compared with the country round about but also because of its apparent lack of man-made features. Villages and farms are few and are found only on the lower and more sheltered parts of the Moor. The roads and lanes which form a close network over lowland Devon are absent from most of Dartmoor. Only two roads cross the Moor, from Plymouth to Moretonhampstead and from Tavistock to Ashburton, with their intersection at Two Bridges. Over large areas of moorland there are only a few indications on the maps of paths and tracks. The moorland walker will, of course, know other pathways not considered important enough to be shown. He will discover trackways, perhaps only short ones, where the ground is difficult and walkers, moormen, sheep and cattle have made the best route clear by repeated use. But even so the number of routeways is small because of the barrenness of the Moor and the consequent lack of incentive for men to make their way there.

Each route will have come into being to meet some particular need. Some linked together the towns and villages of the moorland edge. Others led out into the Moor to the pastures, peat, tin, and other resources. The men who made these roads and tracks no doubt knew Dartmoor well and the routes will have been carefully chosen. In lowland Devon many roads and lanes have irregular courses whose lines were to some degree dictated by the fields, farms and villages which they served. By contrast, the men who chose the moorland routes were free to take the best way to their destination. They would take as short a route as possible, but would also avoid difficult ground. The highest land on the Moor, over about 1,500ft, is level, wet and often has an uneven surface, so is to be avoided. The more steeply-sided valleys, or the marshy bottoms of many of the broader valleys, are also difficult to negotiate. The best ground for walking is on the lower ridges and hilltops and the sides of the broader valleys. It was there that the moormen and travellers went when they could.[1]

Early Routes

Identifying a very early routeway is a difficult task. It should have a smooth, even line, picking the best route across the country for travellers on foot. It will keep as much as possible to high ground and avoid river crossings. This should be true even where it is leading through farmed countryside, because it existed before the farms and fields. We should also find early routeways leading to and from early archaeological remains. On Dartmoor we might hope to find traces of old trackways relating to the many hut circles and other prehistoric remains. To the north and south of Dartmoor there are roads and lanes leading up to the Moor on the ridges of high ground between the valleys of the rivers flowing off the Moor. They are believed to be of prehistoric origin and to have served as routes to summer pastures since Neolithic times. On Dartmoor itself, however, almost all the known trackways are clearly of more recent origin and almost all trace of very early routes has been lost.

Only on the edge of the Moor can a very early trackway be identified with any certainty. It is probable that the A30 to the north of it traces the line of a very early routeway down the spine of the south-west peninsula. On the north-west another route veers off this route and leads down the western flank of the Moor to reach the sea at the Cattewater or at Sutton Pool near to Plymouth Sound. On the opposite shore, at Mount Batten, there existed from the fifth century BC onwards a settlement which had trading connections with the Continent, and it seems as if this route led to it. The old route appears to have left the line of the A30 to the south-west of Okehampton and led up through the hamlet of Meldon. The road junction between Fowley and Hughslade was altered in about 1862. Before that, the present main road climbed steeply and awkwardly off the Meldon lane, which therefore appears to have had more importance in past times. Beyond Meldon the lane ends on the open Moor, but a parish boundary and then field walls mark what was probably the old line as far as the River Lyd. Parish boundaries were not drawn until the twelfth century, but often followed long-established features such as an old trackway. The name 'King Way' has been given to this stretch of track and this name appears beside the parish boundary south of Sourton Tor on the Sourton tithe map of 1844.

The present main road takes a lower way through Sourton village. It may well have come into being to replace the higher way as the woodlands were cleared and the land settled. From the River Lyd southwards the old route seems to be traced almost completely by modern roads, by way of Harford Bridge, Horrabridge and Roborough Down, and so down into Plymouth. The only breaks in the line are where road alterations in 1817 made a deviation from the direct line to Harford Bridge, and where the wartime airfield covered part of Roborough Down and destroyed the road which had existed there.

There are other roads, lanes, and tracks which suggest by their character that they may be very early in origin. One is the road leading up from Buckfastleigh to the moor near Hayford Hall. Another is the track leading out from Skerraton Down towards Aune Head, which is traced by a parish boundary for some distance. From Whiddon Down on the north-east side of the Moor a road runs along the high ground to Drewsteignton. Two apparently-early routes branch from it, one leading south-eastwards by way of Sandypark Bridge to Lustleigh, the other going down to Chagford Bridge and out to the moor past Waye Barton and Metherall. This suggests that the route south and west from Metherall by way of Two Bridges to Roborough Down (the line now followed by the B3212) is very early too. In none of these cases, however, can we suggest a date for their origins.

Recent research has shown that the Romans made a number of roads in Devon. There was one leading south and west from Exeter at least as far as Teignbridge. Another went round to the north of Dartmoor by way of North Tawton and may have passed very close to the Moor at Okehampton and Sourton Down before leading westwards into Cornwall and on towards the tin mines near Land's End. Detailed field research may yet reveal Roman roads on the Moor itself, but the attempts to prove the existence of Roman roads on Dartmoor have not so far been convincing.[2]

Devon was invaded by the Saxons in the seventh century, and there then began a period lasting six centuries or more during which farms and villages were settled and woodlands cleared. It was during this time that many of the farm lanes and local roads of lowland Devon and the lower parts of Dartmoor came into being. The angular and winding character of these routes is partly a consequence of their having originated as ways picked between newly-created fields; the walls or banks with which they are lined would have been built of stones cleared from the land.

It was probably not, however, until towns began to appear in Devon that routeways other than very local ones began to assume any importance. Three of the earliest Devon towns were close to Dartmoor, and it is probably significant that they grew up on and near the early routeways flanking the Moor on the north and west already described. One of the four burghs made by the Saxons in the ninth century was on a hilltop

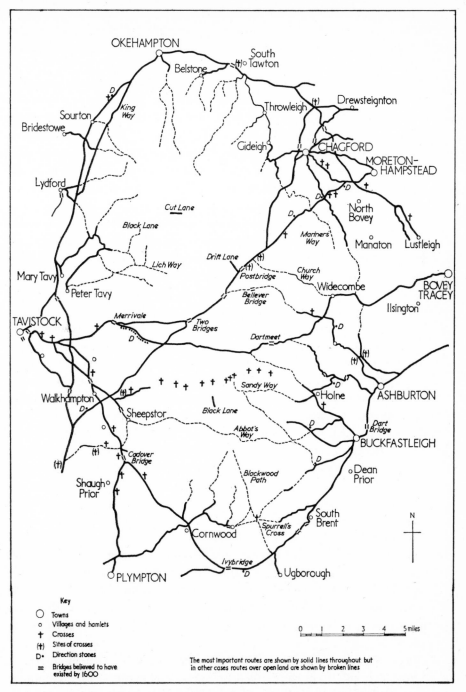

OKEHAMPTON

South
Tawton

Belstone

Drewsteignton

Sourton

Throwleigh

King
Way

Bridestowe

Gideigh

CHAGFORD

MORETON-
HAMPSTEAD

Lydford

North
Bovey

Cut Lane

Black Lane

Mariners
Way

Manaton

Lustleigh

Lich Way

Drift Lane

Mary Tavy

Church
Way

BOVEY
TRACEY

Peter Tavy

Postbridge

Widecombe

Ilsington

Bellever
Bridge

Merrivale

Two
Bridges

TAVISTOCK

Dartmeet

Sandy Way

Walkhampton

Holne

ASHBURTON

Sheepstor

Black Lane

Dart
Bridge

Abbot's
Way

BUCKFASTLEIGH

Cadover
Bridge

Blackwood
Path

Dean
Prior

Shaugh
Prior

South
Brent

N

Spurrell's
Cross

Cornwood

Ivybridge

PLYMPTON

Ugborough

Key

○ Towns
○ Villages and hamlets
† Crosses
(†) Sites of crosses
D• Direction stones
═ Bridges believed to have
   existed by 1600

0 1 2 3 4 5 miles

The most important routes are shown by solid lines throughout but
in other cases routes over open land are shown by broken lines

Fig 23.   Early roads and tracks; the principal roads and tracks on and near the Moor
as they existed before the changes of the last two hundred years.

overlooking the River Lyd, less than a mile from the spot where that
river was forded by the track leading along the edge of the Moor; they
called it Lydford. Near a small settlement on the bank of the Tavy an
abbey was founded in about 974. In later times the town of Tavistock
grew up close to the abbey and was linked to the routeway by roads
which led to Horrabridge and the hill above Harford Bridge. On the route
into Cornwall the Sheriff of Devon built a castle in the eleventh century
and shortly afterwards founded the borough of Okehampton near by.

The main growth of towns came at a later period. Markets, fairs and
town charters did not begin to appear until the twelfth and thirteenth
centuries. We cannot be sure when it was that the various routeways linking the towns of the moorland edge came into being, but it seems reasonable to suppose that it was at this period. Trade was on the increase and
travellers and traders went from town to town. At Tavistock and Plympton in the west and at Chagford, Moretonhampstead, Bovey Tracey and
Ashburton on the east and south-east, there were markets trading in local
produce, and in several towns there was also an expanding cloth industry.
Tin-mining boomed from about 1150, and in the fourteenth century the
importance in the trade of Chagford, Ashburton, Tavistock and Plympton was acknowledged when they were made stannary towns.

Travellers used existing ways where possible but elsewhere made new
routes between the farms or over the open Moor. Tavistock, on the route
to Cornwall, became the focus for the routes leading westwards from
each of the towns on the eastern side of the Moor. Not only did new routes
come into being at this time, but it seems probable that many of the
bridges and wayside crosses of the moor also date from this period.

Travellers probably used the moorland routes mainly on foot or horse-
back. Packhorses were used for transporting goods. The Rev John Swete
describes in his journal for August 1797 meeting a packhorse train near
Chagford with which a man was bringing a supply of lime for the land
up from Ashburton. Strings of packhorses were not generally replaced
in Devon by wheeled vehicles until about 1800, and on Dartmoor these
were probably rare well into the nineteenth century. The Rev Sabine
Baring-Gould wrote in 1912 that it was not so long ago that an old man
in Sheepstor died who could remember the first cart coming into the
village.[3]

Every route over Dartmoor has to cross one or more of the many rivers
which flow off it; in flood these form formidable obstacles.[4] A number
of the bridges on the Moor's edge appear in thirteenth- and fourteenth-
century records, and some were rebuilt in the fifteenth and sixteenth
centuries. These bridges are often fine structures of several arches. Those

on the Moor itself were more crudely constructed, consisting of unhewn or roughly shaped blocks of granite heaped on each other. These are the 'clapper bridges', of which the largest is at Postbridge. It probably dates from the thirteenth century, in common with others, including those at Bellever and Dartmeet and those which existed once at Two Bridges, Cadover, the Cherry Brook, and perhaps Huccaby. Clapper bridges continued to be built on the Moor over many centuries. One went up over the North Teign River in about 1780 to give access to the newly-enclosed Teignhead Farm and others of unknown date span many moorland streams, for example the Wallabrook near Runnage and Babeny.

It has been argued that these clapper bridges as they survive, show only the skeletons of their original form. Nosworthy Bridge, carrying the old road to Kingsett Farm across the river Meavy above Burrator, appears from the road to be an ordinary bridge with a parapet, but from the river bank it is seen to be carried on granite slabs like those in the clappers. Such bridges, with parapets and either a turf or metalled surface, are not uncommon as crossings over the Plymouth leat.

The granite crosses to be found beside many Dartmoor roads and tracks reflect the prosperity of local towns in the Middle Ages and the need to mark moorland tracks and provide landmarks to guide travellers.[5] Most of the Dartmoor crosses are of simple design and were erected over a period of several centuries. The earliest documentary reference appears to be that to Siward's Cross, in the Perambulation of 1240, but many of the crosses may have existed before that date. Perhaps amongst the last to be put up were four erected on the boundary of Brent Moor in 1557, of which Huntingdon Cross is the best-preserved survivor. Crosses of rather more elaborate design, of octagonal section or perhaps simply with the corners chamfered off, were being put up in the fourteenth and fifteenth centuries (Plates pp 143 and 144).

The early maps of Dartmoor enable us to discover which routes over the Moor were considered to be important.[6] There is one map dating from the fifteenth century which, despite its sketchy character, is of considerable importance. It shows the route over the Moor from Chagford to Tavistock, and also the road leading round the southern edge between Exeter and Plymouth. These two routes are also shown in considerable detail in John Ogilby's road book of 1675.

The track from Chagford to Tavistock was part of a route from Exeter into Cornwall which approached the Moor by way of the Teign Valley and, after passing through Chagford, led out on to the Moor past Waye Barton and Metherall. It then led over Hurston Ridge, but it is doubtful whether the track was ever very well defined there. There is now no trace of it. John Swete came this way in 1797 and despite attempts to follow the old route he found himself wandering into a bog. At Statts Bridge this route was joined by another (now the B3212), leading on to the moor from Moretonhampstead; it was marked by Beetor Cross and Bennett's Cross, and there are said to have been crosses at one time also on Merripit Hill and at Postbridge. The route west was by way of the clapper bridges at Postbridge, the Cherry Brook, and Two Bridges.

At Two Bridges the early route went north of the present road, on a line almost directly from Parson's Cottage to the entrance to the drive to Beardown Farm. Traces of the old track can be seen on the hill south-westwards from Parson's Cottage. The track crossed both the West Dart and Cowsic Rivers a short distance above the point at which they meet. It might be supposed that there was once a bridge over both rivers and that the name 'Two Bridges' derived from this fact. This does not seem to have been the case. Ogilby shows only one bridge, and that was over the West Dart, though no trace of it remains now. The *Place Names of Devon* volume gives the earliest form of the name as 'Tobrygge', occurring in the fifteenth century, and suggests that this probably meant simply 'at the bridge'.[7] Beyond Merrivale Bridge, which is shown on the fifteenth-century map of the Moor, the old route lay south of the present road into Tavistock. Leading by way of Windy Post and past Moortown, it went over Whitchurch Down before descending steeply to the River Tavy, which it crossed into Tavistock by the Great Bridge (probably built in the thirteenth century, perhaps about 1260).

The second of the routes shown by Ogilby in 1675 led from Exeter to Plymouth round the southern edge of Dartmoor. The present A38 takes a much lower and easier line than the earlier road because of changes carried out by the turnpike trusts in the nineteenth century, using road building techniques not available in earlier times. Stretches of the old route still exist as by-roads between Buckfast and Bittaford. This must always have been a difficult route because of the number of rivers to be crossed. We hear of bridges on this road quite early: Glaze Bridge and Ivybridge are mentioned in the records in the thirteenth century, Dart Bridge in the fourteenth century.

A higher way round the south of the Moor existed, and may have provided easier going if the weather was good. It diverged from the main route just south-west of Buckfastleigh, and going by way of Gidley Bridge, Shipley Bridge, Harford, and Cornwood, rejoined it near Plympton St Mary church. High on the open moor, east of Harford, this route is marked by Spurrell's Cross.

The maps of Devon which appeared towards the end of the seventeenth century indicated another of the moorland routes, the one linking Tavistock with Bovey Tracey. Veering off the route to Chagford just east of Merrivale it went south of North Hessary Tor, through the site of Princetown, and by way of Swincombe to Dartmeet clapper bridge. The section near North Hessary Tor does not seem to have been well defined, but over Royal Hill it is still very clear. From Dartmeet the way to Bovey is traced by modern roads and lanes, past Corndon Tor and over Ponsworthy Bridge (a stone of which is dated 1666) and round to Widecombe. From there the route to Bovey is up over the high ground around Rippon Tor and Hay Tor, then down into the basin of the River Bovey, and so to Bovey Tracey, with roads beyond to Exeter.

Tavistock and Plympton (with its Norman priory in 1121) were twelfth-century boroughs. They were linked by a route which curved round north-east of the deeper parts of the Walkham and Plym valleys, and followed the high ground down to the creek at Plympton. A number of crosses stand on this route and some, though of simple design, are similar enough to suggest that they were put up at about the same time. There are two on Whitchurch Down and one above Huckworthy Bridge. Then there are Marchant's Cross and the crosses at Cadover Bridge, near Shaden Moor, and at Beatland Corner, where only the socket-stone of the cross has survived.

Huckworthy Bridge is shown on the fifteenth-century map of the Moor, and Cadover Bridge is named in a document of 1291. Between these two there was a route to the north-east of the main one, going by way of Sheepstor Bridge (possibly mentioned in 1326) and Sheepstor village. The section by Lynch Common has been disused for at least two centuries, suggesting that this route declined from some former importance, an idea borne out by the fact that Walkhampton church stands close by it, while the village is in the valley below. Perhaps this route was in use from the twelfth century, when the valleys of the Upper Meavy and Plym were such rich sources of tin, but fell out of use as the mining declined. From Cadover Bridge a route leads through Cornwood to the Exeter road at Ivybridge; it was marked by one or more crosses.[8]

From the Tavistock to Plympton route there veered off another which was marked by crosses and which avoided the highest and wettest land of the centre of southern Dartmoor. The first cross on this line seems to have been at Lowery, above Burrator, because there were a cross pedestal and socket-stone there until some years ago. The first cross still standing on this line is at Cross Gate below Leather Tor; there is another near Crazy Well Pool, and one further east on the same hillside. Siward's Cross was no doubt a landmark on this route, and from there

the way east was marked by a cross near the edge of Foxtor Mire, by
the cross which stood on Childe's Tomb, then by a cross above Fox Tor
Farm, two on Ter Hill, two more on Down Ridge, and Horn's Cross.
A number of these crosses are of similar design, and another like them
stands by an oak tree at Hawson near Holne. If it was part of the series,
they appear to have been leading to Buckfastleigh.

When we look at the maps it seems natural that there should once
have existed a routeway across the southern part of Dartmoor. By taking
advantage of the rather lower and drier ground near Huntingdon Warren, Redlake and Erme Head, one can avoid the high, wet areas round
Cater's Beam and Ryder's Hill on the north, and Shavercombe Head
and Langcombe Head on the south; thus a valuable east to west link
is created. Such a routeway certainly existed; very clear traces of it can
still be seen between Brockhill Ford and Huntingdon Cross (near the
Avon Reservoir), between the Avon and Redlake, and near Broad Rock.
The Ordnance Survey labels this routeway 'Abbot's Way', and a number
of writers have seen it as a link between Buckfast Abbey in the east,
founded in the eleventh century or perhaps earlier, and the two abbeys
on the west: Tavistock, founded in the tenth century, and Buckland,
founded in 1278. The routeway could certainly have served that purpose.
Roads and lanes lead from Buckfast up to the edge of the Moor at Cross
Furzes, and from there the way would have been as already mentioned
by way of the Avon and Redlake to Broad Rock. From Broad Rock it
would presumably have been over the Plym by Plym Steps (mentioned
as 'Plymcrundla' in 1291) and then towards Sheepstor village by the track
which now leads to the ruins of the Eylesbarrow tin mine.[9]

Is the name 'Abbot's Way' justified? Apparently the only early piece
of evidence associating the route with the Abbeys on the edge of the Moor
is the fact that the ford where the track crosses a small right-bank tributary of the Avon was called 'Buckland Ford' in a document of 1557.
The earliest occurence of the name 'Abbot's Way' appears to be in the
papers of one John Andrews, a Modbury attorney, who in 1790–4 called
this track 'Jobber's Cawse (otherwise Abbot's Way)'.[10] The name also
appeared on the first edition of the Ordnance Survey one-inch map published for Devon in 1809.

Whether the so-called Abbot's Way was ever used a great deal by the
monks we cannot be sure. They may well have used it, but it seems
likely that most of those who used it were people from the towns, the
jobbers (workers or traders) to whom Andrews refers. If the monks spon-
sored a route over the Moor it might, as Hansford Worth suggested, have
been the one further north marked by crosses. That route seems to have

been carefully planned to use the easiest areas of high ground, with fewest river crossings, to make a link between Buckfast and the west side of the Moor. It was perhaps intended to replace the 'Abbot's Way', although in fact shows little sign of having been used.

For travellers coming from Ashburton or further east, both these routes over the southern Moor were superseded by the building of New Bridge and Holne Bridge. The structures of both probably date from the fifteenth century, but when we hear of Holne Bridge in 1413 it is being re-erected after destruction by floods. Whenever these two bridges were built over the deep River Dart, they provided a new way to Tavistock by way of Dartmeet and Merrivale.

On the east side of the Moor a road runs directly from Chagford to Ashburton, deviating from a straight course only slightly to avoid valleys. After climbing steeply out of Chagford it keeps to the high ground between the basins of the Bovey and Dart Rivers before descending from the open moorland through woods and fields to the town of Ashburton. Both these towns traded in farm produce, wool and tin, and wagons from a large woollen mill at Chagford were using this road early in the nineteenth century.

The Tracks

Many of the paths and tracks used to get out on to the Moor from the farms and villages in times past are now faded and the memory of them is lost. We have, however, the record of the most important moorland routes made by William Crossing in 1909, when many of them were still in regular use. The parishes of the moorland border include large areas of the Moor, where the inhabitants had the right to peat, pastures, and other resources. Over many centuries tracks out into the Moor have been formed, and in some places worn deeply by men going out to the peat cuttings or taking cattle to the good grazing land. The deep beds of peat are found on the highest land, over about 1,700ft in the northern and 1,500ft in the southern parts of the Moor. The tinners were using peat for fuel in the thirteenth century, and probably the people of the moorland border were using it in their homes for long before that. It must have gained in importance as the woodlands on the lower ground were cleared and wood became scarce.

Many of the tracks must have been used for carrying peat at one time or another; some we know to have been used for this purpose. From Okehampton a track—now a metalled road within the firing ranges—led out to Dinger Tor and the peat cuttings near High Willhays. From Sourton,

Bridestowe and Lydford tracks went up to the peat on the high land near Rattlebrook Head and Kitty Tor. From Wapsworthy in the Tavy valley a peat track called 'Black Lane' led to the area near Walkham Head, and another went over to Blackbrook Head. On Dartmoor 'black' in a place-name frequently refers to peat, the moorland name for peat being 'blackwood'. From Petertavy a peat track went up past White Tor and White Barrow and towards Walkham Head. Peat was also cut extensively around Quintin's Man, Whitehorse Hill and Wild Tor, and was taken in from there to the border farms past Batworthy.

In the south, two tracks led out to Erme Pound, which was used for drifts (the gathering in of cattle), and beyond that the pastures on Green Hill could be reached. One came up from Cornwood by way of Stall Moor, and the other led out from near Wrangaton and was probably used by Ugborough people. Both were used for carrying peat, and the latter actually had the name 'Blackwood Path'.

Some other moormen's routes are known. Black Lane is a way through the peat between Fox Tor and the area near Erme Head, and on the northern part of the Moor a pass, known as Cut Lane, crosses the difficult ground just north of Cut Hill. Sandy Way is a track of which there are very clear traces, leading from Michelcombe near Holne to the highest parts of the southern Moor. In many places there are spaces left between two enclosures, or between an enclosure and a river or stream, where cattle could be driven. One on the right bank of the East Dart just above Postbridge was called Drift Lane.

There is one early trackway for which the evidence is particularly good. The ancient tenements on the lower land near the Walla Brook came within the Forest of Dartmoor and so within the Parish of Lydford. The inhabitants originally had to go over the moor to Lydford Church to take the sacraments and bury their dead; we know this because in a document of 1260[11] the people of Babeny and Pizwell were excused this arduous journey and allowed to go instead to Widecombe. An established route is believed to have existed between the moorland farms and Lydford; it has been given the name 'Lich Way', meaning the route by which corpses were taken. It would have continued in use after the dead ceased to be taken this way because the Forest courts were held at Lydford, and from the clapper bridge over the East Dart at Bellever a very clear track leads over the hill through the plantations to the Cherry Brook. No further trace can be seen until just before the Cowsic. A fairly well defined track crosses the Cowsic at Traveller's Ford and leads to the River Walkham at Sandy Ford; it is named 'Lich Way' by the Ordnance Survey.

The traveller to Lydford would have gone from the Walkham over the hill to the west and then down past Bagga Tor to Willsworthy. A route over the Bagga Tor brook by a small clapper bridge and then across the Tavy by the large stepping stones at Standon Ford might have been taken. Another suggested route takes a more direct line. Leading down the left side of the Bagga Tor Brook it crossed the brook and the Tavy at Cataloo Steps and then climbed up to Willsworthy by a lane long overgrown and blocked; it was cleared again early in 1970. From Willsworthy the way was past Yellowmead and over the open moorland, where there are still very clear traces of a trackway for some distance, to Beardon, from which a path leads to Lydford.

As we should expect, there was a route from the ancient tenements to Widecombe Church. It led from the Wallabrook round the south of Hameldon and down to Widecombe village, and is said to have been called 'Church Way' in 1491.

After the Middle Ages, granite crosses ceased to be put up as guides; where necessary this function was performed by wayside stones. An Act of Parliament passed in 1696 gave the justices authority to erect at crossroads stones or posts bearing large letters indicating the name of the next town. There are a number of these on and around the Moor, and it seems likely that many of them were put up within a few decades of the Act. They can be seen at Cross Furzes, by the Chagford turning between Bush Down and Shapley Common, and at other places indicated on the map on page 185 (Plate, p 144).

On the open Moor where tracks were poorly defined, there was no doubt an even greater need for such stones to prevent travellers becoming lost. On Donn's map of 1765 a number are indicated. In 1699–1700 Plymouth Corporation paid £2 for the erection of 'Moorestones on Dartmoor in the way leading from Plymouth towards Exon for guidence of Travellers passing that way'. These may be the same stones which Donn shows to the south-west of Two Bridges on the road from Plymouth. They have disappeared now, but he shows some other stones which still survive. They stand on the line of the track leading southeastwards from Merrivale. There are said to be thirteen stones to the west and south of North Hessary Tor, each bearing, on opposite faces, the letters T (for Tavistock) and A (for Ashburton).[12]

There is a strong tradition on the eastern side of the Moor that there once existed a routeway used by sailors travelling between the ports of Bideford and Dartmouth; it has been given the name 'Mariners' Way'. This tradition is supported by a number of entries in the Gidleigh church records between 1730 and 1774 recording the giving of alms to sailors.

William Crossing has described its line, and further details came to light when rights of way were the subject of inquiry in 1958. The old route is claimed to have passed down the eastern flank of Dartmoor, very close to a direct line between the two ports; it deviated only to avoid the northern part of the Moor and the rearing mass of Hameldon. This was not a trackway existing in its own right but simply a route which used roads and lanes where possible and elsewhere picked out a way across the fields. It is said to have come south from Bideford by way of the Torridge valley and Great Torrington, through South Zeal, and then by way of West Wyke and Clannaborough to Throwleigh. From there perhaps Deave Lane to Forder was the route, through Gidleigh to Glassy Steps below Gidleigh Tor, and thence by Frenchbeer, Yardworthy, Shapley, Hurston and Jurston. South-eastwards from there the line is indicated on the more recent Ordnance Survey maps by a right of way as far as Natsworthy. Beyond that the course is uncertain, although the best way would be through Widecombe; a route down the Dart valley through Ausewell Woods has been suggested. Dartmouth is then reached past Ashburton and through Totnes.

Most of the Dartmoor roads and tracks seem to have come into being in the Middle Ages and in all probability altered little if at all for several centuries. The map on page 185 shows the situation as it probably was in the eighteenth century and for some considerable time earlier. The lines on this map, however, are in many places clearer than the tracks they are representing. Reporting in 1786 on the possibility of developing mining and farming on Dartmoor, William Simpson, a Duchy surveyor, wrote that 'within the last twenty years there were only three or four very blind roads across the whole, insomuch that going over the moor in *winter* was always considered not only as an arduous but really danger-ous undertaking; and the many lives lost in such attempts is too notorious to be doubted'.[13] Even as Simpson was writing, various improvements were under way on Dartmoor.

Turnpikes

In the eighteenth century, traffic on the roads of England was increas-ing and the long-established system of road maintenance by parishes, which had never worked satisfactorily, was at last found to be intoler-able. From about 1750 groups of landowners and business men co-operated to obtain Acts of Parliament and loans of capital to improve and maintain stretches of road in their localities. They could recoup their investment by levying tolls at toll-gates or 'turnpikes'. About eight

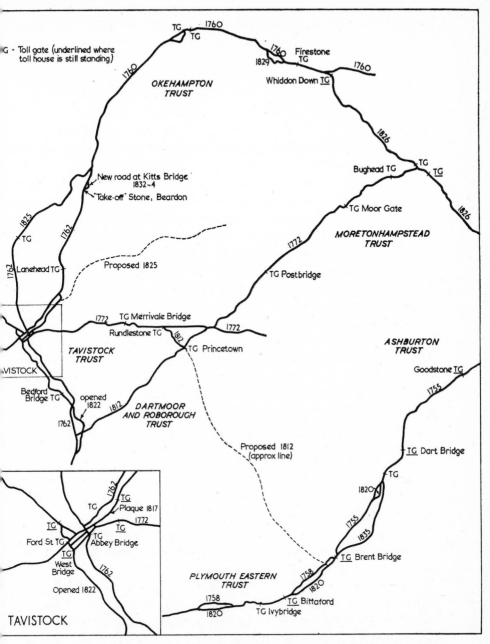

Fig 24. Turnpike roads; the evidence from the Acts of Parliament and from the trust records. Dates refer, except where otherwise indicated, to the authorising Act and not to the carrying out of works. The 'Take Off' stone at Beardon indicated where extra animals hauling vehicles had to be taken off.

turnpike trusts, authorised during a period of over 120 years by almost 50 Acts of Parliament, administered roads round Dartmoor. The evidence relating to the turnpike roads has been gathered on the map on page 195.[14]

The roads around the edge of the Moor were turnpiked first. The Ashburton Trust, set up by an Act of 1755, administered the Plymouth road as far as Brent Bridge, beyond which the Plymouth Eastern Trust (1758) had jurisdiction. To the west and north of the Moor were the Tavistock Trust (1762) and the Okehampton Trust (1760). At first the old routes were not greatly altered, and new methods of surfacing were not introduced until the nineteenth century, so it is unlikely that the new administration made any great impact on these roads for some time, though presumably they were kept in better repair.

When, however, the roads on the Moor itself were turnpiked some important changes were made. The road from Tavistock to Moretonhampstead was turnpiked by two Acts of 1772, although the work on them may not have been completed for twenty years. Under one Act the Tavistock Trust replaced the old route out of Tavistock, which had a steep climb up to Whitchurch Down, with the present road by way of Moorshop to Merrivale.[15] From there the turnpike road followed the old line, but at Two Bridges there was a diversion southwards so that it crossed one river instead of two. The bridge which was built then still stands, though it now serves only as an approach to the nearby hotel. The Tavistock Trust took over the road as far as the Cherry Brook. They also made a road from Two Bridges down to Dunnabridge.[16] This appears to have been an entirely new route; it would have replaced the old way by Royal Hill and Swincombe as the route from Tavistock to Ashburton. The second of the two Acts of 1772 set up the Moreton-hampstead Trust, which administered the road from the Cherry Brook to Moretonhampstead and beyond. The old route through Chagford was ignored, probably because that town was less important than it had once been, and a direct line was taken for Exeter.

When the Acts of 1772 were going through Parliament, opposition was expressed by a number of places in Devon and Cornwall; they believed their interests would be injured and pleaded that Dartmoor was too barren a place for the proposed road improvements. But the road changes in fact prepared the way for those who wanted to develop the Moor and transform its barrenness into prosperity. Prince Hall, Tor Royal, Princetown and other places were developed. The road from Roborough Down to Two Bridges, with a branch past the Prison of War, was turnpiked by an Act of 1812. The tolls from the gates on this road (at

Page 197 (above) *The Burnard family shelters behind an up-turned cart on White Ridge, while on holiday at Postbridge in 1893. George French stands by the wheel;* (below) *one of Bulpins' 'Pride of the Moor' charabancs c 1923*

Page 198 (above) *The Princess of Wales (later Queen Mary) in the Royal Pavilion at Huccaby Races on 11 June 1909;* (below) *the Hon. W. F. Smith, MP, drives off to open Chagford golf course on 8 June 1908*

Princetown and Rundlestone) were paltry, and the Act appears to have expired, the normal period being twenty-one years. A Plymouth guide-book of 1812 shows as 'proposed' the road over the southern Moor from Princetown to the Plymouth–Exeter road. It was of course never made, though the track leading out from Princetown between the Devil's Elbow and the Plume of Feathers is still called Ivybridge Lane. A road was also made at about that period leading from Tor Royal to the mine at White Works. It was metalled during the last war.

When the turnpike engineers altered the lines of the Dartmoor roads their chief aim appears to have been to ease the gradients. They took the roads as low as possible, having the resources to make roads over ground which earlier travellers had avoided. The roads they made or im-proved frequently have long ruler-straight lengths, for example near Two Bridges and near Gibbet Hill. The bends, though suitable for coach and horses, are often too sharp for modern traffic.

It was not until almost two decades of the nineteenth century had gone by that work began in earnest to improve the roads round the edge of the Moor. The valley road north out of Tavistock was made in 1817, a fact still commemorated by a roadside plaque. The road south-east out of the town towards Plymouth was replaced by the one which has become the A386. *The Plymouth and Plymouth-Dock Weekly Jour-nal* for 13 June 1822 recorded the opening of the latter.

> The trustees of the Plymouth and Tavistock Turnpike being met at two o'clock by his Grace the Duke of Bedford and a large party of gentle-men, went in procession over the new road, which presents a variety of picturesque scenery, the carriages preceded by nearly 150 persons on horseback, and the Dock Cavalry bringing up the rear. At the entrance of Tavistock the procession was met by the inhabitants, and received with acclamations, the bells from the venerable church ringing a merry peal.

Enthusiasm at Tavistock for road-building resulted in an Act of 1825 which authorised a number of ambitious schemes. Some of the proposals materialised, but one which did not was for a road as far as the River Dart over the wildest parts of the northern Moor.

On the Plymouth to Exeter road a number of changes were made under an Act of 1820, at Dean Clapper Hill near Dean Prior, south-west of Brent, and west of Ivybridge. It was not, however, until after an Act of 1835 that plans to make the long curving road from Dean to Brent by way of Stidston were carried out. A new road was made past Okehampton Castle, and under an Act of 1829 South Zeal was by-passed. The Tavistock Trust accounts show that the present road at

M

Kitts Bridge was made in 1832–4; the bridge used before that can still be seen on the older and more direct line.

The toll houses have been marked on the map on page 195. The amounts of money collected are known in some cases and give a clue to relative amounts of traffic on the roads. In a twelve-month period in the early 1820s the Princetown and Rundlestone toll houses were bringing in together only about £20 to £30 and the toll house at Postbridge under £100, but at Ivybridge, on the Plymouth to Exeter road, over £500 was collected. None of the trusts were a financial success, however, and tolls began to fall off after about 1840. In the case of the Plymouth Eastern Trust the year of greatest drop in tolls was, significantly, 1849, the year that the railway reached Plymouth.

The railways brought an end to the turnpike system. The trusts were wound up, the toll houses sold off, and the roads handed over to the counties. The first of the Dartmoor trusts to go was Okehampton, in 1863, and the last was the Plymouth and Tavistock Trust (separated from the Tavistock Trust in 1804) in 1882.

The improved roads and increased traffic on the Moor in the eighteenth century led to the opening of a number of wayside inns. Newhouse (later called Warren House Inn) and possibly the Dartmoor Inn at Merrivale are shown on Donn's Map of 1765. The Saracen's Head at Two Bridges was put up by Judge Buller a few years before 1797, and the Greyhound Inn at Postbridge may have been built at about the same period. On the east side of the Moor there was once an inn called New House beside the Chagford–Ashburton road west of Rippon Tor, but it was burnt down some time in the nineteenth century.

The changes made by the turnpike trustees were the last general alterations to the roads on and around the Moor. Other changes since their time have been piecemeal and very local, carried out to serve some particular purpose. A number of tracks were made or re-used to serve the mines. The track up the west side of Newleycombe valley, above Burrator, was in use before the end of the eighteenth century to give access to the Whiteworks Mine, and in the nineteenth we hear of tracks to the Knock Mine from Belstone, to Ringleshutts Mine from Holne Gate, to the Hexworthy Mine and the Huntingdon Mine. Granite workers at Merrivale used a track over the open Moor past Staple Tor to Petertavy. The new settlement at Princetown needed its supply of peat, and this was brought on a track from Blackbrook Head. New pieces of track branched off old trackways in order to reach peat cuttings at Walkham Head and the tin mine at the Rattlebrook. China clay workers made paths and tracks on Shaugh Moor, Crownhill Down and Heddon Down, and a track which leads out from Ball Gate in Brent Parish to the workings at Bala Brook Head.

Two nineteenth-century road schemes were of more general importance. One was the making of the road over Trendlebere Down at some time after 1840. The other was the making in 1874 of the road branching off the Moretonhampstead road and leading down the valley past Grimspound towards Grendon (where the field pattern was changed to its present geometrical form at about the same period).

In the heart of the north Moor, on the highest land between the river valleys, large areas of peat eroded into gulleys make crossing difficult. Frank Phillpotts, a keen follower of hounds, between 1895 and 1905 made a number of passes and causeways through the peat to provide an easier way for hunting and cattle men, though in some cases they were improvements of already existing ways. They are marked in a number of places by short granite posts bearing bronze tablets recording their origin and purpose, and many appear on the most recent Ordnance Survey maps.[17]

Modern Times

In the twentieth century communications on the Moor have changed almost completely. No one now goes out on to it for peat and tin, and the tracks used for centuries have all but fallen out of use. Motor vehicles have replaced the horse and the roads have been surfaced to take them. The amount of traffic on the roads, especially in summer, has been increasing as more and more people have come by car to the most beautiful and easily-reached parts of the Moor.

The improved accessibility of many parts of the Moor during this century has led to the growth of a number of roadside settlements. Horrabridge has extended uphill and along the road by which it was by-passed in 1822. Other roadside settlements are at Blackdown near Marytavy, Postbridge, Yelverton, and Dousland. The beginnings of this growth can be seen on the Ordnance Survey maps of the 1880s, but most of the new houses have gone up in the last forty or fifty years.

Motor buses came to the area soon after World War I. The Devon General Company originated in Exeter in 1919 and within a few years had extended its services to the Dartmoor area. The Devon Haulage Company, also set up in Exeter in 1919, used ex-army vehicles to carry goods. It soon moved to Okehampton and developed passenger services, changing its name to the Devon Motor Transport Company. Its bus services were developed over a wide area, including Tavistock and Plymouth. On the east and south of Dartmoor in the same period Great Western Railways Road Services were operating; in 1927 they took over the Devon Motor Transport Company, and in 1929 merged with the National Omnibus and Transport Company to form the Western National Omnibus Company. The earliest timetables of the Western National show that bus services round the west of the Moor were as extensive and only slightly less full than they are now. The only notable exception was Princetown, which in 1929 had only two buses a day, two days a week.

The increase in motor traffic on the Moor resulted in the need for road improvements. The turnpike bridge at Two Bridges was by-passed by a new bridge in 1931. The banked bridge at Merrivale was made in 1957–8, and the sharp bend at Devil's Elbow near Princetown eased in 1964. In recent years some of the tracks within the firing ranges in the north have been surfaced for motor vehicles. Civilian vehicles use these roads too, now penetrating to the heart of the Moor, a fact deplored by many wishing to preserve its wild character.

Cars were also causing concern elsewhere on the Moor, and in 1962 the Dartmoor Preservation Association produced a memorandum entitled *Motor Vehicles in the Dartmoor National Park: the Need for Effective Control*. This was sent to various bodies including the National Parks Committee, which set up a working party to investigate the problem. The Road Traffic Act of 1960 confirmed that it was an offence to drive a vehicle off a road without lawful authority, except for going up to fifteen yards from it in order to park. The working party proposed that in order to help the enforcement of this law notices bearing the words 'No Vehicles beyond this Point' should be erected at various points of access to the Moor. They also suggested earth banks, boulders and ditches to regulate vehicles. This provoked a good deal of opposition but the Committee went ahead and the scheme was carried out all round the Moor, carefully limited parking places being made off the road in suitable places. The last area tackled was Roborough Down, at the request of the Commoners, where work on earth banks was begun in June 1965. Now this scheme of preventing motorists using the old green tracks into the Moor is generally accepted. Cattle grids have replaced the old moor gates to prevent cattle and ponies coming off the moorland, and now the main road over Roborough Down is being fenced to stop the large number of accidents involving cars and livestock. The amount of motor traffic, particularly in the summer months, is likely to continue increasing for many years. No doubt further facilities for motorists and restrictions on their unreasonable movements will be made.

Most of the increasing numbers of visitors who come to Dartmoor travel by car and do not venture far from their vehicles. Nevertheless a fine summer's day will probably find more people on the Moor, even its remotest parts, than were ever there in times past. More and more people walk on Dartmoor for pleasure. If they are fortunate they will be armed with the *Guide* written by William Crossing, describing the Dartmoor of sixty years ago, when the moormen were still using the old ways which had been in use for centuries.

Notes to this chapter are on pages 293–295.

7

Railways

Michael Ewans

MAIN LINE railways came late to the fringes of Dartmoor; the South Devon Railway to Plymouth did not open till 1849, the London and South Western reached Okehampton only in 1871 and Lydford three years later. Although the Plymouth to Tavistock line was built, after local squabbles had long delayed construction, by 1859, the inadequacy of the SDR to the new economic expansion of Plymouth encouraged the LSWR to apply in 1876 for running rights from Lydford to Plymouth. Only when the expensive independent line from Lydford to Devonport was opened in 1890 were the two major companies, now GWR and LSWR, in open competition, and the challenge encouraged them at last to provide adequately for the railway needs of the city.

The development was not confined to Plymouth. Yelverton acquired even its name from the station (corrupted from Elfordtown, on which estate it stood), and though it was not even built until two years after the opening of the Princetown branch, it was entirely created as a community by the railway in the few years after the station's opening in 1885. For Okehampton, on the other hand, the coming of the railway in 1871 did not bring the expected opening of an era of expansion and progress, but stagnation, as trade was transferred to Exeter.

The railway came too late to Tavistock to convey the last fruits of the booming demand for copper of the 1840s and 1850s; 1887 saw only six mines open, none paying dividends, and over 2,000 miners had left the district by the end of the century. Like Lydford, absurdly over-served by two railway lines beside each other (though to travel from Yelverton to Exeter 'via Lydford' you had to cross Tavistock from one station to the other), the market town was an uneconomical railway stop until the tourist boom during the first decades of the twentieth century. Services, still further extended for the wartime evacuation of Plymouth, never recovered in the period after World War II.

Our main concern is with earlier enterprises, to transport the natural products of Dartmoor; outstanding figures are Sir Thomas Tyrwhitt, the first man to promote such a project, and George Templer, whose more rapid construction on the east side of the Moor, gained the honour of being Devon's first railway for the Haytor granite tramway.

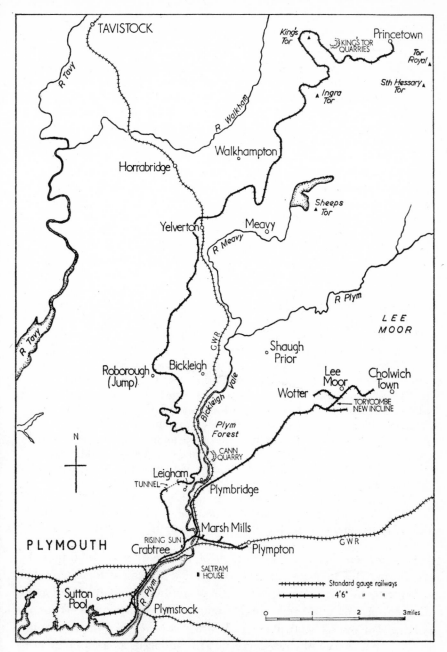

Fig 25.   Map of the 4ft 6in gauge lines.

Plymouth and Dartmoor Railway

This magnificent undertaking (and it truly deserves the name) was first projected by Sir Thomas Tyrwhitt, of Tor Royal, for the cultivation of the Moor, and the application of its granite to architectural and other purposes, employed Mr William Shillabeer, of Walkhampton, surveyor, to mark out a line of connection between Dartmoor and Crabtree, about two miles from Plymouth. In the earliest part of 1818, Sir Thomas, having matured his plans, submitted them to a special meeting of the Chamber of Commerce, at Plymouth, and they being viewed with a favourable eye by that useful body, Sir Thomas published them in a pamphlet.

He next exerted himself in obtaining subscribers, with peculiar success, to the extent of £27,783, being the estimated expense under the first act (passed July 2nd, 1819) for carrying the road from Dartmoor to Crabtree; and under which they were incorporated as the Plymouth and Dartmoor Railway Company.

On the 20th of September, in the same year, the first general meeting of the proprietors took place, when a managing Committee was elected, and Sir William Elford, Bart., appointed Treasurer, Mr Burt, Clerk, and George Day Wood, Collector, Mr William Stuart, Superintendant of the Plymouth Breakwater Works, being Engineer, and Mr Hugh Macintosh, of London, Contractor for forming the road, and Messrs Bailey and Co., of the same place, Contractors for supplying the iron.

It being found necessary to make a branch from Crabtree to Sutton Pool, Plymouth, an act was solicited and passed July 8th, 1820, for that purpose, the estimated expense of which amounted to £7,200.

Some parts of the line being considered as improvable, by . . . excavating a tunnel at Leigham, on the lands of the late Addis Archer Esq., another act was applied for and passed, July 2nd, 1821, with the additional estimate of £5,000.

. . . The total length of the line, from Prince Town to Sutton Pool, is 25 miles, two quarters, and six chains; and is used in conveying up lime, coals, timber &c., and taking back granite and other articles.

Tyrwhitt was MP for the borough of Plymouth from 1806 to 1812, and during this time he obtained Admiralty agreement to the building of Princetown prison, to replace their overcrowded accommodation for prisoners of war at Millbay in Plymouth. The railway, opened as far as King Tor on 20 September 1823, was completed to Princetown only in 1827; but Tyrwhitt's prospectus (1818) adduced, as arguments in its favour, ease of communication with the prison, then three years deserted, and Princetown village, along with the cultivation of Dartmoor and the employment of the poor of Plymouth (then in severe depression). This last point was strongly stressed in the preamble to the Act authorising the

branch railway. The economic basis for the undertaking was thus far
from sound, and the account just quoted of its early years, by Burt, the
Company's secretary, though factually correct as far as it goes, is a fine
example of slanted writing; the periodical which printed this article[1] (which
Burt had written ten years earlier for his preface to Carrington's *Dartmoor*) published in the next issue the following corrective :

> Since the article inserted in last month's *Museum* was written, we
> have been furnished with some further information relative to this
> undertaking; and lest some of our readers may have formed erroneous
> conclusions in reference to the construction of the works, we think it
> our duty, at the earliest opportunity, to set them right on the subject.
> We stated that Mr William Stuart was the engineer, and Mr Hugh
> Macintosh, contractor . . . Those of our readers who were unacquainted
> with the proceedings of the Railway Company would, from this, natur-
> ally suppose, that the whole of the works were done by those gentle-
> men; such, however, was not the case, for after a considerable portion
> of the then intended line of road had been formed, it was discovered
> that about four miles thereof were so steep as to be totally unfit for the
> purposes intended. Mr Roger Hopkins, who then resided at Swansea,
> and had been, for many years, successfully employed as an engineer
> in the forming of railways and other public works, was, therefore, sent
> for in March 1821 on behalf of the Company; and he having ex-
> amined the line that had been laid out and reported thereon, it was
> determined to abandon as useless the part between Shallaford, near
> Crabtree, and Jump, and the lands so occupied were therefore returned
> to their original owners. Mr Hopkins was then appointed engineer to
> the Company, in lieu of Mr Stuart, and requested to lay out a new line,
> which he accordingly did. To effect this, a new act of parliament was
> obtained, and under Mr Hopkins' direction alone, the works were sub-
> sequently completed, and the Tunnel[2] . . . designed and executed. The
> total cost of the undertaking, including the purchase of land, the ex-
> pense of three acts of parliament, the construction of the works, and
> other contingencies, amounted to about £66,000; £28,000 of which
> were borrowed from the commissioners for granting the loan of ex-
> chequer bills in aid of public works.

Tyrwhitt had written in his prospectus[3] that 'the Survey of this undertaking, as now finally terminated, is on every consideration perfectly satisfactory; and what by many, at the commencement, was thought quite
impracticable, has been accomplished by a fall of only half an inch in
three feet, upon a distance not exceeding twenty-two miles'; and the
estimate of £45,000 based on it[4] was released over the name of William
Stuart. The committee put the blame heavily on him, in a strongly-
worded letter of 2 July 1821;[5] but the mistaken levels below Jump
(modern Roborough), according to which formations for a line were

actually made,[6] were Shillabeer's; Stuart wrote to the arbitrators between himself and the company :

> In the printed prospectus my name appears at the bottom of it, indicating thereby that I . . . pledged my professional opinion on the accuracy of the observations, but the fact is that I never wrote a line of the prospectus nor was I consulted about it—I was merely desired by Sir Thomas Tyrwhitt and Mr Burt to calculate the rate of exports and imports; with respect to my consenting to give an estimate on the sections and plans of another I confess I did it but was lured into it by Sir Thomas Tyrwhitt . . . I positively refused to give evidence at the Bar of the House of Commons respecting the line of road, on the ground that I was not the engineer who surveyed it . . . Mr Shillabeer was therefore sent up for that purpose . . .

Tyrwhitt had, however, succeeded in getting Stuart to produce for Parliament a witnessed statement that the railway could 'if not prevented by inevitable accident' be completed in three years, and the arbitrators did not vindicate his character as he desired.

The problems of the railway's construction did not end with the surveys. The proprietors first met on 20 September 1819, and the whole of the sum which the first Act required to be raised before construction could begin was subscribed by 14 April 1820. Nevertheless the committee, meeting on that day, resolved to apply for a loan of up to £10,000 from the Exchequer Bill Loan Commissioners, to avoid the necessity of calls on the shareholders of over twenty per cent per annum, and a further application for £18,000 was resolved on 17 July. Meanwhile, Addis Archer, the obstinate landowner on a crucial section of both the original and the revised line, refused the company's offer of £540 for the relevant portions of his land 'and stated he treated it with contempt'. The company was forced to offer to buy his whole estate of Shallaford at his own price—£2,100—but disputes continued; by 14 May 1821 he proposed to take them to court 'for the balance of the purchase price and for damages'. His pressure caused the Act authorising the deviations to specify[7] that the tunnel should not at its north-east end emerge within his lands, and only his death at the end of 1823 saved the situation.

By 18 December 1820 thirty-two shareholders (102 shares) had defaulted on the first instalment, fifty-six (58 shares) on the second; proceedings were to be instituted against the sixty-seven who held more than two shares each. In the next year Hopkins, appointed assistant engineer and given entire responsibility for the upper section of the line (Ingra Tor to Horrapit Plain), was instructed to report on the state of the rest. The result of his investigations was an order to Stuart to produce the sections on which his specifications were based, and a petition to Parliament for the new Bill to alter the line. On 21 May it was 'resolved that Mr Hopkins be directed to effect such alterations in the road made before his appointment and turnouts as he may think necessary'.

The quality and quantity of the labour was inadequate under both the original engineer and contractor and the new;[8] and the ten per cent call of 4 May 1822 was accompanied by a circular requesting the full amount of subscriptions 'for the purpose of completing the work immediately, there being a demand for granite, the supply of which is much impeded by [the railway's] present unfinished state'. The Exchequer Commissioners refused a further loan. On 1 June the iron contractors' bill could not be met, and it was 'resolved that a letter be written to Sir Thomas Tyrwhitt begging to know whether he has succeeded in his endeavours to procure the advance of a certain sum of money by way of temporary loan on the shares'. Later in the month, arrangements for the collection of instalments on shares were tightened, and control of the undertaking passed gradually to Messrs Johnson and Brice,[9] who had the rights to the King Tor granite quarries—these were to be connected to the railway by an inclined plane—and so were the commercial interest suffering most from the delay in opening. They took over the contract to supply iron and the engineering, 'substituting scarf rails for those at present in use',[10] and continued the construction without pay to give the company a chance to repay Bailey and Co, who had supplied iron since early 1821.

Threats to defaulters continued during 1823, and Sir Thomas Tyrwhitt joined their ranks on 7 February 1824. The company expressed impotent fury at the 'gross injustice' of the exclusion of its granite from the London Bridge contract, which 'can, it is presumed, only be grounded on the idea, that the Dartmoor granite is *inferior in quality*, more scanty in quantity, and more costly in working than the granite coming from Haytor or Aberdeen . . .' But it was grounded, strictly, on the fact that their railway had only just opened, and only as far as King Tor, while the other granites had long been readily available. Letters of early 1819 show that Tyrwhitt had had London Bridge in mind at the inception of the project; but his enterprise was less successful than that at Haytor. The Exchequer Commissioners pressed for repayment immediately after the opening. The reply was that

it is not quite correct to say that the railway is open, as the northern extremity is not yet completed and is suspended (though I hope only temporarily) for the present moment from the present extraordinary rise in the price of iron . . .

As to the south end

> I can assure you that the fact you state that stone and other articles
> have been carried to the shipping place at Plymouth is totally without
> foundation, the railway leading to that port being as yet in a state
> totally incapable of admitting the passage of carts.

Not until 2 January 1827 was the railway completed and certified.

Its history during its working life is largely that of attempts to reach
a compromise with the Johnsons; the company being unable to pay
interest on the mortgage they had acquired in return for completing the
railway, the Johnsons paid no tolls—and were thus themselves in dispute
with the Loan Commissioners. Tyrwhitt died in 1833, and when the committee minutes resume after a ten year gap in 1844, the Commissioners
have given up hope of recovering their £18,000. The minutes cease again
for a longer interval in 1847, and the three intervening years are largely
a chronicle of the company's futile attempts, under a committee controlled by the Johnsons, to oppose the South Devon Railway. By 1865
mortgages of over £75,000 to Johnson and Brice and to the Exchequer
were all in the hands of William Johnson.

A new company was formed by Act of Parliament,[11] and he received
their value in preference shares. In 1874 the new company thought it
worth while to start relaying the track; but the Princetown Railway, a
standard gauge concern connecting the town with the SDR Tavistock
branch, was promoted in 1878, and used the line of the P&D above
Yelverton. The remaining lower section had some sporadic use—179 tons
of small granite traffic passed, for example, in three months of 1881—
but the rails above Rising Sun, junction of the Lee Moor tramway, were
removed for scrap in 1916.

Cann Quarry Branch

As price for his support of the 1821 Act, which was essential for the
modified P&DS line passing through his property, the Earl of Morley,
of Saltram House, exacted from three of its directors an undertaking to
connect his slate quarry at Cann with the new railway at Rising Sun.
Doubts about the legality of this agreement were raised at the P&D committee meeting of 20 August 1824, nine months after the earl had given
the notice required under the agreement that he wished the railway 'to
make a railroad to Cann Quarry in a manner to be approved of by him
and to instal a tenant in Cann Quarry'. On 5 July 1825 Morley
threatened to go to law, and the committee hastily sought the opinion
of counsel; but by early 1826 Morley had still not sued. The com-

mittee decided to try to induce him to build it himself by offering a toll
reduction on the portion of the P&D he would run over between Rising
Sun and the docks. Morley temporised, and the argument over the proposed toll concession continued until, after proceeding to run a navigable
leat six feet wide (the Cann Quarry Canal) from the quarry to near
Marsh Mills, he wrote to the committee :

> Doubts are now pending, whether it will be best to convey the produce
> of the Quarry at Cann to the port by completing the Canal, now in
> great part made, and connecting it with the Lary by a Tunnel under
> the Turnpike Road, or by uniting by means of a private railway the
> canal as far as it is made with the Plymouth and Dartmoor Railroad
> at Crabtree.

The committee, by acceding to Morley's suggestion on the toll concession,
was able to persuade him to adopt the second course, and the junction
was made by half a mile of tramroad, crossing the Plym on two cast-
iron arches to connect the canal basin at Marsh Mills with the P&D at
Rising Sun. The complete system was opened on 20 November 1829.[12]

The railway was extended along the canal towpath to Cann Quarry
by 1834; the canal was then only used as a mill leat. The quarry was
not in regular use after 1855. The second Lord Morley tried to persuade
the South Devon and Tavistock Railway (promoted in 1852) to buy
the Cann Quarry Railway,[13] as part of an agreement under which it
would build a tramway from the Lee Moor quarries owned by him. The
tramway was built, but four years later Morley wrote 'we have been
obliged to retain the Cann Quarry line although I have been put down
to a large figure in shares for the purchase of it.' The CQ branch was
already effectively closed above the junction with the Lee Moor Tramway, since work had stopped in the quarry, though Paley, writing in
1902, reports occasional use by 'a single large truck with a horse', to
bring down slate for paving stones. A proposed extension to Shaugh, to
which the Johnsons were opposed, was never made.

Plympton branch

This branch, running from the canal transfer line at Marsh Mills to
near St Mary's Bridge in Plympton, was constructed by Messrs Johnson and Brice by agreement with Lord Morley in 1834

> to terminate for the present at Colebrook, near Ridgeway and Plymp-
> ton, for the purpose of conveying coal, lime etc to these villages, and also
> to bring down to the port of shipment the china clay rose on Lord
> Morley's forest land.[14]

A railhead for the Lee Moor trade, in fact, before the construction of its own tramway. The possibility of extension to Lee Moor was envisaged when this line was built, but the only extension constructed was a short branch to Farm Quarries, Woodford.[15] The rent paid for the branch by Johnson and Brice in 1840 was £100 per annum. In 1847 the SDR, building their main line to Plymouth parallel with the branch, bought the remainder of the lease from Johnsons for £510 and closed the line.

Lee Moor Tramway

The South Devon and Tavistock Railway was promoted in 1852, with Lord Morley as chairman of the provisional directors and Augustus H. Bampton as engineer.

> Many lines on this route (Plymouth to Tavistock) have been projected from 1840 to this date, all of which were defeated by the conflict of interests, which it is not anticipated will be renewed. The owners of the tramway from Crabtree to the Cann Quarry have agreed to sell the same to this Company, and this tramway will be available for the construction of the proposed line above a distance of two miles.
>
> Arrangements have been entered into, by which a short branch railway from the works of the Lee Moor Porcelain Clay Company, joining the proposed line, will be at once constructed, and . . . will become the property of this Company on favourable terms. Regard being had to the small outlay required, and the increasing importance of the traffic of the Lee Moor Co., it cannot be doubted that this part of the undertaking will be very remunerative.

Like his father, Lord Morley demanded a branch as price of his support for a railway Act of Parliament; he succeeded, and the tramway was built, 4ft 6in gauge, to join the Cann Quarry Railway at Plymbridge. The SD&T was not completed till 1859, but the contract of the tramway specified completion by May 1853, at a penalty of £50 a week afterwards; it was shoddily built as a result. John Foster's report comparing the line and its specifications shows it faulty in every particular. Both the inclined planes were unusable as delivered, and an accident at Torycombe in October 1854 led to its being abandoned after only a month's operation and a new plane being built on a new site. Wotter viaduct was built one bay too short and was unsafe. The ironwork of Plym bridge 'is rusty and appears never to have been painted', 3,854 sleepers were faulty and the ballast was 'soft slate and clay'.

The contractors did not rectify these faults at their own expense, as required by their contract. On 11 July 1855 Phillips, lessee of Lee Moor clayfield, declared that the SDR refused to work the line (as it had agreed

to do), the SD&T had refused to put it into working order, and would not
let him work his own traffic. He had done so none the less in September
—with the disastrous results at Torycombe. On 19 March 1855 Bampton
ordered Phillips' men off; next day Phillips took forcible possession and
'but for that he would not be able to work at all'. He asked Morley to
withhold the advance of £6,000 he had promised to the SD&T, and
not to surrender the land for its own line, until a guarantee of working by the SDR and maintenance by the SD&T were forthcoming. Soon,
however,

> the great object of Lord Morley and the Lee Moor Clay Company and
> William Phillips is to bring the Tavistock Company to abandon the Lee
> Moor branch and to prevent them from at any time disturbing or touch-
> ing the Cann Quarry Railway, and this without any money considera-
> tion whatever.

By 1858, when Bampton was dead and Brunel's new alignment for the
SD&T meant that the CQ line was safe, Morley wrote to Phillips; 'under
the circumstances in which the South Devon and Tavistock is placed I
do not see how we can do further than adhere to the tenth clause of our
agreement'—under which both he and Phillips had power in such circumstances to operate with their own wagons. The line thus effectively
became Morley's free of charge, since the SD&T had agreed in 1856 to
pay the contractors. Phillips rebuilt the defective portions, also extending
the tramway to Wotter and Cholwich Town. An opening ceremony
was held at the new Torycombe incline on 24 September 1858, its celebrations contrasting with Phillips' anger at the loss of trade, 'shutting
our clay out of the market at a good time . . . postponing our getting into
the market until commercial prosperity passed away'.

Wotter viaduct was replaced in 1878 with a curve higher up the
valley, and demolished two years later; and the track between the head
of Cann Wood incline and Torycombe was further relaid in 1899 to
take two Peckett 0–4–0 saddle tanks, Lee Moor Nos 1 and 2, necessary
to deal with a continued increase in traffic. The other levels, above Torycombe and below Cann Wood, remained horse-operated. The Wotter
tramway closed in 1900, and clay was then conveyed from there to Cornwood by steam lorry; the Cholwich Town branch closed around 1933
and the Torycombe incline was then used only for occasional traffic to
Lee Moor village until the line closed for the war in 1939. Only the
section below this incline was worked after reopening on 8 October
1945 and the whole tramway above Marsh Mills closed finally two years
later, to be replaced by road transport, though the section to Laira wharf
remained in use till mid-1960. A pipeline was laid in 1961 on the site

of the tramway above Marsh Mills for the transport of clay, now pumped suspended in water. The two locomotives were preserved in the original shed at Torycombe but Lee Moor No. 2, restored, found a new home at Saltram in July 1970.

Princetown

The Princetown branch railway was promoted at a public meeting at Princetown on 14 March 1877, and the first meeting of the company was held at Paddington on 7 August 1879. Sir Daniel Gooch was in the chair as one of four GWR nominees on the board. In the following year a price of £22,000 in the shares of the new company was offered for the section of the P&D above Yelverton, whose route was to a great extent to be followed. The transfer was complete by 28 April 1882, and work commenced on the 10½-mile narrow-gauge line, though without the convict labour expected by the company. The Home Secretary refused to make any compensation for this, but £25,000 was paid in 1884.

On 21 December 1883 an agreement with the GWR, which was to work the line, was concluded, but the engineer (W. G. Owen) reported that the line would cost £61,800 instead of the £54,581 estimate laid before Parliament, due to 'additional works, extra requirements of the Board of Trade', higher prices and larger station buildings. The company's borrowing powers up to £20,000 were activated, and on 5 July 1883 the 16th was set as opening day. But the Government inspector insisted on more guard rails on the numerous tight curves and, since ballast trains were still being run by the contractors, Owen advised postponement of passenger opening 'there being no siding at the granite quarries'. The railway opened on 11 August, only two days within the five-year limit allowed in their Act of 1878.

Maintenance, nominally the branch company's responsibility, was contracted out to the GWR. By March 1884 there were three trains a day in each direction; the company asked for an extra one for the summer. A Princetown shareholder alleged that 'the line is worked more for the benefit of the GWR co than of the shareholders', and asked for a Sunday service, workmen's tickets at reduced rates, and the reduction of rates for granite.

Suggestions of this kind continued, but the GWR had reason to be unwilling; the first six months of 1884 brought only 82 first class passengers, 342 second and 8,445 third, and made a loss of £543 14s 3d. The Princetown Company directors commented 'these results are not encouraging, and do not realise the expectations which the directors were induced

Page 215 (above) *John Bishop's house, Swincombe, a late nineteenth century enclosure now fallen into ruin;* (below) *raising the dam at Burrator in 1928; the temporary suspension bridge is shown*

Page 216 (above) *The Avon dam on southern Dartmoor in 1968;* (below) *a new dimension in the Services' use of Dartmoor: Royal Marines training with helicopters in the Merrivale area in 1969*

to entertain from the interest evinced locally in the promotion of the line'. The next report, in the same vein, suggests 'that the local shareholders should make personal endeavour to bring the line into more general use', and reveals that prisoners were still being sent from Tavistock by road.

The annual loss continued to be between £900 and £1,000, and by 1889 the directors, noting that 'the granite traffic has increased, but the traffic connected with the Prison Establishment is not what might be expected, and there do not appear many resources in the locality for much further development . . . have come to the conclusion that there is no advantage in prolonging the existence of this Company as a separate undertaking'. They had in fact no control over traffic management or expenses, and the GWR insisted on transferring all freight traffic to the broad gauge at Horrabridge (there was no exchange siding at Yelverton) instead of using the LSWR narrow rails of the mixed gauge line from Yelverton to Plymouth Laira. The GWR initially refused to take over, but eventually did so in 1921. The branch survived, uneconomically, on tourist traffic until 5 March 1956.[16]

Haytor Granite Tramway

On Saturday Mr Templer, of Stover House, gave a grand fête champêtre on Haytor Down, on the completion of the granite railroad. The company assembled at its foot on Bovey Heathfield, and in procession passed over it to the rock. A long string of carriages, filled with elegant and beautiful females, multitudes of horsemen, workmen on foot, the wagons covered with laurels and waving streamers, formed in their windings through the valley an attractive scene to spectators on the adjacent hill. Old Haytor seemed alive; its sides were lined with groups of persons, and on its top a proud flag fluttered in the wind. Previously to returning to dine, Mr Templer addressed the assemblage in a short and energetic speech, which excited bursts of applause. He stated the causes that induced him to engage in such a great undertaking. He pointed out the advantages which it offered to the surrounding proprietors, the employment it would find for the mechanic and labourer, and its tendency to increase in a great degree the trade of the port of Teignmouth. In averting to the Plymouth railway, he expressed his hope that both might prosper, and not endanger, by improper rivalry, the success of either.

George, the third Templer to live at Stover House, may have come a little later to the idea of providing transport for Dartmoor granite than the promoters on the west side of the Moor, but his project was completed promptly and efficiently. The date of the opening ceremony des-

N

cribed in these terms by the *Exeter Flying Post* was 16 September 1820. Three factors contributed to this success; the incentive of a contract in the offing, that for London Bridge; Templer's ability, like his father before him with the Stover Canal, to build at his own expense and on his own land; and the choice of material, for the line was constructed of the granite it was to carry. The name of the engineer is unknown, but the idea of using stone sets instead of iron rails, not attempted elsewhere in a line of comparable length, was highly appropriate to the Haytor granite, one of whose most valued qualities was its ability to resist pressure. It also had the advantage of eliminating entirely the cost of transportation of materials, since the Haytor granite quarries were already in operation.

Blocks of very varied length with a 3in flange on the inside were laid to a gauge of 4ft 3in; and at points the direction to be taken was determined by the position of metal cheek-pieces pivoted on a peg with its socket in the junction stone. Granite was transported on flat-topped wagons; these—alarmingly—had for brake only the primitive device of a pole manually applied to the rim of the wheels, which ran loose on the axles. The trucks were marshalled in trains of about twelve, and a pair of detachable shafts were added for the upward journey, also for the branch to the Holwell quarries, from which alone loaded trains had to climb. Hence the local jingle

> Eighteen brave steed and twelve old car
> To take stone from Ovals Tor;
> The stallion in front they did place
> It was John Murrin's, of Teigngrace.

The Murrin family ran the smithy, inn and stables which had grown up beside the clay cellars at Ventiford, terminal basin of the Stover Canal and start of the tramway; this was single-line until it reached the moor, where branches served the Main Haytor, Holwell and Rubble Heap quarries.

The tramway was almost certainly built for the new London Bridge contract, work on which eventually began in 1825. The interval of five years is natural enough, since Haytor granite, even more than Teign Valley clay, could not even begin to compete commercially until it had efficient transport to the sea. It had to share London Bridge with Aberdeen and Peterhead, and the correspondence of 1833–4 between Templer and Bigg, London agent and secretary of the granite company[17], shows Haytor in a precarious position commercially, since both these two granites and those of Cornwall, in particular of Penryn, were in a position to rival and undercut their prices. Only the particular qualities of the rock enabled it to retain a competitive position. Yet as Bigg claimed in a circular issued during the arduous, unsuccessful struggle for the Blackfriars Bridge contract

> Above 300,000 cube feet of Haytor Granite were supplied to the New London-Bridge, and the same used in all those parts where the current of the tide was most active, and where strength and durability are alike indispensable . . . The Company feel a proud satisfaction in stating that Haytor Granite has been *entirely* used in the New Goldsmiths' Hall; New Fishmongers' Hall; Ramsgate Harbour Monument; Shoreham Bridge; Christ's Hospital; King's College; Waithman's Obelisk; Pitt's pedestal in Hanover-Square; George the Fourth's pedestal in Edinburgh; and the pedestal for the equestrian Statue in Windsor-Park; whilst a large proportion of Haytor has been used in the Covent-Garden and Hungerford Markets; Westminster New Bridewell; Custom-House; Buckingham Palace, etc.

These, the highlights of the first ten years, justify the tramway's construction. But in London Bigg was hard put to win contracts and in fact trade, which was highly dependant on demand, stopped completely from 1841 to some time before 1850; by 1858 the tramway was closed for good. Bigg's constant fear of Penryn, which persists even where the Cornish quarries were not involved in the bidding, points to the conclusion openly stated by Dymond; 'the competition of the Cornish quarries with their better facilities of carrying to the ship-side has proved too strong.'

Moretonhampstead

1858, year of the Haytor tramway's demise, was also that of the promotion of the Newton and Moretonhampstead Railway. This was to run from a junction with the SDR at Newton, making use of the latter company's station there, up the Teign and Bovey river valleys to Bovey Tracey, where it struck northwards to Lustleigh and then on to Moreton up a smaller tributary of the Bovey. Agitation had begun in 1851, and the company was incorporated in 1858, when a survey of the line was made. Nothing much was done until October 1861, when the Earl of Devon reconstituted the company under the name of the Moretonhampstead and South Devon Railway Company. A contract for the construction of the 12¼-mile line was then placed with Brassey and Ogilvie, for £88,500. The authorised capital under the Act passed in 1862 was £105,000 in £10 shares, but the line eventually cost £155,000. The SDR had a controlling interest, and subscribed £500.

The line rose from 50 to 588 feet with a maximum gradient of 1 in 50. Although it was single, the SDR insisted that its bridges should be built to take double track in case the line should be doubled later, but this was never done. The company wished to pass their line through the centre of the Stover estate, and the Duke of Somerset (who had bought out Templer in 1829) held out for a price of £8,000 for purchase of the Stover Canal, alongside which the new railway was to run as far as Ventiford, and the bottom two miles of the granite tramway. The railway company was obliged to provide a transfer siding for the granite trade at the point, one mile south of Bovey, where the tramway left the course of the branch; it is unlikely that this was ever in regular use.

There was some difficulty in raising the capital required for the railway, and it was not opened till 4 July 1866; the SDR, which worked the line for fifty per cent of the gross receipts, provided an inadequate service. It absorbed the M&SDR in 1872, so bringing all the railways south of Dartmoor under its control, but was itself taken over by the GWR in 1877.

The Teign Valley Railway, which bears the unwelcome distinction of having had to seek twelve Acts of Parliament, nine before opening, ran initially from Ashton to Chudleigh Road station on the M&SDR, which was then renamed Heathfield since the new branch gave a station a mile from Chudleigh. Opening was on 9 October 1882—an isolated standard-gauge line with a single tank engine until the Moretonhampstead line was converted, and not completed through to Exeter until 1903.

Traffic on the Moretonhampstead line was sparse until the first decade of this century, when the GWR connected Chagford to Moreton by bus (1908). A considerable excursion traffic to these two places, good starting points for the Moor, and to Lustleigh flourished until World War I. But decline thereafter was steady, despite the addition of two new halts in 1928 (Brimley) and 1931 (Hawkmoor); and the branch closed to passengers on 2 March 1959. A preservation society was unsuccessful, and goods traffic beyond Bovey Tracey ended in 1964. A freight train a day now serves various industrial concerns at Heathfield.

Ashburton

The first project to connect Ashburton with the SDR was for a line to Newton Abbot; the Ashburton, Newton and South Devon Railway Company was incorporated in 1846, to run 10½ miles from Newton to Dart Bridge, near Buckfastleigh. The estimate for the single line was £103,251, and it was to be leased on its completion to the SDR. The prospectus spoke of ready access to Torquay and Teignmouth for the sale of agricultural produce, of the 'rich mineral wealth' of the Ashburton district (thirteen limekilns and five slate quarries, size unspecified) and the romantic scenery of the Dart as incentives to construction. But rivals were already on the ground, with plans to connect via Totnes with Plymouth. Owing to a depression nothing was done for either scheme, however, and the directors made tentative moves towards dissolution in 1849; by 1851,

> the directors . . . having taken into consideration the position and prospects of the undertaking and having determined according as they believe to the general wish of the shareholders that it is not expedient for the present to proceed to carry it into effect propose to return to the shareholders the surplus fund now remaining unemployed . . .

£3,352 was repaid, and nothing further happened until the incorporation in 1864 of the Buckfastleigh, Totnes and South Devon Railway, with a capital of £48,000. Powers for extension to Ashburton were gained in the following year with further capital of the same amount. Maintenance and working were to be by the SDR, which was to pay fifty per cent of the receipts to the BT&SD. The first sod was cut by the chairman's wife on 27 July 1865; at that time the amount of money needed to start (one-third of the whole capital) was only technically made up, the subscription list being temporarily augmented from the directors' pockets. Construction proceeded slowly, as money was raised and land became available. The opening was not until 1 May 1872. The half-yearly report for December 1874 claimed that 'it must be obvious that the rates now charged cannot be remunerative to any but the Working Company, and some revisions and alterations must be required'.

On the amalgamation of the SDR and GWR in 1876, the board offered the working of the line to the latter at a 48 per cent holding, but the offer was declined and they worked it on the same terms as the SDR had done. Later in the year the branch directors compiled a train service of six trains each way, and requested of the GWR that this be put into operation 'at least for the summer months'. Paddington ignored the suggestion, offering belatedly to extend the 4.45 from Ashburton (Saturdays only) to all weekdays.

On 30 September the board offered its first terms for full takeover by the GWR; these were declined and it was not till 1897 that transfer took place. The branch was then still prosperous, but both the wool trade of the Dart valley and the tourist revenue left it in the motor age. It was closed to passengers from November 1958, and to goods from 10 September 1962. Summer reopening has now taken place under the auspices of the Dart Valley Light Railway Company, and the first trains ran to Buckfastleigh on 1 April 1969.

Zeal Tor and Redlake Tramroads

In 1846 L. H. Davy and William Wilkin, of Totnes, obtained from the Duchy of Cornwall the right of 'cutting, manufacturing and vending peat and peat charcoal' in Redlake Mire, a rich source. They constructed the Zeal Tor tramroad in 1847 from Redlake to Shipley bridge, with wooden rails bolted to granite blocks. The venture failed and the partnership was dissolved by 1850, when Davy paid Wilkin £4,000 for 'machinery, tramways, horses and carts'.

The lower portions of the line and the derelict works at Shipley Bridge, originally used for the production of naphtha from peat, were re-used from 1877 by the Brent Moor Clay Works for the transport and pressing of clay; this was extracted from pits near the sources of Bala Brook for a few years before this venture in its turn fell into disuse. There was talk of revival around 1905; but when this was done the Redlake–Ivybridge route was used, since the Redlake and Leftlake pits were now the focus of attention.

A new company, calling itself the China Clay Corporation, was formed in 1905 with headquarters in Ivybridge. After a preliminary survey in 1909, the 3ft-gauge Redlake tramway was built in 1910 under the direction of Hansford Worth. It was $7\frac{1}{2}$ miles long from a specially constructed transfer siding (Cantrell) near Bittaford to the Redlake clay works.

The tramway, whose rails were spiked directly to wooden sleepers, did not carry the clay extracted at the workings; this was suspended in water and piped down to the main line at the siding, where it was dried. The railway itself carried the staff in three rudimentary passenger vehicles; it also took coal up for the pumping engine, returning in the evening with sand for building and fertiliser. The line began with an inclined plane of over 350ft. A shed for the locomotives operating the rest of the line, which rose steadily from 750 to over 1,450ft, remains; one of the locomotives was the *C. A. Hanson* (named after a director of the company), a Kerr Stuart 0–4–2 side tank, which bore the brunt of the traffic until 1921 when, needing major repairs, it was scrapped. Its replacement, a steam tractor named after Lady Mallaby-Deeley, outlasted the line and was sold on its closure. The other original locomotive, a slightly smaller 0–4–2, also from Kerr Stuart and named *Dartmoor*, was unreliable and used mainly for shunting and standby duties.

The Redlake tramway was opened on 11 September 1911, but its trade deteriorated during World War I and in 1921 it was purchased by

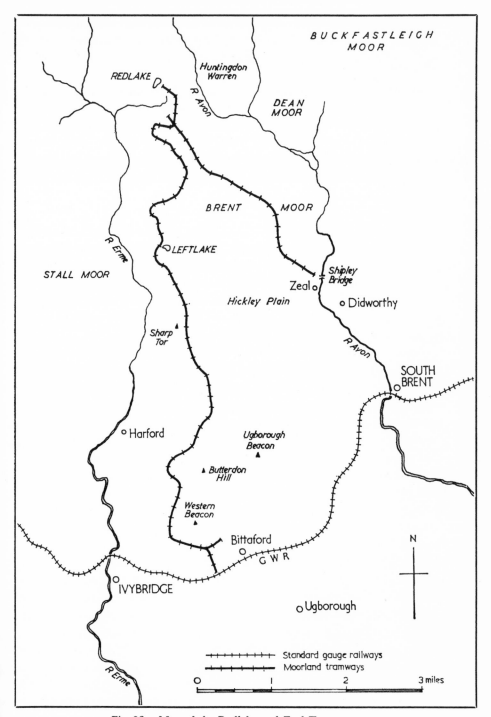

Fig 26.   Map of the Redlake and Zeal Tor tramways.

the chief shareholder, Sir Henry Mallaby-Deeley, and renovated. Left-lake pit, an earlier working on the route of the tramway, was also worked from 1922. But the new firm failed suddenly in 1932, and the engines, rolling stock and rails were auctioned. The GWR removed the sidings and signalbox at Bittaford in the following year.

Rattlebrook Track

The Rattlebrook track was originally the transport for the produce of the West of England Compressed Peat Company, formed in 1877 to work a square mile of land above Bridestowe leased from the Duchy of Cornwall. The line was built in 1879 at a cost of around £6,000, after a ceremony in September 1878 at which the High Sheriff of Devon cut the first sod and a variety of optimistic speeches were made. It was standard gauge and over five miles in length, including a reversal point; on the journey between Bridestowe station, where connexion was made with the LSWR, and Rattlebrook Head (2½ miles as the crow flies) a rise of about 1,000ft had to be made by horse-drawn trucks.

The venture failed almost immediately, probably because of the high cost of the railway, and further attempts to extract peat profitably proved abortive. Between 1917 and 1919 further unsuccessful attempts to extract marketable substances continued, using a petrol-driven truck on the railway. A complete cessation of activity in 1931 led to the removal of the rails, and when the Duchy granted a new licence in 1936 the site of the line was converted to become the access track for road wagons. Attempts to exploit the peat since the conversion suffered as many difficulties as those before it, and the last cutting was for a few years after 1955.

Notes to this chapter are on page 296.

8

Recreation

Brian Le Messurier

THE STORY of recreation on Dartmoor must take some note of medieval times, although it is only in the last hundred years or so that the Moor has attracted visitors in any numbers.

For centuries people spent such leisure time as they had in making their own entertainment. Primitive musical instruments were used to while away the dark evenings, and there are at least two ancient Jew's harps in private collections on the Moor. Singing and dancing round the fire to the accompaniment of the local instrumentalist helped to pass the time; many of our folk songs have their origin in the need to entertain a small group.

Both Sabine Baring-Gould and, in more recent times, Peter Kennedy, have collected old songs from singing-men in the moorland villages. Bob Cann, who farms on the northern Moor[1] and is still in demand for dances, plays a number of traditional tunes on his accordion. There are a few men in the area who can still dance on the washboard, producing the steps that were done at fairs on the tailboards of carts, and the other peculiarly Dartmoor dance was the broom dance, a solo performance in which the legs are swung over a broom handle held in the hand with the broom head on the floor. Every parish had its variation of the broom dance; probably Meavy last saw its own step in the bar of the Royal Oak on Christmas Eve 1939. Since the war the English Folk Dance and Song Society has done much to revive both the songs and the dances, and folk dances are now an integral part of village life from Throwleigh to Horrabridge. Perhaps the most remarkable party was in the Manor House Hotel in the summer of 1962, when a demonstration was put on for delegates to the National Parks Conference being held there, and even the second Earl Jellicoe, then a Minister of the Crown, joined in.

In the early days the only holidays were feast or fair days, when pageants were sometimes held. But an Act of 1466 stipulated that :

Every Englishman should have a bow of his own height, of yew, ash, wych hazel or amburn, and that butts should be made in every town-

225

ship, which the inhabitants were to shoot at every feast-day, under the penalty of ½d when they should omit that exercise.

So even these days were taken from them. The sites of the three practice grounds in Widecombe parish are known; Buttes Park is the village green, Butts Field is at Jordan, and Butts Ware is at Lower Uppacott, Spitchwick.

There were recognised bull and bear baiting places around the Moor, such as the Play Field at Sheepstor, and at Ashburton where the central crossroads is still called the Bull Ring. The same arenas were often used by wrestlers, with fern spread on the ground to serve as matting. The contestants wore a rough uniform; shoes soaked in bullock's blood, worsted stockings, breeches and a short linen jacket—the only part of the outfit by which a hitch or hold could be obtained. In Marytavy churchyard there is a tombstone to the memory of John Hawkins, blacksmith, dated 1721, which shows that wrestling on the Moor goes back at least to the beginning of the eighteenth century. The stone is attached to the south outside wall of the chancel and reads :

> Here buried were some years before
> His two wives and five children more
> One Thomas named, whose fate was such
> To lose his life by wrestling much
> Which may a warning be to all
> How they into such pastimes fall.

That inveterate West Country traveller and diarist, the Rev John Swete, whose volumes of journals are kept at the Devon Record Office, visited Two Bridges Fair in 1795 between six and seven pm and found the women 'had in a great measure withdrawn; and the amusements of the men seem'd to be confined to wrestling and drinking'.

It was a matter of some annoyance to the genteel sensibilities of some observers that parish revels were occasionally held on Sundays. In her *Home Scenes* (1846) Rachel Evans wrote of Lydford village feast or fair being held on a Sunday in the church. 'Let us hope that higher aims and occupations will in time lead altogether to a neglect and disuse of the "revel Sunday" '. Further on she continues :

Some years since I remember going to the church at Peter Tavy on a revel Sunday. My feelings are best expressed by saying that, although but a child, I was *ashamed* to be there. Standings for fairing and toys were erected in close vicinity to the churchyard; parties were engaged in noisy vociferations over their favourite game of kayles (or nine pins); shouts of drunken laughter came from the village inn, and even at an early hour men passed along in a state of intoxication.

'Fairings' were an assortment of sweets, made of almonds, cinnamon and caraway seeds, covered with sugar, gingerbread and nuts.

Up to about the beginning of the last century the Holne Ram Feast retained its ancient tradition of rustic barbarity. On the day of the revel a party of young men seized the first ram they could catch on the Moor, took it down to the field in the village still called Play Park, killed the animal and roasted it. Dancing, wrestling, games and much cider-drinking occupied the rest of the day. Holne takes its annual pleasures more soberly now with a flower show and a gymkhana.

Whortleberry gathering was formerly looked upon as an extension of the harvest, and parties of women and children from all the moorland villages took to the open Moor to collect the fruit. The Ashburton and Holne people favoured the Ringleshutts area, for the Ausewell berries, although nearer, were not so abundant. They kept cooking utensils on the Moor through the season and sometimes stayed out overnight. Other well-known whortleberry-gathering grounds were at Stony Bottom on the Erme, and at Foxholes on the Doe Tor Brook.[2]

Not many whorts are picked nowadays; the local reasons given being the depredations of the Scotch Blackface sheep, and too-frequent swaling. But another reason must be that the class of people who formerly made whortleberry picking an excuse for an annual break from routine can now go away on holidays themselves.

The deadly dull day-in, day-out monotony of the ordinary people was broken only briefly by these red-letter occasions. For the men 'night-work', poaching, brought a little excitement into life and helped provide food for the family.

Other, more irregular events occurred from time to time and were made the excuse for local junketings. The peace of 1815 was marked by bonfires and a general carousing late into the night. The Queen's jubilees, the end of the Crimean War, the armistice and victory celebrations were other important events which the Moor dweller supported as enthusiastically as his lowland neighbour. Even the marriage of the Prince of Wales in 1863 was marked by festivities at Lustleigh.

At intervals of several years it is the custom of many parishes to 'beat the bounds'. This serves the purpose of instilling into the members of the younger generations a knowledge of parish limits, and to encourage their attendance some special food treat is usually provided. Belstone parish beats its bounds every seven years and solemnly moves one of the boundary stones a few yards into South Tawton, which parish equally regularly moves it back again when it beats its own bounds, before the Belstone parishioners make their next perambulation. Belstone includes a picnic at Cullever Steps; South Brent takes two days to get round its large parish, and arranges for rounds of beef to be at Dockwell Mires for the walking party. Parish sports are arranged at the same time.

Hunting is the oldest pursuit still carried out on Dartmoor. In early times the quarry was sought for food, but later the central part of the Moor, the Forest, became a royal hunting preserve, and here the sport was pre-eminent. The unfortunate Childe is probably the first individual of whom there is any record to go hunting on the Moor. The traditional story tells how Childe of Plymstock lost his way while hunting in mid-winter and, being benighted, killed his horse, disembowelled the animal and crept within its carcass to shelter from the cold—dying nevertheless. Near Fox Tor on southern Dartmoor there is a restored monument called Childe's Tomb, which is supposed to mark the site of the huntsman's death. Professor Finberg has made a study of the background to this pre-Norman story in the 1946 *Transactions of the Devonshire Association*.

His quarry is not recorded. The Duke of Bedford's hounds are said to have exterminated deer on Dartmoor by 1780, and in the 1830s a pack of hounds was kept at Two Bridges for hunting polecats. The queerest hunt of all must have been that of George Templer, the Haytor railway man, who not only kept two packs of hounds at Stover but a yard full of chained and kennelled foxes which would be given twenty yards grace and hunted with a special pack of small hounds when the wild foxes were not giving sport. This pack of hounds was so disciplined and the master so close on their heels that they were not permitted to kill; one fox in the season of 1824–5 was turned out thirty-six times and survived. Templer is even said to have hunted hare in Stover Park with his pack of foxes.

George Templer had to give up his hounds after the financial crash which cost him Stover, but after a couple of years the fantastic figure of Sir Walter Carew took over this country, and from his mastership (1829–43) dates the name of the South Devon Hounds. Extremely wealthy and arrogant (when yachting he was capable of cursing the royal yacht itself if it got in his way), he rode as hard as he drank. Two bottles of port would see him through dinner, and he once told the Lord Lieutenant's wife that 'Time is wasted on women which you can give to hounds.'

For the hunting man Dartmoor is described as rough country, with wild, tough foxes. There are no coverts for them and they are liable to get up in view and go away with the pack on their back. 'You can't ride anywhere except where you can' is the classic description; clitter and rocky country is impossible, and country that looks good too often ends in bog. In 1892 the South Devon had six horses up to their bellies in a bog at the same time. Ralegh Phillpotts, who hunted the northern quarter with a private pack when the Mid-Devon was out of action after World War I, once had a foot meet at Cranmere because it was considered impossible horse country, and the Eggesford Pack was on one occasion lost in the northern Forest for several days. But the men who hunt the Moor get to know it as intimately as any walkers; Commander C. H. Davey, the master of the Dartmoor for twenty years who was lost in *Campeador V* on naval service in the last war, was reputedly one of the few men who could find a path through Fox Tor Mires.

The South Devon, with kennels at Denbury, roughly has the south-east quarter of the Moor. The Dartmoor, which dates back to 1827, before which the country was hunted by J. S. Pode of Slade, has kennels at Ivybridge. John Crocker Bulteel was master when Walter Carew had the South Devon; a joint meet must have been a rare kindling of spirits. After Carew came the redoubtable Squire Charles Trelawney, master for 30 years. In his day a meet would attract a field of 300 mounted followers. Their country is now approximately between Plym and Avon, down to the sea.

What was the western part of their country is now hunted by the Spooner and West Dartmoor pack, with kennels at Sampford Spiney. Clarence Spooner was master of the Hunt which took his name from 1911 to 1925, and he was succeeded by Sylvia Spooner, the first woman to match herself against the Dartmoor fox as both master and huntsman. The north-western quarter of the Moor is rather left alone, but the Mid-Devon has the north-eastern quarter, with kennels at Chagford.

The Dartmoor Otter Hounds, like the Dartmoor Foxhounds, were established by Pode of Slade in 1827, and from the kennels at Bow their country now extends right to Land's End.

For many years they were hunted by the resourceful Miss K. Y. Varndell, who became master in 1952. The other hunting family of modern times is the Whitleys, who have supplied nearly every master for the South Devon since 1915.

In spite of the anti-blood sports agitation of modern times, hunting has as large a following as ever, though the great country magnates of immense wealth have faded from the scene and the hunt today is a much more democratic organisation. Apart from foxhounds, the Dart Vale and Haldon Harriers flourish, a post-war combination of two packs which both date back to the mid-eighteenth century. Since the war two packs of beagles have been formed, the North Dartmoor, launched in 1960 with Charles Hooley, then master of the Mid-Devon, as master; and the South Dartmoor, with kennels at Sampford Spiney. During 1964–5 these beagles were hunted by the King's Shropshire Light Infantry, stationed at Crownhill. They were maintaining an old tradition, for the Plymouth Garrison and the naval officers there were great hunting men before World War I, and hardly a hunting reminiscence of the time misses a few rude words about sportin' young subalterns larkin' about.

Crossing and Douglas St Leger–Gordon have both written about hunting on the Moor,[3] and there is a fund of stories in Edward Tozer's *South Devon Hunt*, published in 1915. Its frontispiece is a picture faced by an apposite poem, 'George Templer's Farewell to his old Horn.'

The great event in the Dartmoor hunting calendar until the early 1930s was Bellever Day, held on a Friday in April, when people flocked to Bellever Tor from miles around. This was the holiday of the year for many country folk, and champagne (for the gentry), sloe gin, ale and cider flowed freely. There were many who failed to get home in the evening, and slept the night by the roadside, huddled under the newtake walls.

As an offshoot of hunting, the racing of horses has been a popular pastime at certain places on the Moor. Rachel Evans, in *Home Scenes,* evocatively describes the races on Whitchurch Down.

> . . . a busy multitude in gay attire . . . Ballad singers bawled their loudest ditties to the listening rustics; our old friends Punch and Judy fought and chattered as loudly as ever, while a band of musicians played our national airs amidst the increasing din and uproar. Vehicles of all descriptions lined the course; booths with gay streamers denoted the vicinity of good cheer, while a handsome stand protected the charms of a number of ladies from the sun.

Other moorland courses were on Butterdon Hill, where the track may still be seen marked out by stones just east of the Hangershell Rock (last used about 1870), Henlake Down (used in the 1790s), Haytor Down (early 1900s) north of Dunnabridge on the slopes of Laughter Tor (before and just after the last war) and near Huccaby Tor. The Prince and Princess of Wales (later King George V and Queen Mary) were visitors to these races on 11 June 1909 (see page 198). Crossing also states[4] that the Princetown and Hexworthy Races were held in Lower Watern Newtake. This is the area to the south of the B3212, just east of the Ockery.

The South Brent Steeplechases were held at Palstone, just east of the town, and the course actually crossed the present A38. After a certain dignitary had been delayed by a race as he journeyed to Plymouth he caused such a furore that the course was abandoned.

Unlike the northern moors, Dartmoor proper has virtually no shooting. Some rough shooting is done on the edges but now that myxomatosis has decimated the rabbit population there is little more than the odd pigeon and the rare woodcock. Partridges are sometimes put up, and pheasants, apart from the few that stray, only exist where they are bred, on the Maristow estate and above Cornwood, for instance. Since there was no native red grouse stock on the Moor, some north-country birds were introduced about 1910 or 1912 in the hope that the Duchy would benefit thereby. Whether it was the abundance of foxes or the country, the birds have never thrived, and would not be worth organising a shooting party for. In the past they seem to have preferred the blanket bog areas, particularly of northern Dartmoor. Recent observations indicate, however, that they are extending their territory outwards, for birds have been seen on Hameldon, near the Longstone on Chagford Common, and on the eastern slopes of Kennon Hill.

Snipe and plover can be found, too, but local knowledge is required unless the seeker is prepared to trudge miles on the offchance of finding some.

Fishing is a much more certain sport on the Moor. Given the right conditions, baskets of a hundred or so trout a day are not unknown. The size may be small, but the flavour amply compensates for this deficiency. Like hunting, fishing had its origins in the necessity to obtain food, but this has ceased to be the motivation which brings anglers to Dartmoor year after year. For certain hotels, such as the Manor House Hotel, the Forest Inn, the Mill End Hotel and the Two Bridges Hotel, the fly-casting fraternity forms a considerable part of their patronage.

As long ago as 1846 Rachel Evans was writing that the Duchy Hotel at Princetown (now the prison officers' club) afforded 'accommodation for anglers and sportsmen, who range the Moor for their desired game.'[5] No doubt fishing on Dartmoor received a certain boost when the Prince Consort tried it. He is said to have caught his first Dartmoor trout on the O Brook near Saddle Bridge.

It is towards the end of the eighteenth century that one first begins to read of people setting out across the Moor for purposes other than business. A South Devon lawyer, John Andrews, made a number of excursions on Dartmoor between 1788 and 1808. As he visited Cranmere Pool in 1789 he is probably the earliest visitor to record his arrival at the place which, above all others, has become a point of pilgrimage for Dartmoor walkers. His notes came to light as the result of a paper salvage drive during the last war; they were edited by R. Hansford Worth and published in the *Transactions of the Devonshire Association* for 1941.

John Swete is the next recorded visitor to arrive; his observations of Two Bridges Fair have already been quoted. On the same tour he visited Postbridge (he had his cousin with him, and two servants in tow), and the two of them had lunch on the old bridge. At the end of their meal Swete ordered his servants to divide the remnants of the meal 'among the poor children of the miners that had flocked around us from the neighbouring houses'. Clearly such an event was unusual in the neighbourhood.

During these years, and into the nineteenth century, great changes were effected on central Dartmoor. The prison was built, and from it grew its satellite, Princetown. Vast enclosures were made and roads constructed. Where hitherto the Moor had been largely a trackless waste, the way was now clear for a trickle of visitors to make their way over it, staying at the various inns which had sprung up; the Plume of Feathers at Princetown and the Saracen's Head at Two Bridges. The present Warren House Inn (formerly Newhouse) dates from 1845, but a previous building, probably dating from when the road was made fifty-odd years earlier, stood on the opposite side of the road and a little nearer Postbridge.

In 1810 Wordsworth published his famous *Guide to the Lakes*. He is usually credited with being the first person to plead for a 'national park' although, to be accurate, he wrote of 'a sort of national property, in which every man has a right and interest who has an eye to perceive and a heart to enjoy'. But the movement towards positively enjoying 'romantic', picturesque scenery had begun, where up to this time the same landscape had been spoken of in fear and awe (according to the *Oxford English Dictionary* the word 'scenery' as applied to landscape only dates from 1784).

Then, from 1826 onwards, several important books about Dartmoor were published in the space of a few years. N. T. Carrington's poem *Dartmoor* went through several editions, and as it included vignettes, etchings and copious notes to the text it is an interesting source-book for the period. Ten years later the letters of Mrs Bray to the poet Southey were published in three volumes under the title *The Borders of the Tamar and the Tavy*. (It was subsequently published in two volumes in 1879.) The letters consisted largely of extracts from the journals of Mrs Bray's husband, the Rev E. A. Bray. Other publications about this time were two books by Sophie Dixon telling of her wanderings on the Moor, and two volumes describing the scenery and antiquities of the Ashburton and

Moretonhampstead areas by the Rev J. P. Jones. In themselves all these books can only have made a small impact on the reading public, but they indicate that writers and others were beginning to discover Dartmoor.

It was in the 1840s that Dartmoor lost its remoteness for ever. The railway reached Exeter in 1844 and had pushed on to Plymouth by 1849. The branch line feeders came later; the Moretonhampstead line in 1866, the Ashburton line in 1872, and the Princetown line in 1883. The north-about route of the LSWR through Okehampton was not complete until 1871.

The publication of the Rev Samuel Rowe's *Perambulation of the Antient and Royal Forest of Dartmoor* in 1848 was an important event. It was the first and, until William Crossing's *Guide to Dartmoor* appeared in 1909, the only comprehensive Dartmoor book available. It can still be read with pleasure, although the reader will discount the druidic theories with which it abounds.

Samuel Rowe devoted several pages to Chagford, but at the time he was writing the little town had not yet awoken to the possibility of attracting the holiday-maker. It was a new rector, Hayter George Hames, who succeeded his father in 1852, who was largely responsible for making Chagford the inland resort we know today. He planned a drainage system and a water supply, and introduced gas in 1869 and electricity in 1889. In White's *Directory* for 1850 there is no mention of any boarding houses or hotels, but as the years go by the entries begin to appear. The first hotel was known as Niner's Hotel (after its proprietor, Mrs Isabella Niner) for about three years from 1869. Niner's was taken over by H. C. Bolt in about 1872 and has since been known as the Moor Park Hotel. Some years later a woollen goods drying store and warehouse were converted into the now well-appointed Moorlands Hotel.

The years from 1860 to 1890 saw a great deal of new building at Chagford. Sturdy stone villas sprang up on all sides, and many of these were advertised as 'apartments'. A reading room and library were established, a parish magazine was published regularly, the painter W. S. Morrish set up a picture gallery, and in 1862 the old market house in the square was demolished and the present building erected. Chagford's metamorphosis was achieved with surprisingly little damage to its character. No doubt the new villas appeared stark and raw at the time, but the stone has mellowed and trees have thrived in the spacious gardens.

For one man to have accomplished so much in a small Devon country town seems incredible, but to the Rev H. G. Hames must go the credit for putting Chagford on the map. He first persuaded a number of dis-

o

tinguished people to stay at the local inns and, when they saw
what beauty Chagford had to offer, personal recommendation did
the rest.

While the rector looked after the cultural, domestic, and spiritual com-
fort of the town, J. Perrott, Dartmoor guide and fisherman, saw to it that
the visitors enjoyed to the full the surrounding countryside. Besides per-
sonally guiding people over Dartmoor, James Perrott ran a flourishing
posting business. Carriages of every description—broughams, waggonettes

J. PERROTT & SON,

SQUARE, CHAGFORD.

Fishing Tackle Manufacturers

⟵ and Guides to Dartmoor.

Over 50 years thoroughly acquainted with every object of interest
on the Moor. Those desirous of investigating the Moor apply to
the above.

✦•✦

SADDLE HORSES, PONIES, CARRIAGES of every description
at Moderate Charges.

PHOTOGRAPHS OF THE NEIGHBOURHOOD SUPPLIED.

Fig 27. Advertisement from *Dartmoor and its Surroundings*, second edition 1900.

and pony carriages—were available for hire, and trips to the north coast
of Cornwall were arranged.

James Perrott began the Cranmere Pool pilgrimage in 1854 when he
built a small cairn there in which he placed a bottle to act as a repository
for the visiting cards of those who reached this remote spot; postcards
had yet to be introduced. A small book was also provided in which people
signed their names. Over the years a number of different objects served
as containers, including a pickle jar, but in 1937 a tall stone
box was built after an appeal launched by *The Western Morning News*.
The top section, with a different door, still does duty over thirty years
later. James Perrott died in 1895, but he left four sons who carried on
the guiding tradition through the Edwardian period.

A personal account of a trip to Cranmere Pool undertaken by three
ladies in 1889 and guided by 'Perrott junior' has survived,[6] and shows
that the guides were in the habit of driving their clients through Fernworthy as far as Teignhead farm before setting out to walk the rest

of the way. Needless to say the passengers were regaled with local anec-
dotes during the drive. On reaching the Pool

> there was a small cairn of stones erected by Perrott, and concealed in
> the cairn was a tin case, and in the case a little book in which the
> adventurous few who reach Cranmere Pool inscribe their names. The
> trio, of course, added theirs to the roll call of heroes and heroines of
> Cranmere and great excitement prevailed which found vent in hand-
> shaking all round and in drinking sherry.[7]

Transport links with various points on the railway system were as
competitive as the railways themselves. The GWR, with its branch to Moretonhampstead, 5 miles away, had the closest link with Chagford. The
LSWR ran a horse bus service to Yeoford which lasted from the early
1860s until Clarkson steam buses were introduced direct to Exeter in
1904.

Other places on Dartmoor's eastern border were attracting the discern-
ing holidaymaker too, but on a smaller scale. Belstone and Lustleigh both
developed at this time, and the Victorian stone villa is much in evidence
in both parishes. The LSWR line to the west stopped short of Okehampton
in 1867 at a temporary terminus called Okehampton Road but, when
the track was opened beyond, the station was renamed Belstone Corner.
In 1872 it was again changed, to Sampford Courtenay, and thus it has
remained.

Like Chagford, Belstone had its Dartmoor guide, a local character
called William Ellis, but he never achieved the same fame or status as
James Perrott, despite an impressive list of trades and qualifications. In
addition to his guiding activities he was a watch repairer, photographer,
picture postcard retailer, manure and seed merchant, churchwarden,
organist, bellringer, lay reader, dog-breeder and dealer in game.

Lustleigh developed after the Moretonhampstead branch line opened
(the main road passes it by), and most visitors came to the village to see
the Cleave. Lustleigh Cleave is one of those beauty spots which it is not
so fashionable to visit nowadays, but in late Victorian and Edwardian
days it was very popular. Even in the 1930s there was a tea room by the
Cleave road at Hammerslake, but few people go there now compared
with the crowds on other parts of the Moor.

The development of Yelverton as a holiday and residential neighbourhood can be attributed to the opening of the station in 1885, and
its proximity to Plymouth. Apart from its suburban function it also
claimed a health value, particularly for heart cases, because walks could
be taken on the level.

Coach proprietors were not slow to realise the growing interest in Dartmoor, and the story is told in detail in Crossing's *Dartmoor Worker*. Coach services for visitors to the Moor began to run from Bovey Tracey in about 1880, and other towns to start their own trips were Newton Abbot, Ashburton, Moretonhampstead, Tavistock and Okehampton. Horse-drawn coaches were running from Chagford as late as 1920.

In retrospect one realises that the thirty or so years from about 1885 to the start of World War I were the golden years for Dartmoor. In 1883 the Dartmoor Preservation Association was formed, and began to awaken the public to the dangers which threatened the Moor—army training, the destruction of antiquities and new enclosures. The Association's publication in 1890 of *The Rights of Common upon the Forest of Dartmoor* by Birkett and Moore remains the indispensable reference book for all interested in the historical background.

The pre-history of Dartmoor remained unknown, however. The Druids had been put to flight, but a vacuum remained. What sort of people had lived in the huts whose ruins are so numerous on the Moor? Robert Burnard, an early secretary of the Dartmoor Preservation Association, was determined to find out, so during the summer of 1893 he carried out an excavation at Broadun Ring, Postbridge, assisted by the Rev Sabine Baring-Gould. The results were so promising that the Dartmoor Exploration Committee was formed and work started the following year at Grimspound.

No doubt the 'digs' were unscientific and heavy-handed by present-day standards, but excavations went on steadily at a number of places during the next twelve years and a great deal was discovered.[8]

As this group tried to unravel the past, two of the founder-members of the Committee, Robert Burnard and Hansford Worth, were concerned for the future. Each felt that, with the need for recreation which was building up, the Moor should become some kind of park. Burnard (1894) wrote of a 'county park',[9] and Worth (1888) of a 'public park, similar to, though smaller than the great American National Parks'.[10] W. F. Collier was also urging similar action during the last years of the nineteenth century.

Interest in the moor was being engendered in other ways. Eden Philpotts had just started writing, and the first of his many Dartmoor novels, *Folly and Fresh Air*, was published in 1891. Eleven years later William Crossing's *The Ancient Stone Crosses of Dartmoor* came out. Crossing was at this time writing regularly about the Moor in Devon newspapers, and his famous *Guide to Dartmoor* was first published in 1909. The demand for cheap literature about the Moor was satisfied by the appearance of Ward Lock and Homeland Association guide books towards the end of the nineteenth century.

During the early years of the twentieth century several private sanatoria opened their doors to consumptive patients. There was a small one at Birchy Lake, Belstone, run by a Dr Gwyn and another at Throwleigh in the charge of Dr Rashleigh. Other sanatoria were established at Thorn (Chagford), Hawkmoor and Didworthy. When they saw the success of these establishments, many doctors in Exeter, Torquay and Plymouth recommended their patients to take the Dartmoor air, even though they did not need sanatorium treatment.

English golf was born with the Royal North Devon club's foundation in 1864, and both the leading courses on Dartmoor are North Devon offspring. The Tavistock course on Whitchurch Down, formed in 1890, was the idea of a Royal North Devon member, J. R. Divett, and not only is it the second oldest surviving course in Devon but the pioneer heather course in the country, the first to move away from the natural sand dunes. At 6,233 yards it is the longest of the moorland courses, and has been described as 'top-class'—'a fine test of golf.' Yelverton's first course was a nine-hole affair laid out in 1904 on fields beside Roborough Down under the direction of Charles Gibson of Westward Ho! The original clubhouse is now the professional's shop and caddie house. This course was extended to eighteen holes in 1909, and opened in May 1911 when J. H. Taylor and Harry Vardon played over it. Half the course was ploughed in World War I, and in 1918 an entirely new course was planned, on the open down. Virtually the golfers moved from Yeoland Mine to Yeoland Consuls Mine for their new architect, Herbert Fowler of Walton Heath, took the last seven holes through the surface workings of Yeoland Consuls, whose adit runs horizontally from beside the Meavy under the down. Apart from the ravines, pits, mounds and air shafts of the mine, Fowler also used the old Devonport leat and declared that artificial bunkering was almost unnecessary. Various changes have been made to the course since, but Yelverton is still described as a course of severe punishment for wild hitters.

Stover, half way between Bovey Tracey and Newton Abbot, was laid out in 1894 by Major H. St Maur as a private course and taken over by the club in 1899. Ploughed up in World War I, it was laid out afresh by James Braid in 1930 and then lost ten holes on the Bovey side to an American Army hospital in World War II. The modern course is a little shorter than Braid's, and is a parkland course in pines and heather. Wrangaton, the only other course on open moorland, was laid out in 1895 but has never grown beyond nine holes. Greater distance from Plymouth and poor roads have kept down its popularity, as compared with Yelverton with its larger membership, where Sunday morning golfers have to be out at 8 am to get a good start, or Tavistock with its 650 playing members.

Chagford opened its own nine-hole course on 8 June 1908. The Hon W. F. Smith MP drove off before 300 people (see page 198) after lunch at the Moor Park Hotel. There were high hopes that it would become an eighteen-hole course in time, but this never came about. The professional, a Mr Quick, doubled as greenkeeper, and when he left in the early 1930s nobody could be found to take his place and the club closed down. The Manor House Hotel, only three miles away, had just opened, with a full-size course in the grounds, and this drew many potential players away from the Chagford links. The old clubhouse is now a private bungalow by the side of the road where it passes over the southern shoulder of Meldon Hill. The lockers are still in situ, and the word 'Ladies' may be seen through several layers of paint on one of the interior doors. The first tee is just across the road.

Okehampton golf course opened in 1913, and a few years earlier a nine-hole course was laid out in the grounds of Prince Hall, Two Bridges (to the east of the drive), but it only lasted a short time. Similarly, a nine-hole course planned and run by the Fox and Hounds, Lydford, in the area just north of the hotel, had a brief life and is reported to have been 'very primitive'.

Chagford refused to be dismayed at the loss of its golf course and built (largely by voluntary labour) a swimming pool instead in 1933. The site was the old mill pond for Rushford Mill. Moretonhampstead also has a swimming pool adapted from a mill pond, and at Petertavy a disused mill pond is used for bathing—unofficially.

In addition to the places already mentioned, holiday accommodation began to be available at Ashburton, Bovey Tracey, Ilsington, Lydford, Princetown, and the Two Bridges area. Looking through guide books of the first ten years of this century we see what seem now to be rather quaint 'attractions' in the hotel and boarding house advertisements. For example 'trap to meet trains' (Mrs Courtier, Ilsington); 'piano' (Spaders Cottage, Two Bridges); 'lit by acetelyne gas' (Two Bridges Hotel); 'perfect sanitation' (Yellam farm, Chagford); 'tuberculosis cases not taken' (Fernleigh, Yelverton); and 'electric light' (Moorland Hotel, Ilsington).

Advertisements in the 1909–10 edition of *Dartmoor and its Surroundings* (Homeland Handbooks) show that only the larger hotels had garage facilities, and the Dolphin Family Hotel at Bovey Tracey listed its extensive horse-drawn coach services. Six years later it was still 'The Premier Coaching and Posting House', but with 'motor cars for hire'.

The GWR ran a day excursion to Dartmoor from London as early as the summer of 1911. This became possible on the completion in 1906 of the Westbury–Castle Cary 'cut-off' route which avoided Bristol. The train travelled non-stop from Paddington to Newton Abbot, where passengers divided into four groups, lunching at various hotels before leaving in solid-tyred 'observation cars' for a variety of tours, some of which went as far as Two Bridges. The return train left Newton Abbot at 7.20 and arrived at Paddington at 10.48.

World War I made little impact on Dartmoor, and the Army training areas were not extended. Competition between the rival railways was now fierce, as the 1915 guide-book advertisements show. For some years after the war the railways, particularly the GWR, ran a fleet of motor coaches over the Moor; after 1923 these were painted in the well-loved chocolate and cream livery.

Other companies were running motor coach services too during this period of post-war transport expansion, some of them using vehicles built from Army-surplus chassis. The Devon General Company was founded in 1919, and about the same time Bulpins of Newton Abbot started their 'Pride of the Moor' coach services (see page 197). Bulpins was bought out by Grey Cars (A. Timpson & Sons Ltd) about 1930, and in 1932 the Devon General took over Grey Cars, but retained the name for touring.[11]

This was the great coach touring period on the Moor, when the well-known tripper spots became firmly established—Lydford Gorge, Princetown, Dartmeet, Haytor and Becky Falls.

But the railways had not forgotten the visitor. In 1936 the GWR opened a new stopping place on the Princetown branch line—Ingra Tor Halt—and were solicitous enough to provide a notice on the platform which read :

Great Western Railway Company
NOTICE
In the interests of game preservation
and for their own protection against
snakes, dogs should be kept on a lead.
By Order

The same railway published a slim booklet for walkers in the early 1930s called *Rambles in South Devon,* and to help this type of visitor day and weekend walking tour tickets were available.

The walker using the railway to reach the Moor had one great advantage over the modern motorist. From Plymouth he could, for example,

Fig. 28. Advertisements from *Dartmoor with its Surroundings*, tenth edition 1915.

leave the train at Yelverton and walk to Cornwood Station, using the same ticket for his return journey; there were many variations of this cross-moor walking and many still cherish the memories of winter walks, coming off the Moor in the last light, down through the lanes under the stars, and waiting for the train by a blazing waiting-room fire. Of a Saturday afternoon Mutley Station, Plymouth, would be crowded with heavy-booted men and women waiting for the 2.10 to Tavistock. For many years before the war the 'Woolworth' ticket (because it was first 6d return, only later 9d) was available from Plymouth to all stations to Yelverton in the summer months, and on fine evenings hundreds of people used this concession.

In the meantime a country-wide movement to create some form of national park system for the best landscape areas in the country was under way. The Council for the Preservation of Rural England submitted a memorandum to the Government in 1929 inviting it to make 'inquiries and preliminary surveys', and a committee was set up to consider the whole question of national parks. Despite a singular lack of action by the Government after the report (published in 1931) had been received, interest continued to grow. The Standing Committee on National Parks of the CPRE was set up in 1936 and interested MPs continued to press the Government for action on the 1931 report, but nothing was done before the outbreak of war in 1939.

At the local level, the Dartmoor Preservation Association was strongly in favour of the Moor becoming a national park, and passed the following resolution at its 1937 general meeting :

> That the Association reaffirms its expressed belief that the best interests of the Nation and of all having rights in or over Dartmoor would be most readily and fully secured by the creation of a National Park, to include the Forest of Dartmoor and the Commons of Devon.

As the war progressed the climate of opinion was moving in favour of national parks, and this culminated in the famous Dower Report of 1945. A committee under Sir Arthur Hobhouse was then formed to consider the Dower Report, and its own conclusions were published in July 1947. Two-and-a-half years later the National Parks and Access to the Country-side Act received the Royal Assent and Dartmoor's designation as a national park was confirmed on 30 October 1951.

Hopes were high at this time that Dartmoor was now safe from unseemly development, although Mrs Sylvia Sayer, now Lady Sayer, Chairman of the Dartmoor Preservation Association, warned that 'the voluntary preservation societies must not relax their vigilance'.

How has the ideal worked in practice? First it must be said that this special status has not prevented undesirable developments of many kinds. The BBC put a television mast on North Hessary Tor (the ITA did not site theirs on Dartmoor). Many tracks on northern Dartmoor have been turned into tarmac roads. Overhead powerlines are sited in beautiful places when they could be undergrounded. The china clay works on southern Dartmoor have grown extensively; their waste tips rear up over the sky lines and are visible far into the Moor. Helicopters often use the Moor for exercises, creating noise and danger to horse and pony riders. Open country has been planted for commercial afforestation, and large areas of broad-leaved woodland felled for the same purpose. A pumping station has been built on Taw Marsh. The ploughing of extensive areas of open moor has taken place. Lastly (though one could go on, for the list is formidable), are the decision to build the Meldon reservoir in the West Okement valley and the acquisitive looks being cast by water authorities elsewhere on Dartmoor.

Successive governments have paid lip service to the need for conserving our last reserves of wild country, and Mr Harold Macmillan, when Minister of Housing and Local Government, asserted that 'in national parks, amenity is the overriding consideration'. That this doctrine has gone by default (if it ever held good) is only too evident to those who have the future of the Dartmoor National Park at heart.

Against the failures, there are the gains. Car parks are being constructed. Some measure of control of the cars which infringe the Road Traffic Act by driving more than fifteen yards from the highway is being undertaken. A summer information centre is provided. A head warden, supported by a deputy and a number of voluntary wardens, helps and assists the public. Rights of way are being cleared, signposted and waymarked, and disfigurements removed. As with the other list, one could go on. But the point must be made that in the big issues the national park authorities, whether it be the Countryside Commission (formerly the National Parks Commission) or the Dartmoor National Park Committee, are helpless. These bodies may vituperate as much as they like, but the Services continue to fire live ammunition over vast areas of the national park and fly helicopters whenever they want. Water authorities, too, operate with seeming impunity.

These conflicts do not seem to worry the average visitor to the Moor, who apparently seeks only a place where he can park his car and lay out his family's picnic paraphernalia. However, when the Devon County Council Planning Department carried out a survey of landscape and amenity in August 1966 one of the report's comments was as follows:

Within the Dartmoor Park . . . a fair percentage, especially of visitors
to the Dartmoor Park, suggested that no improvements should be made,
other than the banning of army exercises on the moor, in order that
the natural state of the Park might be retained.

Since the war the two recreational developments which have made the
most impact on Dartmoor have been the family car and adventure training.

The latter has grown from the small scout-hike type of camping to elaborate expeditions using temporary or permanent base camps. Several
local authorities, youth organisations and schools now have quarters on
the Moor from which they organise expeditions, rock climbing, canoeing,
pony trekking and ecological and scientific study projects. Dartmoor is
ideal for such activities, although the closure of large areas of the northern
Moor for so much of the year for live-firing practice does inhibit the use
of that part of the national park presenting the greatest challenge.

Rock climbing has developed tremendously in recent years. The main
centre is the Dewerstone, a massive crag between the rivers Plym and
Meavy, but many of the larger tors provide rock climbs of varying difficulty.

On Dartmoor the private motorist has discovered a place where he
can get out in the open and yet not be too far from his car. At most seaside
resorts the car parks are some distance from the beach, and unless the
family wants to use the sand or sea as such, the outing can just as well
be taken on the Moor. If water is available as well, so much the better,
and this accounts for the popularity of such riverside spots as New Bridge,
Dartmeet and Cadover Bridge. The time of year seems to make little
difference, and the car park at Haytor is as likely to be full on a fine
Sunday afternoon in January as in midsummer.

It would be unfair, however, to give the impression that visitors to the
Moor do nothing but laze about or drive aimlessly from one 'beauty spot'
to another. An increasing number are taking an intelligent interest in the
features which Dartmoor has to show—the antiquities, the flora and
fauna, the old farmhouses and the ancient tracks across the high moor.

To do this a walk is often necessary, so visitors are combining exercise
with education. Public rights of way, whether footpaths or bridleways,
will be used more than they have been for years as the traffic pressure
in the lanes reaches thrombosis-point in the years to come. Other visitors
are finding that a pony trekking holiday is a good way of enjoying the
Moor. There are riding centres in nearly every parish, and many provide
accommodation.

A few more years and a motorway will have reached Exeter, and a dual carriageway to Plymouth will pass along the southern boundary of the national park. With such easy traffic access we may expect even more people to visit Dartmoor. As it is, 3,823,000 people are estimated to have visited the Moor in 1969, with a peak of 57,700 on Sunday 2 August. With increasing leisure, proliferating car ownership, easier access, and a growing interest in the countryside, it is only to be expected that Dartmoor will become more important as a national 'lung' for those who desire peace, beauty, and historical associations. It is important that we who are its trustees should see that those who come after us have something left to enjoy.

Notes to this chapter are on pages 296–297.

9

Exploitation

John Somers Cocks

Enclosure and the Improvers 1780–1815

IT is difficult to assign a precise date to the beginning of the chain of events which resulted in Dartmoor changing from its ancient, almost medieval ways into something recognisably modern. Although enclosure had already begun on a fairly wide scale before then, the year 1780 may perhaps be selected as marking the start of the work of the 'improvers' who ultimately had such a profound effect on the Moor. The fact that change began when it did was not a matter of chance; it was rather that for the first time a number of conditions which were necessary for such change were simultaneously fulfilled.

The latter part of the eighteenth century was a time when there was an upsurge in the seeking out of knowledge and a flowering of inventiveness, when mechanical power began to be harnessed in man's service, and agricultural experiments were carried out to discover new means of increasing the yield of the soil. It was certain that when conditions were right Dartmoor would come under close scrutiny. Here was a very large and almost uncultivated area, yet obviously well watered; moreover it belonged for the greater part to the Prince of Wales, who could be expected to show a lead in such matters. Only new-found knowledge of agricultural improvement, determination, and above all capital, were wanting to transform its barren acres into fertile land—or so it was believed—and men were ready to do just that if the Duchy would permit them. Indeed, putting such an area to a proper use was seen as hardly less than patriotic, more particularly after the outbreak of the war with France, when great emphasis was placed upon home-grown food. It could be a task to profit the enterprising cultivators as well as the Prince; but if they were prompted by self-interest, it was an enlightened self-interest.

The men and the capital were there, but the fact that they were able to visit Dartmoor and with increasing ease as the years went on was due to the improvement in the roads leading to and across it, notably the Moretonhampstead–Two Bridges turnpike. Without this development it is doubtful if much of the rest would have taken place.

The position in about 1780 was a somewhat confused one, and to understand how it had arisen it is necessary to go back to the earlier years of the century. The Duchy had in fact rather lost interest in Dartmoor, and had allowed the relaxation of its former careful supervision and administration. Between 1738 and 1770 the Forest was granted out and no manor courts were held, so that thirty years' developments had gone unrecorded. In particular, details of fresh newtakes were unknown, though there had been much activity in that direction. By the 1780s, when the Duchy was taking stock of the position, it was seen that this lack of control was operating against its own interests.

The right of making newtakes, the permanent enclosure of the waste, was one claimed by the ancient tenement holders upon succession, provided that the tenement had been held for at least two generations and that the newtake did not exceed eight acres in extent. A 'rent' of $1\frac{1}{2}$d. per acre was payable to the Duchy for the privilege, but as long ago as 1621 Sir Edward Coke had given his opinion that the practice was illegal since the original Duchy charter expressly stated that no part of the Duchy's possessions could be granted away. The custom continued, however, and was now being seriously abused. It was being claimed that the eight acres was exclusive of bog and rock, so that enclosures of sometimes 100 acres were being made. In 1766 another similar legal opinion was given, after which Mr Heywood, who was tenant of the Forest at the time, had thrown down some newtakes and demanded rent from others. But only one shilling for any newtake, whatever its size, was forthcoming, and because rents of all descriptions had never been revised they were in any case more relevant to medieval than to modern conditions. The fact was that considerable areas of land had become annexed to the copyhold tenement farms and had passed from Duchy control. It was this loss of control more than the enclosure that worried the authorities. In 1796 the custom of newtaking was forbidden, an edict which by no means stopped enclosure.

Development of Dartmoor in the 1780s was being carried out in two ways; first by the improvement of the tenement farms and their newly-won enclosures, and secondly by enclosure of vast areas of commons within the Forest under grants made by the Duchy to certain individuals. A number of the ancient tenements had come into the hands of a few gentry, including James Templer of Stover and Mr Gullet. The latter (who seems to have been the Christopher Gullet connected with the Duchy) had Prince Hall and began improvements there in 1780; he was among the earliest to do so. All others were eclipsed, however, by Mr Justice Buller who at first held three tenements at Sherberton, one-and-a-half at Huccaby and, as trustee, that at Brownberry, apart from numerous newtakes. He had acquired Sherberton and Huccaby in 1784, and in the following year he took Bellever in place of Templer. A few years later he obtained Prince Hall from Gullet, and by the time he had finished was possessed of some 2,000 acres, a power to be reckoned with.

Francis Buller was a distinguished lawyer with local connections. Born in 1746, the fourth son of James Buller of Morval near Looe and of Downes near Crediton, he was married at the age of seventeen to the only daughter and heir of Francis Yarde of Churston. He was a KC in 1777, becoming a judge of the King's Bench in the following year before transferring to Common Pleas, and received a baronetcy in 1790. His

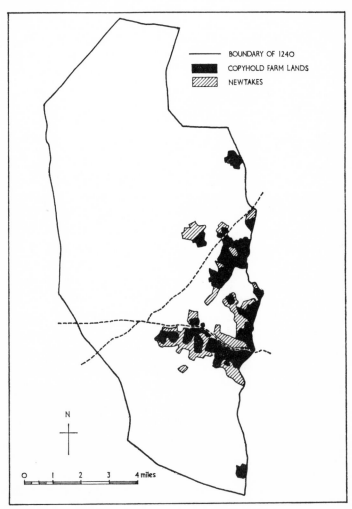

BOUNDARY OF 1240
COPYHOLD FARM LANDS
NEWTAKES

N

O 1 2 3 4 miles

Fig 29. Enclosure in the Forest, c 1750

legal duties did not prevent him taking a great interest in his Dartmoor estate, centred on Prince Hall which he rebuilt, and he caused the Saracen's Head at Two Bridges to be erected at the western end of one of his newtakes. It is now the Two Bridges Hotel. He had the reputation of a kindly employer.

Several other names loom large at this period. They were the men who obtained grants from the Duchy in about 1780 or soon after to enclose enormous areas of the Forest and form entirely new estates. First and foremost was Thomas Tyrwhitt, whose labours on Dartmoor, beginning at Tor Royal in 1785, are recounted in a separate section. He was preceded by Edward Bray, a solicitor employed in managing the Duke of Bedford's Devon properties, who carved an estate for himself at Beardown just west of Two Bridges and enclosed 900 acres, spending what his daughter-in-law, Mrs Annie Elizabeth Bray, called a small fortune in doing so. A barn on his property was licensed as a chapel for Divine Service for the benefit of those living nearby. Soon after the turn of the century they could have included the Rev J. H. Mason, another Duchy official as well as vicar of Widecombe, who enclosed 600 acres around Crockern Tor, upon which he erected a flagpole, and built himself a cottage by the turnpike road. Further north still, Thomas and John Hullett took over a grant made to a Mr Paterson of a huge area lying to the west of the turnpike. Their enclosures totalled at least 3,000 acres of what had been commons, and they founded the village of Postbridge with its Greyhound Inn. It appears that they had intended to have what is now Stannon Farm as their residence, and they erected suitable entrance lodges on either side of the drive in Postbridge itself—where they may still be seen—but their grandiose ideas never prospered. Further enclosure was also going on at Fernworthy where, apart from the long-established farmland, a total of 278 acres had been taken in by 1802.

Meanwhile Buller came upon the scene again with a proposal to enclose the entire Forest. The suggestion was first made to the Duchy Council by Mr Robert Fraser, and a company with a capital by subscription of £100,000 was formed for the purpose by Mr Charles Cole. Buller drafted the necessary Bill for dividing and allotting it and for forming it into its own parish; amongst those who signed it was Edward Bray. The Bill was in draft by early 1791, but Duchy officials were divided as to how much support it should enjoy. One of the Duchy officers at that time was Richard Gray, who held the posts of deputy auditor and clerk of the Prince's Council, and deputy surveyor general to the Duchy, sharing from 1780 the first-named post with his son, also Richard. It was largely his interest in and knowledge of Dartmoor affairs which caused the Bill to fail.

The petition for enclosure had come ostensibly from the tenants and newtake holders in the Forest, but Richard Gray's opinion, conveyed to the Duchy's legal advisers, was that they merely wished to 'confirm their newtakes and usurpations, and to wrest every part of the Forest worth taking from the Prince—to throw off The Duchy Yoke . . .' He complained that Buller had already named a string of commissioners and declared that the Prince's rights should be properly guarded in a way which the Bill with its 'flagrant partiality' clearly did not, adding that while deliberations proceeded encroachments were going on as usual. Even Gray was unable to discover exactly what the total acreage of newtakes was; a man sent to find out was refused the necessary information. In spite of Gray's advice the Prince approved the Bill at the next council meeting in February, but later revoked his decision. In August we find Mr Simpson, another Duchy adviser, attacking the Bill clause by clause, presumably on Mr Gray's advice. Amongst the points he made was the fact that the rights of the venville men on the Forest were entirely ignored, as were the rights of those who cut peat for their hearths and for converting to charcoal for smelting tin ore. The Bill had stated that a great part of the Forest was capable of being improved and brought into cultivation, whereas he asserted, 'it will not bear the plough' and could only be improved by depasturing more and better cattle. In the end the Duchy decided that it objected to the Prince's share being allotted by commissioners and that in any case the share must be at least one-third. Agreement with the sponsors was not forthcoming and the Bill lapsed.

Arising out of this contretemps was a report which gave the exact position and extent of the newtakes and ancient tenements in the Forest, based on a survey by Mr Thomas Gray of Exeter in 1802, and headed 'On the general contents of the Forest, the quantity already granted out by lease, and the expediency of suspending for the present all further grants.' The figures given are as follows : Ancient customary tenements, 2,876 acres; newtakes, 5,274 acres; land at Fernworthy, 278 acres; remainder of Forest, 45,812 acres. It seems from these figures that the grants of common lands to men such as Bray and Tyrwhitt came under 'remainder of Forest', for the report says that the idea was then being put forward that the Duchy might agree to an enclosure of the Moor giving it one quarter, and that tenants' illegal newtakes should be included in their share of allotments. But, it pointed out, the Prince had already granted out 14,265 acres on long leases, which was more than a quarter. Further grants, it said, should cease, especially as many lessees had 'no interest whatsoever in the Forest' (it is unlikely that the whole 14,000 acres had been enclosed), so that 'much jealousy had been excited in the Country, and some

P

of his Royal Highness's Lessees have experienced opposition from neighbouring Commoners who have broken down part of their fences.' The
only exception might be allotments made to ancient tenement holders in
exchange for their ancient claim to newtakes.

But the enclosures went on. Fernworthy, owned by the Davie family,
took in another great tract of land on either side of the South Teign; a
farmer called Windeatt made Fox Tor Farm and dismantled Childe's
Tomb, an ancient burial chamber and cross, in the process; on the surviving Hullett, Thomas, deciding to give up his labours at Postbridge the
Rev Mr Vollans took over; and down in the southern part of the Forest,
Huntingdon was enlarged to 790 acres in 1808. A grant in the same year
of 904 acres beside the upper reaches of the North Teign made to Mr
Crawford caused certain difficulties.

Crawford employed William Rogers as his agent to make this farm,
with its long lengths of stone wall enclosures. It lay right on the boundary
of the Forest and there can be little doubt that the boundary was taken
to be that shown on the map which Thomas Gray had produced in 1804
after his investigations of two years before, and upon which the Rev J. H.
Mason had apparently given advice. The advice here was certainly
erroneous and the line was (and still is on Duchy maps) drawn too far
to the east on the north-east side, with the result that the enclosing walls
of Teign (later known as Teignhead) Farm began to cross Gidleigh Commons. What happened is luckily preserved in the records, because the
boundary line had to be settled by a Tithe Commissioner in 1842–3 in
order to draw up the correct apportionments, and the evidence collected
includes that of William Rogers himself, who made a full and frank
statement of what had happened in 1808. The Gidleigh commoners, on
seeing what was afoot, arranged a very well-attended perambulation of
their bounds and threw down the offending wall. Crawford and the
Duchy were most annoyed, but Rogers then rebuilt it so that only a comparatively small portion crossed Gidleigh Common where the commoners, although threatening further action, allowed it to stay. When
collecting stone for the walls, Rogers came across some awkward evidence
inside his enclosure in the shape of stones marked G, which he proceeded
to obliterate or build into his wall, and he was later instructed by Mason,
acting for the Duchy, to try to reach agreement with Gidleigh. He received co-operation from one farmer only, but between them they erected
new stones on a different line—for which, of course, there was no historical basis—and cut DC and G on them as well as on the Longstone, where
the lines coincided. The Duchy surveyor thought the letters should have
been embossed, as looking more ancient.

Thus the farm came into being and the commoners were deprived of a big area of common land. One tradition relating to it is worth recalling. When the clapper bridge giving access across the Teign was formed, it is said that the heavy slabs forming the imposts were brought down from Manga Hill by being slid over hard-frozen snow to the river bank below.

Enclosure was certainly taking place on the surrounding parish commons too, but it is often difficult to discover the dates of these encroachments though it seems that many were later than those in the Forest. It is significant that no Dartmoor commons were included in any Enclosure Act or Award. The 1809 Act to enclose Ilsington Common which is sometimes quoted as an exception refers in fact to the Heathfield near Liverton and not to Haytor Down.

Thomas Tyrwhitt and Princetown

Thomas Tyrwhitt was born in 1762 at the parsonage at Wickham Bishops in Essex and had no previous connection with Devon. He came to know Dartmoor through his friendship with the Prince of Wales, to whom he was introduced when up at Christ Church, Oxford, taking his MA degree. This led to his being appointed the Prince's secretary, and in 1786, a year after he had begun operations at a spot a little south of Two Bridges, which he called Tor Royal after his patron, he was appointed auditor to the Duchy of Cornwall. He was then twenty-four and was described as a small, active man, courteous to everyone and of sanguine and optimistic temperament, qualities quite essential to his persistent and single-minded pursuit of the improvement of Dartmoor, which he carried to a degree unequalled by any of his contemporaries.

Between 1785 and 1798 he was forming his 2,300-acre Tor Royal estate, building the house itself and various others in the neighbourhood such as Bachelor's Hall, Peat Cot and Swincombe Farm. His lodges were on the spot where the present Methodist Church and the house opposite stand, and as well as forming fields for cultivation he had a large enclosure known as Tor Royal Newtake or Cattle Park. Unlike the other improvers, he was not content to have just his own farm estate, but strove to build up a little community which he hoped in the fullness of time would become virtually self-sufficient. He therefore erected a few cottages and an inn called the Plume of Feathers near by, and improved the road from Dousland to Two Bridges as well as forming a new one from Rundlestone to his lodges. To this tiny settlement he gave the name of Prince's Town, or Prince Town as it soon became called.

It failed to flourish, and one of the reasons was its position. It is not known what caused Tyrwhitt to choose the particular site he did; it was about 1,300ft above sea level and, being perched almost at the top of the col between the Meavy valley to the south and the Dart basin to the north, was in one of the most exposed spots imaginable. This original mis-siting, which the shelter of North Hessary Tor to the west only slightly mitigates, has been an important factor in the area's subsequent history, for it made any development through successful cultivation even less likely to succeed, and what might be termed artificial stimulants had to be resorted to in order to try to offset the natural disadvantages.

Fortunately for Tyrwhitt, his closeness to the Prince Regent, his position as an MP (he represented Okehampton 1796–1802, Portarlington 1802–6 and Plymouth 1806–12) and his abiding interest in Dartmoor, which he visited whenever his duties permitted, all served him in good stead. He was in as good a position as any to pull wires in official circles when that was needed. It was not long after the completion of Tor Royal that he realised that the cultivation of Dartmoor and his dream of acres of corn and flax, of root crops and plantations, was going to be harder to achieve than he had expected and that Prince Town needed something more than reclamation to support it.

In 1805, the year in which he was appointed Lord Warden of the Stannaries, a high Duchy post, the authorities were becoming alarmed at the number of prisoners of war confined in hulks in the Hamoaze and elsewhere at Plymouth, and were looking around for some suitable alternative accommodation. Here was Tyrwhitt's chance. He made his views known, and in July an official of the Transport Board wrote from Tor Royal to say that he had met Mr Daniel Alexander the architect and, after visiting with him many possible sites on Dartmoor for building a prisoner-of-war prison, they had fixed upon one not far from Mr Tyrwhitt's lodges. A 99-year lease of 390 acres was negotiated and the future of the settlement assured for as long as the war lasted. Initial work on the prison began almost at once, and on 20 March 1806 Tyrwhitt laid the foundation stone.

The story of the war prison need only be outlined here. The difficulties of building it owing to the climate and remoteness bankrupted more than one contractor, even though stone was close at hand at Swell Tor quarry. 'This hath been a hindering week' wrote one of them in November, 'the sun hath scarcely made its appearance, and we may safely say that £120 hath been lost in wages'. But in May 1809 it was sufficiently advanced for the first draft of 2,500 men to march up from Plymouth, with another 2,500 following the next month. It was said that, together with the military barracks, it eventually cost £200,000. The bleakness of the situation and the epidemics amongst the French and American prisoners, who at one time numbered about 9,000, caused a good deal of criticism in Parliament and newspapers of the Board of Transport's choice of site. There were conditions of gross overcrowding, and on one occasion a suspected break-out was countered by the guards being ordered to fire on the prisoners with resultant loss of life.

For Thomas Tyrwhitt, knighted in 1812 and appointed Gentleman Usher of the Black Rod, the coming of the prison was an opportunity to expand his village, and he seized it at once. A market was soon established with a tremendous demand for goods and foodstuffs; at Bachelor's Hall a corn-grinding mill was constructed; there was a brewery behind the building now known as the Duchy Hotel, which had been built to house officers, and about thirty other houses went up in the vicinity. Princetown (to give it its modern rendering) was thriving in a way which must have warmed his heart. Yet he must have realised that a prosperity based on something other than permanent local industry could only be short-lived and, when the war ended, decline inevitably set in. The last prisoners left in 1816, life ebbed away, and after a few months grass was growing in the street. He had spent over thirty years already in trying to achieve his life's ambition; he was not going to give up trying now. Standing close by was a series of large buildings whose lease had reverted to the Duchy and which might be put to another use. In the next few years he was to inspire a number of suggestions for them.

Quite by chance a select committee of the House of Commons was at that moment investigating the state of prisons in London, but it was no coincidence that in its report there was a section extolling the climate of Dartmoor and suggesting that 2,000 convicts could be removed at small expense to the vacant prison, where they would 'cleanse the land and render it fit for cultivation' by cutting granite, which might then be conveyed to Plymouth by an iron railway. Nothing came of the idea, though it was revived from time to time, and the next suggestion came in 1818 with a proposal that schools of industry might be set up there. Orphan children were mentioned, and in 1820 a meeting at the Mansion House put forward a more specific plan to fill the buildings with numerous poor children removed from their 'profligate associates' in London, to give them religious education, and to teach them the culture and dressing of flax. Mercifully nothing was done to implement this plan either, and meanwhile Tyrwhitt was putting all his energies into yet another scheme to bring prosperity to Princetown.

He had realised that its future must lie in the profitable use of the

prison buildings and, as the convict scheme of 1816 shows, he had already
seen the advantage of improved communications. If the two schemes of
filling the empty prison and building a railway could not be carried out
together, then, he argued, the prior completion of a railway could well
lead to a scheme for the prison receiving much more careful consideration from the authorities than it might otherwise have done. So, un-
daunted, he set about the task of obtaining the necessary moral and financial support for a project which was more than ordinarily speculative
and, in view of the difference in height between the two proposed
terminals of Plymouth and Princetown, very advanced for its time. It
speaks volumes for his powers of persuasion that he won the backing
of the Plymouth Chamber of Commerce and had sufficient subscriptions
to inaugurate the work of construction in 1819.

He published the arguments he had used at the meeting of the Chamber in a pamphlet dated 1 January 1819. In it he outlined the uses to
which such a railroad could be put. They are of great interest, not least
in demonstrating that his aspirations as an improver remained undimmed
after over thirty years of varying fortunes. His whole credo is summed
up in one paragraph of the preamble.

> To reclaim and clothe with grain and grasses a spacious tract of land,
> now lying barren, desolate and neglected; to fill this unoccupied region
> with an industrious and hardy population; to create a profitable inter-
> change of useful commodities between an improvable and extensive
> line of back country and a commercial sea-port of the first capabilities
> . . . to provide employment and subsistence for the poor of several
> parishes; and to alleviate the pressure of parochial burthens, by a
> method, at once simply ingenious and comparatively inexpensive, form
> altogether such a stimulus to adventure and such a scope for exertion,
> especially to a wealthy Company, as must dilate the benevolent heart
> of the patriot, whilst it emboldens the capitalist gladly to lend his assis-
> tance in carrying the plan into execution.

Put briefly, he proposed that the line should carry up to the Moor com-
modities such as lime and sea sand for fertiliser, timber and other
materials for building, and coal and groceries, while the exportable com-
modities would chiefly be granite, quarried not only at and around Swell
Tor but taken off the ground when the land was being made fit for
cultivation, though there would also be some traffic in peat, minerals,
flax and hemp and, he hoped, a two-way movement of convicts.

The building of the line and its subsequent chequered history are
dealt with in chapter seven; suffice it here to say that it never prospered
and that in Tyrwhitt's lifetime the prison remained empty and Princetown languished. In 1828 he put Tor Royal up for sale together with

the 'wharf' he owned on Roborough Down. He resigned his twenty-year
tenure as Black Rod in 1832, an office he had held with distinction
and in which he earned praise for refusing, contrary to precedent, emolu-
ments for appointments made in virtue of his position, a forbearance
which is said to have made him some £9,000 the poorer. Next year he
died abroad, aged seventy.

What was there to show for his labours? Some achievements were
plain to see—houses, fields, cattle where there had been only moorland
before, a small village, a railway even; and always the hope of something more when economic times were more propitious. But his success
fell far short of the vision he had seen of waving corn, of woods and lush
pasture, of industrious labourers in a thriving community sending their
produce to Plymouth and receiving their everyday necessities in return.
In truth such a dream was beyond his or anyone else's ability to fulfil and
it is a matter for surprise that he persisted in its pursuit so long after it
must have become obvious that it was unattainable. By the time he sold
it, he had put upwards of £47,000 into Tor Royal.

There can be no doubt that in the view of contemporary public
opinion as well as in his own eyes he was performing a patriotic service,
and that he met with partial success. Yet even by the standards of the
day, by which alone he must be judged, he failed to profit by experience
or to grasp certain essentials which any Dartmoor farmer of long standing could have pointed out to him. Nor should it be overlooked that
his enclosures, with the others, occasioned considerable hardship to those
same farmers by depriving them of much of their best common pasture
without any compensation whatever.

He epitomised the improvers and all they stood for, and if today he
is for the most part forgotten, Princetown still stands, for better or worse,
as his memorial.

Later Enclosures

By 1820 the majority of the Forest enclosures had been made and the
momentum of the improvers was largely spent. A traveller, the Rev J. P.
Jones of North Bovey, passing across the Moor on the Moretonhampstead–Two Bridges road about this time, recorded what he saw. Near
Postbridge he noted signs of small estates well cultivated, probably the
Merripits, but after passing through more enclosures he was surprised at
the appearance of the new farms. 'A few years before,' he said, 'the
rage for improvement was great, but now quite the contrary is the case
—the houses were shut up and falling to decay, the fences were torn

down and Dartmoor was fast hastening back to its original uncultivated
state.'

What had gone wrong? Jones himself goes far to provide the answer
when he says that the improvements had been on too large a scale and
that success would never be so great as some speculative heads had
imagined. It was extremely difficult to obtain manure, communications
were bad, shelter insufficient, and labourers were not attracted by the
Moor. He continues :

> The gentlemen and adventurers who commenced the improvements
> were altogether mistaken with respect to the soil and produce of Dart-
> moor : it will produce oats, potatoes, and turnips in abundance; during
> the summer there is good grazing for cattle . . . On the failure of their
> hopes, many were anxious to dispose of their estates, this was found to
> be exceedingly difficult and several persons experienced a great loss by
> their speculations. A general opinion now prevails that Dartmoor must
> be left to its original cultivators, or that a greater degree of experience
> and judgment than has been already displayed must guide future
> attempts.

He mentions that these 'original cultivators' lived hard with small profit
and spent the long winter in a 'state of inactivity and seclusion,' the
cattle being driven into the enclosed country before the cold weather set
in. Finally, and with every justification, he blames the agricultural depression which had set in at the end of the Napoleonic Wars.

One further point he might have made was that the wholesale enclosure which by then stretched right across the Forest in the centre,
cutting it in two, deprived the commoners of a great part of their grazing, including some of the most favoured areas. The original grants for
new enclosure may have been made on the principle that improvement
of manorial waste is permissible provided that sufficient common is left
for the full exercise of common rights, and that much common land remained. This remainder, however, was to a large extent the high blanket-
bog and virtually unpasturable; moreover with such an extensive class
of commoner as had rights on Dartmoor—the whole county save Barnstaple and Totnes—sufficiency of common could hardly be pleaded.
Furthermore, it is necessary to draw the distinction between improvement and mere enclosure. Over vast areas no attempt at improvement
was ever made. Operations savoured more of land-grabbing, of taking
large tracts of common land for a nominal sum (one figure quoted was
sixpence per acre for the first thirty years of a ninety-nine year lease) and
then renting them out to the commoners for whatever it was thought
could be got. The venville tenants were the worst affected and could

obtain no redress for having often to pay to enjoy what was really theirs by right. In drawing up the credits and debits to the local economy this fact must not be lost sight of. It caused much bitterness and resentment; a hundred years later, when another scheme involving common land was being mooted, an old farmer gloomily observed that they were likely to be robbed in the same way that their grandfathers had been.

In spite of past experience there were still those who urged that further reclamation should be tried, that it was only a failure to apply the correct principles that had brought difficulties. In an article in the *Morning Post* at the beginning of 1820, inspired by Tyrwhitt's experiments in growing flax, it was argued that although previous attempts to bring the Forest under cultivation had failed, the cause of failure was now understood—the lack of a proper dressing of lime. The Rev T. Moore, writing in 1829, thought that the absence of proper roads for carrying lime into the Moor was hampering future operations, 'but if it were possible to extend canals into the centre of the Moor, these of course would be preferable, and of the practicability of such plans some writers who have paid attention to the subject are fully persuaded.' He continues by suggesting that a canal for small craft might be formed on the extensive summit level with a larger one on a lower level, the boats being passed between them by an inclined plane if locks could not serve, with lime and sea sand being brought in and granite, copper, etc sent out.

Moore's remarkable ideas were equalled perhaps by another scheme of 1840, when a survey was carried out by the engineer James Rendel for the construction of a railway across Dartmoor from Plymouth to Chagford and Exeter. It was to have reached the Moor at Sheepstor Bridge, gone through a tunnel near Nun's Cross, run through the Swincombe and Cherrybrook valleys to Postbridge, passed up the Wallabrook to another tunnel near Newhouse, and so via the Metheral and Teign to its destination. The steep ascents to the Moor at either end were to be achieved by rope-haulage, the power being derived from water-wheels fed by leats taken from specially-constructed reservoirs, one in the Blackabrook valley, one in the Cowsic valley and one about three miles above Postbridge on the East Dart. Between these two inclines locomotives would be used. It is no surprise to learn that the scheme came to nothing.

The Duchy made considerable efforts to regularise the position created by the earlier extensive grants, the terms of which they later realised were not favourable to them and about which there was even some doubt as to legality. They were also engaged in trying to assert their ownership of some of the newtakes made by the ancient tenements.

In 1822 an Act was obtained making it lawful for the King in his position as Duke of Cornwall to make leases under certain conditions and to legalise the position where doubts had arisen as to title. The leases were to be for three lives or for thirty years, but 'whereas certain Parts of the said Duchy are capable of considerable Improvement by the Erection of substantial Buildings thereon, and by the Cultivation of Waste Lands' which could not be undertaken by the lessees for a short term of years, it was enacted that in those circumstances a term of up to ninety-nine years was permissible.

Twenty-two years later a memorandum was drawn up by J. R. Gardiner, Secretary to the Duchy Council, outlining further steps which he thought should be taken to rectify the position. He felt that the extensive encroachments should be restored and that the Deputy Forester should be granted permission to destroy any new enclosures. As to the older enclosures some progress had been made; Judge Buller's executors had given up their right to the unauthorised ones in 1804 and had been re-granted them on leases. Messrs Sanders, Barker & Co, Solicitors of Exeter, had resisted demands for forty years, Gardiner said, but were thought to be about to settle for leases at Brimpts. So far as Mr Vollans' estates were concerned, he reported that Mr Frean of Plymouth had obtained them along with Mr Bray's Beardown property, about 5,000 acres in all, and had agreed to surrender them for leases. (One wonders what the conditions of the original grants could have been.) The Duchy was recommended to support him because he had already begun improvements 'in a spirited manner' and had 'zeal, industry and enterprise,' his proposed gunpowder works (at Powder Mills) should be granted, and the sole turf-cutting rights which, he said, were bringing the Duchy little profit, should also be let to him for a short term at fourpence a load on at least 3,000 loads per year. Finally Gardiner reported that the lease of Teignhead Farm had been much sold and resold without proper record. No rent had been paid for several years and it should be repossessed.

It is clear from the above that enclosure and improvement were by no means frowned upon, provided that the works were not carried out in a way which deprived the Duchy of actual ownership or control. Enclosure was in fact continuing during the middle part of the century, though on a much smaller scale than before. Chief amongst the later improvers was Mr G. W. Fowler of Liverpool, who bought Prince Hall in 1846 and carried out large-scale works, making the land bear heavy crops but at great expense. The 'original cultivators' remained sceptical; they allowed that he produced enormous turnips, 'proper gert benders, zure 'nuff' they said according to Crossing, but 'most 'o mun was holla.' After eight years, he too had to come to terms with the Moor and was obliged to sell his oxen, changing over to summer pasturage for cattle. Unfortunately perhaps, this decision was made a few years after he had given advice to the government, which influenced it in deciding to make use of the still-empty war prison buildings.

These buildings had been kept in some sort of repair, and in 1846 the British Patent Naphtha Co had taken a lease of land near Holming Beam and of part of the prison for the conversion of peat into naphtha and other derivative products, including candles and gas for lighting the premises. Although the works cost £19,000 they closed after a year or so, and soon afterwards the decision for which Tyrwhitt had pressed more than thirty years earlier was at last taken; the buildings were to be converted into a convict prison with its own farm.

By September 1850 part had been repaired by local free labour, and in November the first convicts arrived. The initial cost for housing up to 1,300 prisoners and their guards amounted to £26,000, provision also being made to expand accommodation to 2,000 if necessary. The site was, of course, no less exposed than before, but with such a permanent establishment Princetown at once came to life again and indeed expanded, with much new building. The convicts laboured at taking in land up to the Tavistock–Two Bridges road, extending northwards in the 1870s beside the Blackabrook. By the end of the century, of a total grant of 2,000 acres, 1,300 had been reclaimed, most of it common land.

The opening of the prison gave another impetus to the would-be improvers, particularly Henry Tanner, a land agent of Exeter, who produced a prize essay on the subject. His plan for Dartmoor was all-embracing and today is of interest largely for its quality of the absurd. Both Forest and surrounding commons were to be reclaimed, and the methods to be employed, drainage, ploughing, fertilising, the terms of leases and the crops (including timber) to be grown are all exactly costed, as are the financial yields to be expected; indeed so confident was he that he apparently thought it unnecessary to set aside any sum for contingencies. Bogs were to be drained—all of them, including the 'fen'. One looks eagerly to see how this was to be done at £2 per acre. An aperture was to be cut in the side of the bog in a suitable place, with main and branch ditches. The work would, he admitted, require great judgment and care, 'but with their aid no practical difficulties will present themselves.' It was as easy as that. Vancouver had said much the same in 1807, but nearly fifty years of experience had been bought since then, and it is perhaps surprising that any agricultural society of 1854 was ready to award him a prize.

However, the capital for such projects was not now to be found, and any further enclosures in the Forest were sporadic and of comparatively small extent. Camps Farm (later known as Harter Farm) in about 1860, Spaders, where an island of common was enclosed by Mr D'Arcy Linton in 1868, and John Hooper's Nun's Cross Farm of two years later, are examples. Mr J. N. Bennet's Archerton estate, formed a little earlier, may have been carved out of existing enclosures. As late as 1937 another 140 acres of commons were taken in by the Prison Commissioners in pursuance of an earlier Duchy lease.

Encroachment was also going on all round the Moor on the Commons of Devon and elsewhere. The Ilsington commoners, perambulating their

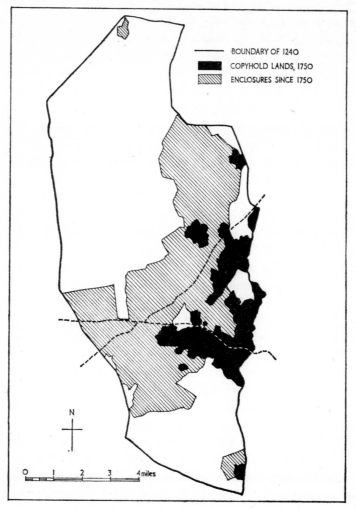

BOUNDARY OF 1240
COPYHOLD LANDS, 1750
ENCLOSURES SINCE 1750

N

O   1   2   3   4 miles

Fig 30.   Enclosure in the Forest in 1880.

bounds in 1834, found that a wall enclosing about 150 acres had lately been set up on Rippon Tor and they were unable to secure its removal. By the middle of the century enclosures had spread up the Walkham to above Merrivale, while others appeared on Belstone and South Tawton Commons. The Duke of Bedford took in 136 acres near Butterford in Petertavy about 1865 and there were many others, albeit on a fairly modest scale.

By the early 1880s an influential group of local men who had become alarmed at the continuing creep of encroachment for various purposes, and were anxious to try to protect the local antiquities, formed the Dartmoor Preservation Association. One of their first actions was to have a thorough search made in the old records to ascertain what the rights of the commoners really were. The search proved most fruitful and illuminating, showing quite clearly that most of the enclosures for nearly a hundred years had been unlawful. These revelations proved decisive on future schemes, and projects over the next few years to enclose parts of Petertavy, Holne, and South Tawton Commons, and the whole of Dean Moor, were opposed and had to be abandoned.

If the commoners' rights could have been asserted at an earlier stage the nineteenth-century history of Dartmoor would have been written rather differently. In reply to a question in the House in 1898, Mr Seale-Hayne was informed that over 15,000 acres of Dartmoor had been enclosed since 1820 alone. It was all common land.

Water Supplies

The diversion of the flow of Dartmoor streams has been going on since the first tinners built leats to take water power to their smelting houses, but with one exception the use of such water for supplying towns and large rural areas dates only from the later years of the eighteenth century. It was natural that, with an ever-increasing population's demands to be met, minds should have turned to Dartmoor, whose rivers have a relatively high dry-weather flow due partly to the peat's absorbent qualities and partly to its action of serving as an insulating blanket against evaporation of the water percolating beneath it. The high rainfall of the area, between sixty and eighty inches in most parts, gives rise to the larger rivers of Devon, with the exception of the Exe, Otter and Axe, so that Dartmoor is the source of much of the lush fertility of the areas lying below it. Where these rivers cut their way from one moorland level to another or through the altered rock surrounding the granite, they form steep-sided gorges on which the eyes of the water engineer have sometimes fallen as sites suitable for constructing dams to impound the periodic flood waters.

The earliest domestic water scheme was the completion in 1591 of Drake's leat from a weir on the Meavy near Sheepstor and across Roborough Down, seventeen miles to Plymouth. When this project was first mooted in 1560 it was only natural that expert advice should have been sought from a tinner, a class of person with ample experience in such matters. With certain alterations and improvements, Drake's leat was to remain Plymouth's water supply for another three centuries, and may still be followed for many miles.

It is quite possible that the next scheme also had the benefit of tinners' advice, as it was another and much longer leat. In 1793 powers were granted to the Plymouth Dock Waterworks Company to supply water to Devonport (then called Dock) by making an artificial watercourse up to ten feet wide, taking in the headwaters of the West Dart, the Cowsic and the Blackabrook, and passing Tor Royal, Peat Cot and Whiteworks, near which it entered a tunnel before crossing into the Meavy watershed, and so across Roborough Down to Crownhill and Devonport. It is curious that when the war prisons at Princetown were built the 'foul leat' conveying effluent was taken to Tyrwhitt's Tor Royal newtake on a contour very close to and just higher than the Devonport leat, which in fact it crossed at one place, giving rise surely to problems of occasional pollution. The company's leat was acquired by Devonport Corporation in 1902 and soon afterwards, on the amalgamation of the Three Towns, passed to Plymouth and was diverted into its Burrator reservoir. Much of the lower, disused portion may also still be seen, particularly on Roborough Down close beside Drake's leat.

Towards the end of the nineteenth century Plymouth's water supply had become inadequate. The open leats sometimes caused trouble when they became choked with snow, as in the great blizzard of 1891, and there was much talk of an impounding reservoir. The choice of sites lay between the Head Weir on the Meavy and the Harter Brook higher up, the latter being championed by Sir Massey Lopes, who did not wish his farm land flooded and who believed his rights to water from the existing leat would be interfered with. The other faction, flatly denying he had any such rights and saying they belonged solely to Plymouth, eventually carried the day.

After some trouble over the dam's foundations it was completed in 1898 at a cost of £150,000, the reservoir flooding 117 acres. The purchase of the catchment was not made by the corporation until 1916 (it meant the end of a number of hill farms), and in 1928 the dam was lengthened and heightened, the reservoir being increased to 150 acres with a yield of ten million gallons a day. While this work was being carried out the road to Sheepstor across the dam had to be closed and a temporary suspension bridge was built beside it to take the traffic.

The purity of Dartmoor streams was such that, while the Burrator Dam was under construction in 1894, a Bill was actually promoted by London County Council to take a supply of water from the Moor, but it was ultimately dropped although considered for a few years more.

The next town to come to Dartmoor was Paignton. (Torquay had already built reservoirs near Hennock, just off the Moor proper). It seems that Teignmouth was also looking in that direction and surveyed a site on the East Webburn above Widecombe, but decided in the end to take a supply from Paignton, which in 1900 obtained powers to construct a dam on the Venford Brook on Holne Moor. This was completed in 1907 and made a thirty-three acre lake. The Act gave the public right of access on about 650 acres of the catchment area involved.

A lull during World War I ended in 1919 with a highly speculative scheme for harnessing streams for hydro-electric and water supplies put forward by Dr J. A. Purves's Dartmoor and District Hydro-Electric Supply Company. When full details were published in the next year it was found that eight reservoirs together with broad leats—canals almost —and various pipelines were contemplated. Power stations were to be built at Skaigh Wood (Belstone), Leigh Bridge (Chagford), New Bridge (Widecombe), Marytavy and Ivybridge, served by reservoirs on the rivers above them. The scheme caused an outcry, partly on aesthetic grounds, partly on the doubtful economics involved, and most of all on the un-desirability of allowing the control of much of the county's water supply to pass into the hands of a company operating for private gain. This last point weighed heavily with local councils, none of whom opposed it on purely amenity grounds. The sponsors eventually dropped the whole idea.

By then proposals were following each other in rapid succession. In 1926 Paignton was having to augment its supply by constructing an in-take with a small reservoir in the Swincombe valley connected to Venford by a pipeline, increasing the yield to three million gallons a day, and in the next year Torquay came to Dartmoor for the first time to build an intake works just below Fernworthy Farm, from where the water was piped direct to the lowest of its Trenchford reservoirs. It was hoped that this extra supply would suffice for twenty years, but the history of water supply is one of underestimation of future consumption, and seven years later it was having to think again.

Thus it came about that Torquay obtained powers in 1934 to construct a dam at Fernworthy to replace the intake. A new road had to be built round the head of the reservoir and certain difficulties, including the onset of World War II, caused delays in completion. Work actually began in 1936, but trouble was experienced with the underlying formation of part of the site, the locally-quarried granite proved unsuitable for the dressed masonry (it was the last granite-faced dam to be built on Dartmoor), and finally a memorable thunderstorm on 4 August 1938 brought about three-and-a-half inches of rain in eight hours—nearer six inches in many surrounding parts—causing an inundation of water and silt which completely flooded the works. Some two million gallons of water had to be drained and 13,500 cubic feet of sand and silt removed before construction could be resumed. The final cost incurred by the time the works had been completed in 1942 was £246,000 against the estimate of £180,000. The lake so formed was seventy-six acres in extent and provided Torquay with about another two-and-a-half million gallons a day.

Just when work was beginning at Fernworthy, Dr Purves reappeared on the scene with another company, South West Utilities Ltd, and a proposal which was in effect inspired by part of his unsuccessful 1919–20 hydro-electric scheme. His company promoted two Bills, one to sell water, the other to build a very large dam and reservoir at Taw Marsh, fed not only by the Taw but also by the Blackaven being diverted into the East Okement and a diversionary tunnel built to the Taw valley. From the reservoir water was to be piped down to what was described as a 7,500kW generating station above Sticklepath, and overhead grid lines were to take the electricity to the West Devon and Exe Valley Electric Companies.

With Dartmoor's name being more frequently mentioned as a possible national park the amenity criticisms were very strong, particularly as no-one had asked for such a scheme. *The Times* urged the Duchy to refuse to sell, and the quoted figure of 7,500kW was challenged as involving 10,000 hp which, with a fall of 520ft, required over 120 million gallons per day—an impossible figure. The twin Bills came up for second reading in the House of Lords in April 1937 and were thrown out there and then.

One of the reasons for their summary rejection was the growing realisation that schemes affecting Dartmoor as a watershed were being put forward in a haphazard and unco-ordinated fashion. This applied to commercial peat-cutting as well as water proposals. At a meeting of the Tamar and Plym Fishery Board early in 1937 a speaker referred to Dartmoor as 'Tom Tiddler's ground', saying that although it was the most important watershed in the south-west anyone could put forward a scheme, whether wanted or not, with little consideration for any interest than that of the promoters. This criticism of piecemeal development was undoubtedly a valid one both then and for some while in the future, and it was partially to meet it that in 1938 the county council itself put forward proposals to construct intakes on the Taw and West Okement to supply North Devon. However, the matter was still in the tentative stage when war broke out and caused it to be shelved.

Post-war developments have been based on a gradual enlargement of fewer water-supplying authorities. The first moves were to set up the North Devon Water Board in 1945 and the South Devon Water Board a few years later, each taking over a few small local undertakings. In the early 1960s there were further amalgamations, Plymouth taking over Plympton's intakes on the Erme, Yealm and Butterbrook, and a new South West Devon Water Board being created from the old South Devon, Torquay and Paignton undertakings. Though leading to less overlapping than before, it can hardly be said that the reorganisation has resulted in fewer schemes for using Dartmoor rivers being advanced.

The North Devon Water Board's Act revived the Devon Council's 1938 proposals, but only the West Okement intake was constructed. Water was piped to new filtration works at Prewley near Sourton and from there distributed over a wide area. Powers for building the Taw intake were not proceeded with as it was discovered that the reliable yield would not be sufficient to make it worth while under the terms laid down.

In south Devon, activity on the part of the new board centred on proposals to build a dam across the Avon above Shipley Bridge. There were already intakes on the Bala Brook and Avon; the former was to be retained and the treatment works were to be extended, but the Avon intake was to be superseded. First mooted in 1948, even before the Board had come into being, an inquiry into the proposed Order was held towards the end of the following year and was something of a curiosity, for the planning authority was never officially informed of the inquiry and took no part in it. When it discovered the position it was too late and the minister gave his approval in 1950. Considerable argument regarding siting and details ensued, partly through efforts being made to minimise the damage to antiquities which abounded in the area, and partly in an unsuccessful attempt to have the dam faced in granite.

Work eventually began in 1954, and 110 acres of common land were taken in for the purpose. A road was constructed beyond the old intake up to Brockhill Foot and a quarry opened up nearby. The dam was con-

Q

structed to allow of its being raised at a later date to increase the yield above the slightly more than two million gallons a day at present obtained.

While the Avon dam was being constructed, the North Devon Water Board applied for powers to sink trial boreholes in Taw Marsh to investigate the possibility of there being an underground 'lake' in the gravels beneath, and after much argument the Dartmoor National Park Committee (created in 1952) consented. The Board pointed out that if water could be found and pumped out from wells it might be unnecessary to build a far more disfiguring dam and reservoir. Boring began in 1957 and some months later the discovery of a 'huge' underground reservoir was announced.

Subsequently the Board introduced a Bill to obtain the necessary powers to put down permanent wells and construct a pumping station which was to be partly underground. The only objectors were the Dartmoor Preservation Association and a few other amenity societies which doubted whether the scheme was as sound as it had been declared to be, and thought that unwarrantable damage to the national park was likely to ensue. Parliament overruled objections and the work began, but later events proved that the societies were not far out in their forecast. The water was found to be radio-active and in Taw Plain an expensive aeration plant had to be built, which emits radon gas. Yield was expected to be at least two, rising to probably three million gallons a day, but experience has shown that under one can be relied on. So far from making another reservoir unnecessary, even before the works had been completed the Board was looking round for a site for one, the position being aggravated by the West Okement intake yield also being rather less than calculated.

The South Devon Water Board meanwhile had obtained a further supply from gravel beds near Totnes weir, but Torquay sought parliamentary powers to divert part of the headwaters of the East Dart and North Teign into Fernworthy reservoir via the old Vitifer mine leat, which conveniently passed across the already utilised South Teign watershed. The proposals aroused great hostility in many quarters on grounds of the damage to the river flows and to amenity in general, and the Select Committee threw the Bill out. Shortly afterwards Torquay joined in with the enlarged South West Devon Water Board.

In 1962 the North Devon Water Board announced that it would need a new reservoir after all for its southern division. Its choice fell upon the West Okement river and, after abandoning its original idea of a dam below Stengator as likely to meet with serious opposition, it chose a site a little way above the Meldon viaduct, further downstream. There was opposition nevertheless; the park committee and amenity societies opposed the whole idea as being highly damaging to the national park. After the minister had given his consent to the trial boreholes to test the underlying rock formation, these were made and proved satisfactory. The planning authority maintained its objection to the scheme and in March 1965 a public inquiry was held in Exeter. Sixteen months later the minister's decision in the Board's favour was announced. The engineering inspector supported the scheme but the planning assessor who sat at the inquiry with him disagreed, saying that more attention should have been paid to the alternative outside the national park at Gorhuish.

The amenity societies then decided to take the matter, as they were entitled to do, to a select committee of both Houses of Parliament (the planning authority was unable to join them due to a technicality) where their petition was eventually heard in mid-1967. The committee decided that it preferred the Gorhuish alternative and that the Meldon site should not be proceeded with unless Gorhuish, after proper investigation, proved impracticable or significantly more expensive. These further investigations, complicated by the belated discovery of arsenic in the soil on part of the Meldon site, went on for more than a year. It was announced in November 1968 that the costs for Gorhuish, according to the Board's and the Ministry's figures, were thirty-seven per cent higher than for Meldon. The protection of the national park presumably not being considered worth that amount of extra money, permission to build the dam at Meldon was finally given. Work on the site began early in 1970.

The utilisation of Dartmoor valleys for water supply continues. Even while the last stages of the Meldon controversy were being fought out a huge new £14 million scheme for damming the Swincombe and flooding Foxtor Plain to satisfy the growing demands of both Plymouth and the South West Devon Water authorities was announced. The Bill laid before Parliament for consideration in 1970 not only proposed a 760-acre reservoir at Swincombe but an enlarged Devonport and Prison leat, together with pipelines and a second reservoir of about 30 acres at Miltoncombe off Dartmoor. It met widespread opposition on amenity grounds.

Afforestation

The planting of trees on open moorland dates from the time of the 'improvers' on Dartmoor. Before then the high, windswept plateau of the Moor had seemed altogether too unsuitable for any attempts to be made, but when Francis Buller took over Prince Hall in 1785 or soon after he realised that trees might be grown not only as a crop but, perhaps more importantly, as shelter belts. The species of trees suitable and available at that date were limited to Scots pine, Norway spruce and the European larch for the softwoods, and oak, beech and sycamore for the hardwoods.

Buller's attempts at afforestation were in the main unsuccessful. He planted about 40,000 trees at Prince Hall, but they largely perished some years later. Bray at Beardown and Tyrwhitt at Tor Royal worked on a smaller scale and were more successful on the whole, but the trees which survived were hardly more than mere shelter.

Tyrwhitt did not lose sight of the possibilities, though he was unable to carry them into effect. In his railway prospectus of 1818–19, under the heading of Planting, he says: 'In the progress of colonisation the formation of plantations will become essentially requisite, as much for the sake of rural embellishment, as to protect the newly inclosed grounds and buildings,' though he warns that no immediate returns could be expected except to nurserymen. Henry Tanner in 1854 envisaged afforestation of no less than 50,000 acres of open Dartmoor interspersed amongst the reclaimed land, but he entirely misjudged the effect of climate, believing that the improvement of Dartmoor would itself lead to improved climatic conditions.

Some planting was being carried out by landowners around the edge of the Moor in the earlier part of the nineteenth century to replace or to augment supplies used for shipbuilding during the Napoleonic Wars. It seems that areas such as Bagtor Woods in Ilsington derive from then, as certainly did one of the largest schemes of all, the purchase of Ausewell Common in Ashburton and the planting of trees, including larch and fir, there and in Buckland, on what was for that time a very large scale— for which patriotic act the owner, Col Bastard, received the thanks of Parliament.

Nothing further appears to have been done until 1862 when the Duchy bailiff, Mr Charles Barrington, went to live at Brimpts and planted another 40,000 trees, including many conifers. Most of these, softwoods and oaks, were felled during World War I, largely by Portuguese labour, the logs being sent to Princetown station by an overhead ropeway suspended from rickety lattice towers. Shelter belts were also made in various places in the 1860s and 1870s, notably at Grendon, across Cator Common, and at Princetown by convict labour, though the belt known as Long Plantation does not seem to have been formed until a little later.

It was not until 1919 that developments took a significant turn. The war had brought home to the country how dependent it was on overseas softwood supplies, and because of the shortage of shipping the available home timber resources had been nearly exhausted. The government of the day determined not only to make good the loss but to increase the acreage planted, and to that end created the Forestry Commission and gave it a target of 1,700,000 acres by 1980, a figure which was calculated to represent three years' strategic reserve.

The effect on Dartmoor was immediate. The Prince of Wales, advised by the Commission, decided to plant 5,000 acres of open moorland, partly to replenish the country's woodland and partly to give impetus to local employment. He began operations at Fernworthy (purchased in 1917) where the farm was abandoned, with smaller plantations at Frenchbeer above Chagford and at Beardown; Brimpts was replanted from 1921–2. Sitka spruce was the chief species used in these early days, with some Douglas fir. By 1930 Fernworthy plantation had extended to more than 800 acres on either side of the South Teign.

In this year, however, all the planted areas came under Forestry Commission management, together with a new area at Bellever and Laughter Hole of 1,350 acres, making a new Commission holding of some 3,100 acres, of which about 1,200 were already planted. Up to then there had not been much public comment on the afforestation, but with the prospect of a big increase of conifers on the Moor in the Bellever-Laughter Hole newtakes and on much of the remainder of Fernworthy, considerable disquiet began to be expressed.

The criticisms arose on several grounds. First, it had not been forgotten that the newtakes had originally been for the most part unlawful inclosure, and if they were planted up the last right of the public, implied if not legally defined, to walk across them would be lost. Then it was felt that, as some of the trees were not doing well, the newtakes would in any case be of more value as rough grazing. There was the question, too, of the changed appearance of substantial tracts of the Moor and the over-planting of antiquities, for it unfortunately happened that at both Bellever and Fernworthy there were a number of substantial remains, including fine stone rows and a stone circle. Though these could be preserved, there could be no argument that they lost much of their impressiveness when deprived of their age-old natural setting. All these points were put forward strongly in order to minimise new developments, but with little effect; the public advantage was held to lie in more planting.

The Council for the Preservation of Rural England was in consultation with the Commission as to how some of the effects on the landscape might be mitigated in certain cases; and in 1932 the Commission informed it that there was no intention to plant on Bellever Tor and the surrounding land, though the first area south-west of the farm was already under trees. A few years later there was a change of policy and the slopes of the tor were in fact planted, with a strip being left along the top of Lakehead Hill. Work continued in the area up to 1943.

Another authority began afforestation soon after World War I. Plymouth Corporation had acquired its Meavy catchment during the war and all farms were abandoned. It was natural that it should turn to forestry when the need was drawn to its attention. Accordingly it started planting in 1921, at first in the old fields surrounding the Burrator reservoir and later up on some of the newtakes above. Today there are some 700 acres of softwoods still owned by the Corporation.

World War II brought a fresh reappraisal of the forestry programme. In 1943 the target area for the country as a whole was raised to no less than five million acres of which three million were to be new afforestation, the whole to be achieved in fifty years. Such an increase was bound to affect Dartmoor, and so it came about that the Duchy leased their Soussons Farm with its land to the Commission in 1945. In the next few years another 550 acres were fenced, deep-ploughed and planted, the whole of Soussons Down being covered. One near casualty here was the only stand of Dorset Heath on the Moor, which had been planted over before anyone had realised it, but which was rescued by the trees on it being removed.

Work at Soussons was completed by 1949. Apart from necessary replanting, other areas affected in the immediate post-war period were Fernworthy, where the planting of the higher parts above roughly the 1,500ft contour was completed in 1951, mainly with Sitka spruce; and Beardown, which was enlarged northwards in 1949–50 to just over 100 acres. The ten houses built at Bellever for forestry workers date from about this time.

The passing of the 1949 National Parks Act, and Dartmoor's designation in 1951 as such a park, had a considerable effect. The Act specified that agriculture and afforestation were normal pursuits within these areas and would not be susceptible to planning procedures. Nevertheless the local planning authority and the Forestry Commission had an agreement that proposals emanating from the latter would be the subject of consultation when they lay within the national park. Under this procedure plans to afforest Cuckoo Ball and about 150 acres of Haytor Down were dropped.

Of recent years the emphasis has shifted to private forestry. Apart from the felling of hardwoods and their replacement with the commercially much more attractive conifers, there was much talk of planting large areas of open moorland—figures of up to 30,000 acres were even mentioned. The rise of private forestry came about not merely through the desire to increase the country's production of timber, but through government encouragement in the form of grants and tax concessions, which had the effect of tempting into woodland ownership those who wished to arrange their affairs so as to attract the least taxation.

The result of this and its possible future consequences on the national park's appearance could not be overlooked. There was much public agitation from the late 1950s for some sort of planning control. Clearly, it was argued, the 1949 Act had not envisaged forestry on the scale now contemplated which would change the character of Dartmoor, since it specifically stated that the typical landscape should be preserved. Eventually it was decided that the planning authority and forestry interests, each in consultation with certain other bodies, should come to an agreement on the preparation of a map showing open land on the Moor divided into three degrees of acceptability or otherwise for afforestation, to serve as a guide for future demands. As a result, some further planting of open moorland seems inevitable in the future.

Military Training

It would not be far wrong to say that the modern use of Dartmoor as a training ground for troops dates from 1873. It had, it is true, been used long before then; occasional exercises were held during both the Napoleonic and Crimean Wars, and there was an encampment on Harford Moor and Ugborough Moor in 1861. All these were sporadic and small-scale affairs, but the autumn manoeuvres of 1873 were on a quite different scale and, moreover, led to other developments.

The army's mobility had been greatly increased through the growing network of railways, and the possibility of using a West Country venue for manoeuvres was being considered many months in advance of their proposed date. In January 1873 the town clerk of Okehampton was instructed to write to the War Office suggesting northern Dartmoor as a suitable site. He received the reply that its advantages would receive due consideration, but in the end a different site was chosen, first the Hameldon area and then, probably because of supply difficulties that would have arisen, the south-west of the Moor.

Over 12,000 men and 2,100 horses came by rail to Exeter in August and marched across the Moor to Yennadon, Ringmoor and Roborough Downs. Unfortunately the weather broke and the exercises had to be curtailed after many days of rain and mist, with troops floundering in bog and water.

The eyes of some senior officers must, however, have been opened to the possibilities of using Dartmoor, with its very large uninhabited spaces, for artillery practice, which up till then had usually been carried out in conditions far removed from those met with on active service. The War Office agreed to a search being made for a new range, and in June 1875 Dartmoor was visited. The Duchy was as anxious as ever that these barren acres should be exploited in some way. It was ready to grant licences or leases for such projects as the commercial utilisation of peat; the idea of wholesale enclosure and reclamation for agricultural purposes had had to be abandoned, so that when they were approached about this new project they readily agreed to it. After the eastern part of the Moor had been examined the visiting committee, mindful of the town clerk's letter of two years earlier, came to Okehampton and at once chose it 'in view of the camping ground in the park, good water supply, and the Moor forming part of the Duchy, and being in every way suitable as a practice range.' By the beginning of August the first camp was set up in Okehampton Park with nine-pounder and sixteen-pounder guns firing over about 3,000 acres between the East Okement and Taw rivers.

It seems that next year there was no camp, but from 1877 it became an annual affair, lasting usually about six weeks in the earlier years but gradually lengthening in duration. Soon the War Office was renting eighty acres of the park to build a permanent camp, and by 1895 had acquired a licence from the Duchy to use the whole of the north quarter of the Forest as a range and danger zone. Firing took place on any day of the week from May until September, flags being hoisted near the camp and on Yes Tor to warn the public when it was in progress.

Though the traders of Okehampton were highly delighted with the arrangements, the commoners whose beasts had to be driven off the ranges felt they should be entitled to compensation. A committee was formed in 1881 to deal with the authorities, who in the following year made a formal agreement. A lump sum of £50 was made available for the committee to distribute as it thought fit, with an annual payment of £10, later rising to £25 and increasing again in 1895. The Okehampton commoners kept the whole sum, much to the annoyance of those of Bridestowe, Sourton and Belstone, whose rights were also affected. Arguments on the subject continued for many years.

The public expressed some unease at the spread of the firing range, partly due to the very inadequate warning arrangements of those days. Their apprehensions were increased when in 1900, during the South African War and after several years of trying, the War Office acquired Willsworthy manor from the Calmady-Hamlyn family to make a 3,200-

acre rifle and field-firing range over a part of the commons which included the famous Tavy Cleave.

Even more startling was the introduction in 1901 of the Military Manoeuvres Bill, with sweeping powers. Under it the military authorities could have taken over compulsorily the whole of an area such as Dartmoor for twenty days in a year for manoeuvres and artillery practice. No access to the area, even to occupiers, would generally have been permitted and only a fortnight's notice, with no opportunity for discussion, was required. The country was altogether unprepared to sanction such an authoritarian measure and after much opposition, including local outspokenness, the Bill was dropped.

An account of military training would be incomplete without mention of the volunteer camps held on Haytor Down between 1884 and the early years of this century, when for a few weeks various battalions of the Devonshire Regiment and occasionally the Duke of Cornwall's Light Infantry exercised and had rifle practice in the area. Over 3,000 men were under canvas at the same time in the later years; their activities were a source of much local interest, particularly on Sunday afternoons when many visitors made their way to the camps.

By 1900, therefore, the pattern was set of military occupations of parts of Dartmoor that was basically to remain unchanged for almost forty years. Changes took place within the areas; on the Okehampton range the few green tracks made by the peat-cutters of old were gradually increased and given better surfaces of macadam to facilitate the movement of guns, notably in 1906–7 when nearly seven miles of new tracks were made; and at Willsworthy the destruction of tumuli on White Hill led to the Secretary of State ordering the erection of cautionary notices. World War I led, if anything, to a diminution of the use of the ranges, but the military returned as before on its conclusion, the guns used now being mainly eighteen-pounders with a range of about 9,000yds. Mechanical transport had superseded horses, so that the tracks were still further improved.

Apart from a scare in 1935 that a tank exercise was to take place, matters proceeded comparatively uneventfully until 1938, when the War Department sought to increase the danger zone at Willsworthy by the acquisition of over 550 acres (originally said to be 450) on Doe Tor Common. The demand was hotly contested by Lydford parish and had not been resolved when war broke out again in 1939.

At once everything was changed. By agreement or under the defence regulations most of the Moor north and west of the Tavistock–Two Bridges–Moretonhampstead road was used as a firing range; another rifle

range was made on the flank of Rippon Tor; much of the south-eastern
sector of the Moor, known loosely as Scorriton, became an area for training with rifles, machine-guns and anti-tank weapons; an airfield on
Roborough Down and a hutted camp at Plaster Down were built; Penn
Moor and Ringmoor Down were used for further training. Finally, an
area around Haytor and Houndtor was set aside towards the end of the
war to train troops for service in the Far East. With all this activity it
was inevitable that damage to antiquities would occur, and there were
some regrettable casualties. Yet with local vigilance (here that noted antiquary Richard Hansford Worth played an invaluable part) and co-operation from senior officers, the losses were fewer than might have been
expected.

For some while after hostilities ceased, so far as the services' intentions
were concerned, all was uncertainty and confusion. Promises had been
made that areas taken during the war would be released, but there was
little sign that they were even being cleared of dangerous missiles. As it
was known that Dartmoor would fairly soon become a national park,
and in any case much of it was dangerous for depasturing stock, local
feeling began to run very high and was given point in a protest meeting
in November 1946 attended by almost every local authority and other
interested organisations. Some days later the military requirements were
announced by the Government. They amounted to rather over 70,000
acres, from 52,000 of which the public was to be permanently excluded.

The question of range acreages at that period is most confusing, with
public announcements often conflicting with each other, but the following
gives an approximation:

Okehampton	20,000 acres
Willsworthy	4,000 acres
Merrivale etc	19,000 acres
Ringmoor, Penn Moor etc	17,000 acres
Scorriton	11,000 acres
Rippon Tor, Plaster Down etc.	1,000 acres
	72,000 acres

The widespread outcry which greeted the announcement caused second
thoughts. By the time the Government had conceded the necessity for the
public inquiry which was held in July 1947, demands had been reduced
to about 43,000 acres. The inquiry was much criticised as being held
at less than three weeks' notice with insufficient detail released in
advance, while the county council had come to an agreement beforehand

with the service authorities and did not oppose their demands. The minister's decision reduced the acreage to about 33,000, but this was exclusive of the 5,000-acre Ringmoor–Roborough Down and the 830-acre Rippon Tor range areas. The former was the subject of another inquiry in 1952. The public were to be excluded from the ranges only when firing was in progress.

Subsequently there were several small reductions and one larger one, the latter being the release of the 4,200-acre Merrivale East non-firing area, where in fact training occasionally carried out was little different from that carried out on other parts of the Moor outside the actual training areas. Following a fatal accident at Cranmere Pool in 1958, the warning system was revised and, in order to simplify the marking of the boundaries of the four separate ranges (Okehampton, Merrivale, Willsworthy and Rippon Tor) on the ground, further adjustments were made to the lines on the map so that the acreage inside the ranges is now less than that actually held for the purpose.

In recent years the type of training carried out has altered. The old roads have in part been given tarmac surfaces, there has been much more cross-country driving, making ruts on the moorland, and a new dimension has been added with the ever-increasing use of the helicopter. For a national park this has presented a sore problem which can only be solved at the highest level. Having maintained steadfast opposition to the type and frequency of military training carried out all the year round, amenity bodies headed by the Dartmoor Preservation Association petitioned the Duchy of Cornwall at the end of 1968 not to renew licences to use the Moor for damaging forms of training after their expiry in 1970. They recorded their belief that such a use was not compatible with Dartmoor's status as a national park and was gradually destroying its wild character. The Ministry of Defence demanded a twenty-one-year renewal of the licence, but in the end the Duchy would only agree to one of seven years.

Dartmoor cannot indefinitely continue to be exploited for purposes of agriculture, forestry, water supply, military training and so on and still retain its character as a national park, with the overtones of landscape protection which that implies. But the nation has not yet made its choice.

Notes to this chapter are on pages 298–299.

APPENDIX

The Forest Boundary

John Somers Cocks

THE EARLIEST record of the Forest bounds is contained in the perambulation of 1240 on the granting of the Forest to Richard, Earl of Cornwall. It lay wholly within the parish of Lydford because it was appurtenant to that manor, and its bounds may, with only one or two slight uncertainties, be identified today. No further full record exists until 1608 when minor differences were noted. Other surveys were made in later years.

In spite of these records considerable confusion has arisen, for it will be seen that the old bounds do not in all cases mark the present boundary of Lydford and that Duchy maps of the nineteenth century do not always agree either with the old bounds or the modern parish. Attempts have been made in the past to identify the boundary marks, but these have usually taken the Duchy maps as a basis and have endeavoured to fit the old names along a line of sometimes very doubtful authenticity. A fresh attempt at identification is made here, accounting for discrepancies so far as is possible.

The following is the return of the 1240 perambulation, the Close Roll copy being given (in translation), with alternative spellings in variant copies noted in brackets:

> . . . The hill of Cossdonne and thence in line to a little hill which is called Little Hundetorre, and thence in line to Thurlestone, and thence in line to Wotesbrokelakesfote where it falls into the Tyng, and thence in line to Heighestone (Hengheston), and thence in line to Langestone (Yessetone), and thence in line through the middle of the turbary of Alberysheved (Aberesheved), and so along the Wallebroke, and thence in line to Furnum Regis, and thence in line to Wallebrokeshede, and so along the Wallebroke to where it falls into the Dert, and so by the Dert to the other Dert, and so by the other Dert going up to Okesbrokysfote, and so going up the Okebroke as far as la Dryeworke, and so going up to the Dryfeld ford, and so thence in line to Battyshull (Cattyshill, Gnattishull), and thence in line to the head of Wester Wellabroke, and thus by the Wester Wellabroke to where it falls into the Aven, and so in line to Ester Whyteburghe, and thence in line to la Redelake (Rodelake) where it falls into the Erme, and thence in line to Grymsgrove, and thence in line to Elysburghe, and so in line to Syward's Cross, and thence

to Ysfother, and so through the other Ysfother, and thence through the middle of Mystor (Mistmore) to Mewyburghe, and thence to Lullingesfote (Hullingssete), and thence to Rakernesbrokysfote, and so to the head of that stream, and from there to la Westsolle, and thence in line to Ernestorre, and thence in line to the next ford east of the chapel of St Michael of Halgestoke, and thence in line to the said hill of Cossdonne in the east part . . .

In commenting on the above it is necessary to refer also to the return made by the jurors at a court of survey held at Okehampton in 1608; in many cases they related the 1240 bounds to the names existing in their day. From Cosdon they said the line went 'one mile or more' eastward to Little Hound Tor. The direction here should in fact have been southward, but in any case it has naturally been presumed that the present Little Hound Tor at just over a mile from Cosdon (the Cawsand rendering is a nineteenth-century mapmaker's error) is the hill in question, though the jurors' estimate of three-quarters of a mile to the next point, Thirlestone, would then be a serious underestimate of the actual distance of just less than two. It was probably this mileage discrepancy, coupled with the nineteenth-century Duchy maps' identification of Wotesbrokelake with the Teign Wallabrook, which caused so much confusion to those such as Whale, Prowse and other writers of the last hundred years.

Recent research has revealed that, contrary to expectation, the old parva hundetorre is the Hound Tor of modern maps and that the modern Little Hound Tor is a fake. Its name until 1834 was usually White Hill, but in that year the renter of the north quarter of the Forest realised that if he could make people believe that it was the Little Hound Tor of old he would have more grazing. In spite of local derision he brought stones up to make a tor of it, as it unfortunately had no natural rocky outcrops. This almost unbelievable story is told in one of the proofs of evidence taken to determine the true Lydford boundary at the time of the tithe apportionment survey in 1842. It at once makes the distance between Hound Tor and Thirlestone more credible as being rather over one mile.

Of the next point, Thurlestone, there can be no doubt. The 1608 jurors supposed it to be Waterdontorr, the modern Watern Tor, and to this day one part of the tor, forming a kind of arch, is known as Thirlestone, the 'thirled' or pierced stone. This identification is supported by other surveys since 1608, as is the next point, Wotesbrokelake, with the Woodlake, the stream which comes down to the North Teign from Manga Hill. The jurors and modern opinion concur on this. The Wallabrook theory can-

not be supported on either etymological or historical grounds; it seems
to be nothing more than the guess of a Duchy mapmaker going back
not more than about 150 years.

The Heighestone, alias Hengheston, of 1240 is the Hingeston or High-
stone of 1608, the well-known bondmark of Longstone on modern maps,
while the next mark was Langestone (Yessetone) in 1240 and Yeston or
Geston 'now commonlie called Hethstone' in the later survey. It seems
clear that there were once two longstones on either side of the South
Teign, whose names became mixed up. The present Heathstone, near the
road entrance to Fernworthy plantations, is not a longstone, though it
may conceivably have lost its top. In *Britannia Depicta or Ogilby Im-
prov'd* of 1720, John Owen shows the Heath Stone beside the Chagford
to Tavistock track further up the hill, but no other evidence seems to
support that position. There is a small marker stone near the top of
Assycombe Hill, but it is not a longstone.

The turbary at Albery Head was the 'fenny place called Turfehill'
in 1608 and is Metheral Marsh today, whence the line went to the easily
identified King's Oven. However, the 1240 bounds give an intermediate
direction when they suddenly record 'and so along the Wallebroke'
though they have not previously brought one to a river and fail to
record where one should leave it, merely making one arrive at the water-
less King's Oven. The entry is an obvious error in transcription, the
identical Latin words occurring a little further on. Yet the os maps give
the headwaters of what just lower down they call the Bovey as being the
North Walla Brook, presumably on the strength of this meaningless in-
terpolation.

From the (genuine) Walla Brook down to the East Dart, to Dartmeet,
up the West Dart and the O Brook, formerly the Okebroke, the line is
clear. It left the O Brook at Drywork, the old tin-streaming works where
the Drylake joins, and ran up to Dryfield, alias Crefield Ford, presumably where the Sandy Way crosses it just south of Wellaby Gulf. Battys-
hull or Gnattishull was in 1608 identified with Knattleborough, the present-
day Ryders Hill with its summit cairn, whence the boundary went down
the Western Wellabrook to the Avon.

In 1240 the next bound is Eastern Whitebarrow, and, although a
survey of 1344 seems to infer that Western Whitebarrow was the southernmost point of the Forest, Eastern is repeated in 1608. There seems to
have been some variation later, and the parish boundary is now drawn
to Western. There does not seem to be much doubt that historically the
lower but more conspicuous Eastern Whitebarrow is correct and that an
encroachment has been made at the expense of the Forest. At all events

Redlake Foot is not in question, and the jurors must have been correct in saying that the now vanished Grymsgrove was in the hollow by Erme Head.

In the perambulation the bounds went next in line to Elysburghe, crossing the Plym close to where a small stream comes in from the west. Yet in 1608 an intermediate point right off the line was put in when it was taken next to 'Plimheadd' and from there to Elisborough, the modern Eylesbarrow, partly agreeing with the present Lydford boundary but being irreconcilable with the 1240 one. Isabella de Fortibus's charter of 1291 supports the latter route. Her boundary in these parts ran from Eylesbarrow to Plymcrundla, which was almost certainly the tin workings (crundel seems to have a quarrying significance in place-names) by where this little stream joins the Plym just south of Plym Ford, and so down the river. Plym Head is not mentioned. Clearly there has been another adjustment here over the centuries.

The western boundary presents few difficulties. It ran to Syward's or Nuns' Cross, to South and North Hessary Tors (Ysfother in 1240) and, in 1608, 'through the midst of Mistorr moore to a rocke called Mistorpann,' presumably Great Mis Tor, through Mistor Pan is now the name given to a rock basin on the tor. A little surprisingly the jurors identified Mewyburghe with Deadlake Head, as White Barrow would seem a more likely choice. Lullingesfote or Hullingssete they held, probably correctly, to be Luntesborowe or Limsboro' on Lynch Tor, and then put in an extra bound, Wester Redlake, taking the line a little further into the Forest before going from the foot to the head of the Rattlebrook or Rakernesbroke.

Westsolle is probably Steinegtorr or Stenga Tor, whence in 1240 the boundary went straight to Ernestorre. This may then have been the name given to the whole ridge which has Yes Tor at its northern and High Willhays at its southern end. But Ernestorre ('Eagle's Hill') lingers on as Yes Tor, and is likely to have been the point to which the line was taken. In 1608 the jurors put in the extra bound of Sandy Ford, the place where the steep-sided valley is crossed, but omitted any reference to Ernestorre, going straight on to the ford east of Halstock Chapel, now called Cullever Steps, in which it agrees almost exactly with the present Lydford boundary. The 1240 boundary, however, ran fairly close to West Mill and Row Tors, as claimed by the Duchy today and as confirmed by a survey of Okehampton Park made in 1532–3. It appears to be the more correct of the two—indeed the sudden vagueness of the 1608 jurors, probably mostly drawn from the Okehampton neighbourhood, leads one to suspect that they deliberately swore to an imprecise line in order to increase their grazing at the Duchy's expense, for only one farm in Oke-hampton (Halstock) had venville rights in the Forest.

Finally, all accounts agree that from Cullever Steps the boundary ran straight back to the summit of Cosdon, and no evidence has so far been discovered to show why the Lydford parish boundary now goes via Smallbrook Foot on the Taw to White Moor Stone, leaving out Cosdon altogether. It appears to have no historical basis at all. The Duchy claims that the northern cairn is the correct point, but had it been other than the summit it would surely have been specified. Moreover, Irishman's Wall, an attempt to enclose the Forest against Belstone Common, is exactly on the line between Cullever Steps and the summit.

From the above it will be seen that the significant discrepancies, with the exception of Plym Head, lie between the West Okement and South Teign. Between the Okement and Cosdon the modern boundary is not the historical one according to the available evidence, and the Duchy line is very nearly correct. But from Hound Tor onwards the modern line is almost exactly the historical one, the discrepancies on the Duchy map being introduced hardly more than 150 years ago. Surveys, evidence in tithe suites and even a seventeenth-century Gidleigh perambulation agree in almost every particular. Proofs of evidence taken in 1842 tell of how boundaries could be tinkered with by bondstones being defaced or built into walls, and new ones being erected on lines having no historical basis. No large-scale maps of the Forest could be made much before 1800 owing to the huge size of the area to be surveyed, and when they were made the surveyors sometimes had difficulty in relating old names to physical features. In these circumstances the records of earlier centuries are a surer guide than modern maps.

Notes to this appendix are on page 299.

Notes, References and Sources

CHAPTER 1

(Pages 21–52)

The Physical Environment of Dartmoor: Denys Brunsden and John Gerrard

(*a*) Geology, landscape history and vegetation

THE Memoirs of the Geological Survey, describing the one-inch sheets, No 325, *Exeter* (1902); No 338, *Dartmoor* (1912); No 349, *Ivybridge and Modbury* (1912); No 355, *Kingsbridge and Salcombe* (1904); No 339, *Newton Abbot* (1912); No 348, *Plymouth and Liskeard* (1907); No 337, *Tavistock and Launceston* (1911); No 350, *Torquay* (1903 and 1933), are very useful summaries of the older literature. Modern work is included in I. G. Simmons (ed), *Dartmoor Essays*, Devonshire Association (1964), and in K. F. G. Hosking and G. J. Shrimpton (eds), *Present Views on Some Aspects of the Geology of Cornwall and Devon*, Truro (1964). An alternative view on the history of the landscape (pp 26–9) can be found in *Exeter and its Region*, British Association for the Advancement of Science (1969)

Albers, G. 'Notes on tors and the clitter of Dartmoor', *Trans Devon Assoc*, 62 (1930), pp 373–8

Archibald, J. F. 'Wistman's Wood Forest Nature Reserve, Devon', unpublished report to the Nature Conservancy (1966)

Bate, C. S. 'On the clitter of the tors of Dartmoor', *Trans Devon Assoc*, 4 (1871), pp 517–19

Blyth, F. G. H. 'The Lustleigh fault in North East Dartmoor', *Geol Mag*, 94 (1957), pp 291–96

Brammall, A. and Harwood, H. F. 'The Dartmoor Granite : its mineralogy, structure and petrology', *Min Mag*, 20 (1923), pp 39–53

Brammall, A. 'The Dartmoor Granite', *Proc Geol Assoc London*, 37 (1926), pp 251–77

Brammall, A. 'The Dartmoor Granites : their genetic relationships', *Quart Journ Geol Soc London*, 88 (1932), pp 171–237

Brunsden, D. 'The denudation chronology of the River Dart', *Trans Inst Brit Geogr*, 32 (1963), pp 49–63

Brunsden, D., Kidson, C., Orme, A. R., and Waters, R. S. 'Denudation chronology of parts of south western England', *Field Studies*, 2, No 1 (1964), pp 115–32

Brunsden, D. 'The origin of decomposed granite on Dartmoor', in *Dartmoor Essays*, ed I. G. Simmons (1964), pp 97– 116

Brunsden, D. *Dartmoor:* British Landscapes through maps series. Geographical Association (1968)

Butcher, N. E. 'Age of the orogeny and granites in south-west England', *Nature,* 190 (1961), p 253

Chandler, M. E. 'The Oligocene flora of the Bovey Tracey Lake Basin, Devonshire', *Bull Brit Mus (Nat Hist),* 3 (1957), pp 73–123

Clayden, A. W. *The History of Devonshire Scenery,* Exeter (1906)

Clayden, B. and Manley, D. J. R. 'The soils of the Dartmoor Granite', in *Dartmoor Essays,* ed I. G. Simmons (1964), pp 117–140

Dearman, W. R. *Dartmoor: the North-west Margin and other selected areas,* Geol Assoc Guides, No 33 (1962)

De la Beche, N. T. *Report on the Geology of Cornwall, Devon and West Somerset,* Mem Geol Surv, 28, HMSO, London (1839)

Dewey, H. *South-west England,* Brit Reg Geol, 2nd ed, HMSO, London (1948)

Dines, H. G. *The Metalliferous Mining Region of South-west England,* Mem Geol Surv, HMSO, London (1956)

Green, J. F. N., 'The terraces of southernmost England', *Quart Journ Geol Soc,* 92 (1936), pp 58–88

Green, J. F. N. 'The high platforms of East Devon', *Proc Geol Assoc,* 52 (1951), pp 36–52

Green, J. F. N. 'The history of the River Dart', *Proc Geol Soc,* 60 (1949), pp 105–24

Greenslade, P. J. M. 'A note on Wistman's Wood, Dartmoor', *Proc Bot Soc Brit Isles,* 7, pt 2 (1968), pp 159–63

Groves, A. W. 'The unroofing of the Dartmoor Granite—the distribution of its detritus in the sediments of southern England', *Quart Journ Geol Soc,* 87 (1931), pp 62–96

Harvey, L. A. and St Leger-Gordon, D. *Dartmoor,* New Naturalist Series, London (1953)

HMSO, *The New Forests of Dartmoor,* Forestry Comm Booklet, No 10, London (1967)

Jones, T. R. 'Notes on some granite tors', *Geologist,* 2 (1859), pp 311–12

Jukes-Browne, A. J. 'The valley of the Teign', *Quart Journ Geol Soc,* 62 (1904), pp 319–34

Linton, D. L. 'The problem of tors', *Geogr Journ,* 121 (1955), pp 470–87

Orme, A. R. 'The geomorphology of southern Dartmoor', in *Dartmoor Essays,* ed I. G. Simmons (1964), pp 31–72

Palmer, J. and Neilson, R. A. 'The origin of granite tors on Dartmoor, Devonshire', *Proc Yorks Geol Soc,* 33, pt 3, No 15 (1962), pp 315–40

Pickard, R. 'Glaciation on Dartmoor', *Trans Devon Assoc,* 75 (1943), pp 25–52

Simmons, I. G. (ed). *Dartmoor Essays,* Devonshire Association (1964)

Te Punga, M. T. 'Altiplanation terraces in southern England', *Biul Peryglacjalny,* 4 (1956), pp 331–8

Waters, R. S. 'Pseudo-bedding in the Dartmoor Granite', *Trans Roy Geol Soc Cornwall,* 18 (1954), pp 456–62

Waters, R. S. 'Aits and breaks of slope on Dartmoor streams', *Geography*, 38 (1954), pp 67–76

Waters, R. S. 'Differential weathering and erosion on Oldlands', *Geogr Journ*, 123, pt 4 (1957), pp 503–13

Waters, R. S. 'Erosion surfaces on Dartmoor and adjacent areas', *Trans Roy Geol Soc Cornwall, Proc, 2nd Conf* (1960), pp 28–9

Waters, R. S. 'Involutions and Ice wedges in Devon', *Nature*, 189 (1961), pp 389–90

Waters, R. S. 'Altiplanation terraces and slope development in Vest-Spitsbergen and south-west England', *Biul Peryglacjalny*, 11 (1962), pp 89–101

Waters, R. S. 'The Pleistocene legacy to the geomorphology of Dartmoor', in *Dartmoor Essays*, ed I. G. Simmons (1964), pp 39–57

Waters, R. S. 'The geomorphological significance of Pleistocene frost action in south-west England', in *Essays for A. Austin Miller*, ed J. B. Whittow and P. D. Wood, University of Reading (1965), pp 39–57

Wooldridge, S. W. 'The Upland Plains of Britain', *Adv Science*, 7, No 26 (1950), pp 162–75

Wooldridge, S. W. 'The physique of the South West', *Geography*, 39 (1954), pp 231–61

(*b*) Flora and fauna

Archer-Lock, A. and Slade, L. W. (1968). 'The Birds of High Dartmoor', *Devon Birds* (Magazine of the Devon Bird Watching and Preservation Society), 21, No 4, Nov 1968, pp 62–64

Bellamy, J. C. (1839). *Natural History of South Devon*

Devon Bird Watching and Preservation Society. Annual Reports

Dare, P. J. and Hamilton, L. I. (1968). 'Birds of the Postbridge Area, Dartmoor'. *Devon Birds*, 21, No 2, pp 22–31; 21, No 4, pp 64–78

St Leger-Gordon, D. (1950). *Devonshire*, County Book Series, R. Hale. Chapters on 'Plant life of the Moorland' and 'Birds of Moor and Woodland'

Harris, G. T. (1938). 'An Ecological Reconnaissance of Dartmoor'. *Transactions of the Devonshire Association*, 70, pp 37–55

Harvey, L. A. and St Leger-Gordon, D. (1953). *Dartmoor*, New Naturalist Series, Collins, London (1953). Has chapters outlining the flora and fauna of different habitat on Dartmoor

Johns, E. (1957). The surveying and mapping of Vegetation on some Dartmoor pastures. Geographical Studies, 4, No 2, pp 129–137

Martin, W. Keble and Fraser, G. T. (1939). *Flora of Devon*, Arbroath (1939)

Mathew and D'Urban (1892). *Birds of Devon*

Moore, R. (1969). *Birds of Devon*, David & Charles (1969)

National Parks Guide. (1957). *Dartmoor*. Chapter on natural history

Simmons, I. G. (1962). 'An outline of the vegetational history of Dartmoor'. *Transactions of Devonshire Association*, 94, pp 555–574

Simmons, I. G. (1963). 'The Blanket Bog of Dartmoor'. *Transactions of the Devonshire Association*, 95, pp 180–196

Simmons, I. G. 'Pollen diagrams from Dartmoor', *New Phytol*, 63, pt 2 (1964), pp 165–80

Simmons, I. G. 'The Dartmoor oak copses : observations and speculations',
   Field Studies, 2 (1965), pp 225–35
Tansley, A. G. (1949). *Britain's Green Mantle*, London (1949). Scattered
   references to the oak woods and vegetation of the Moor.
Worth, R. W. (1967). Worth's *Dartmoor*, David & Charles (1967)
Worth, R. W. (1930). 'Vegetation of Dartmoor', pp 55–66 in *Physical
   Geography of Dartmoor. Transactions of the Devonshire Association*. 62,
   pp 49–115
Worth, R. W. and Christie, M. (1922). 'The ancient Dwarfed Oak Woods of
   Dartmoor'. *Transactions of Devonshire Association*, 54, pp 291–342

CHAPTER 2

(Pages 55–75)

Early Men: James Barber

1   Bray, Mrs. *A Description of the Part of Devonshire Bordering on the
    Tamar and Tavy*, 1 (1836), p 55

2   Brailsford, J. W. 'Bronze Age Stone Monuments of Dartmoor',
    Antiquity, 12 (1938), p 457

3   Hooker, John. *Synopsis Chonographical of Devonshire* (c 1599). Quoted
    by Blake, W. J. *Transactions of the Devonshire Association*, 47 (1915),
    p 345

4   Gough, R. (Ed) *Britannia* by William Camden, 1 (1789), map opposite
    p 25. Examples of early references to Spinsters' Rock are Chapple,
    William. *Description and Exegesis of the Drewsteignton Cromlech* (c
    1779), quoted in J. Brooking Rowe's edition of Samuel Rowe's
    Perambulation of . . . Dartmoor (1896), pp 42, 111, 115; Polwhele,
    Rev R. *History of Devonshire*, 1 (1797), pp 140, 153–4; and, with
    illustration, Lysons, Rev D. *Magna Britannia*, 6 (1822), pp cccvii–cccviii

5   Bray, Mrs. *A Description . . .*, 1, pp 62, 90, 153

6   Polwhele, Rev R. *History of Devonshire*, 1 (1797), p 192, first footnote

7   Bray, Mrs. *A Description . . .*, 1, p 393. There is much of archaeological
    interest in this volume, derived in part by Mrs Bray from her hus-
    band's journal which recorded fieldwork on Dartmoor beginning in
    1801

8   Polwhele, Rev R. *History of Devonshire*, 1, pp 140, 151

9   Lysons, Rev D. *Magna Britannia*, 6, p cccvi

10 *Transactions of the Plymouth Institution*, 1 (1830), pp 179–212

11 Rowe, Samuel. *A Perambulation of the Antient and Royal Forest of
    Dartmoor* (1846); revised edition Rowe, J. Brooking (1896)

12 'First Report of the Dartmoor Exploration Committee', *Transactions
    of the Devonshire Association*, 26 (1894), p 101

13 *Dartmoor Pictorial Records*, 4 vols (1890–94)

14 Now Plymouth City Museum and Art Gallery, Drake Circus, Ply-
    mouth. Other significant collections of prehistoric material from Dart-
    moor can be seen at the Museum of the Torquay Natural History and
    Antiquarian Society, Babbacombe Road, Torquay, and at Rougemont
    House, Castle Street, Exeter

15   Burnard, R. *Early Man*, pp 341–372; Wall, J. C. *Earthworks*, pp 573–630

16   Brailsford, J. W. *Antiquity*, 12, pp 444–63

17   Radford, Dr C. A. Ralegh. 'Prehistoric Settlements on Dartmoor and the Cornish Moors', *Proceedings of the Prehistoric Society*, 18 (1952), pp 55–84

18   Worth, Hansford. *Dartmoor*, Spooner, G. M. and Russell, F. S., Eds. (1953)

19   Ibid

20   'Excavations at Kestor, an Early Iron Age Settlement near Chagford, Devon', *Transactions of the Devonshire Association*, 86 (1954), pp 21–62; 'Celtic Fields and Farms on Dartmoor', *Proceedings of the Prehistoric Society*, 20 (1954), pp 87–102; 'Excavations on Dean Moor, in the Avon Valley, 1954–1956', *Transactions of the Devonshire Association*, 89 (1957), pp 18–77

21   *Proceedings of the Devon Archaeological Society*, 26 (1968), pp 21–30. Lady Fox discussed the Dartmoor material in its broader regional context in her *South West England* (1964), and has summarised more recent developments in the *Proceedings of the Prehistoric Society*, 35 (1969), pp 220–228

22   *Transactions of the Devonshire Association*, 94 (1962), pp 555–574; *Proceedings of the Prehistoric Society*, 35 (1969), pp 203–219

23   cf Bray, Mrs. *A Description* . . ., 1, p 126

24   Bray, Mrs. *A Description* . . ., 1, pp 53–54

25   Worth, Hansford. 'A Flint Implement of Palaeolithic Type from Dartmoor', *Transactions of the Devonshire Association*, 63 (1931), pp 359–360

26   Evans, J. *The Ancient Stone Implements of Great Britain* (2nd ed 1897), pp 492–5

27   *Proceedings of the Devon Archaeological Exploration Society*, 5 (1953), pp 8–26

28   Radford, Dr C. A. Ralegh. *Proceedings of the Prehistoric Society*, 18, pp 68–9

29   Piggott, Stuart. *The Neolithic Cultures of the British Isles* (Cambridge, 1954), p 33

30   A full account of the collapse and re-erection of Spinsters' Rock is given in Worth, Hansford. *Dartmoor* (1953) pp 180–1

31   Eogan, George and Simmons, I. G. 'The Excavation of a Stone Alignment and Circle at Cholwichtown, Lee Moor, Devonshire, England', *Proceedings of the Prehistoric Society*, 30 (1964), pp 25–38. See also Proudfoot, V. B. 'Soil Report, Cholwichtown Stone Row', *Proceedings of the Prehistoric Society*, 35 (1969), pp 217–19

32   Anderson, J. C. *Scotland in Pagan Times; The Bronze and Stone Ages* (1886), pp 125–35

33   Bray, Mrs. *A Description* . . ., 1, p 125

34   Baird, J. G. A. 'Account of the Excavation of Two Hut Circles of the Bronze Age, in the Parish of Muirkirk, Ayrshire', *Proceedings of the Society of Antiquaries of Scotland*, 48 (1913–14), pp 373–381

35   Four of the axes were presented by the landowner, the Duke of Bed-
     ford, to the Royal Albert Memorial Museum, Exeter, the remainder
     going to the British Museum
36   A single, almost complete drinking cup of late style, with shallow
     tooled decoration and two lug handles perforated for suspension, was
     found in 1960 in extraordinary circumstances by the late Michael V.
     Rabley. The vessel lay broken in two halves at the back of a small
     crevice halfway up the eastern face of the Crow's Buttress, a rocky
     outcrop some three hundred yards north east of the Dewerstone, Meavy,
     at a point where a small ledge of rock, which could have afforded a
     site for a temporary encampment, projects from the cliff face. *Trans-
     actions of the Devonshire Association*, 95 (1963), pp 78–9
37   Excavation by Plymouth City Museum Archaeology Group. Publica-
     tion forthcoming
38   Simmons, I. G. *Proceedings of the Prehistoric Society*, 35, pp 209, 210,
     213
39   *Transactions of the Devonshire Association*, 99 (1967), pp 316–18; Fox,
     Lady (Aileen) and Britton, Dennis. *Proceedings of the Prehistoric Society*,
     35 (1969), pp 220–8
40   Settlements of the Early Iron Age broadly contemporary with Kes
     Tor have been excavated elsewhere in the south-west, notably at Dain-
     ton in Devon and Bodrifty in Cornwall. It has recently been suggested
     that settlements of the Kes Tor type, but possibly of Bronze Age as
     well as of Iron Age date, may have been formed within much larger,
     perhaps tribal systems of landholding indicated on the ground by
     parallel reaves or boundary banks several miles in length. Gawne, Eliza-
     beth and Cocks, J. V. S. 'Parallel Reaves on Dartmoor', *Transactions of
     the Devonshire Association*, 100 (1968) pp 277–291
41   Polwhele, *History of Devonshire*, 1, p 192

CHAPTER 3

(Pages 76–99)

Saxon and Early Medieval Times : John Somers Cocks

ANYONE writing a history of this period must be greatly indebted to the
works of W. G. Hoskins. His *Old Devon* (1966) and parts of his *Provincial
England* (1963) contain much that is relevant for the Saxon and later periods,
while his *Westward Expansion of Wessex* (Leicester University Press
Occasional Papers No 13, 1960) gives a plausible interpretation of the
chronology of the English conquest of the South West.

Other works for the Saxon settlement include Gover, Mawer and Sten-
ton's *The Place Names of Devon* (8 and 9 of the publications of the English
Place Names Society 1931–2), an indispensable work but in need of revision,
and H. P. R. Finberg's *Early Charters of Devon and Cornwall* (Leicester University Press Occasional Papers No 2, 1963).

Not a great deal is in print regarding the types of settlement and their
field systems apart from Hoskins, quoted above. A most valuable survey of
Dartmoor sites is contained in Mrs C. D. Linehan's 'Deserted Sites and

Rabbit Warrens on Dartmoor, Devon' printed in *Medieval Archaeology* 10 (1966), and A. H. Shorter has a paper entitled 'Ancient Fields in Manaton Parish, Dartmoor' in *Antiquity* 12 (1938). Mrs. E. M. Minter's excavation of Houndtor village is not yet completed, but brief reports by her are to be found in *Medieval Archaeology* 6–7 and 8 (1962–3, 1964). Likewise results of P. V. Addyman's Lydford excavations are only available in three dupli-cated interim reports.

For the Norman Conquest, the Domesday Survey and following period, the basic books are Hoskins' *Old Devon* and *Provincial England*, O. J. Reichel's numerous articles and special supplements in the series 'The Hundreds of Devon', published in the *Transactions of the Devonshire Association*, and dealing with the problems of manorial identification, *The Devonshire Domesday and Geld Inquest* (1884–92) published in two volumes by the same association and giving extended originals and translations of the Exchequer and Exon Books—an invaluable work—and H. C. Darby and R. Welldon Finn's *Domesday Geography of South West England* (19—), setting Dartmoor in the wider context of the south-west peninsula. Other works containing some material include *Tavistock Abbey* by H. P. R. Fin-berg (1951), whose article on Lydford Castle in *Devon & Cornwall Notes & Queries* 23 (1947–9) is also of interest, and Mrs C. D. Linehan's article in *Medieval Archaeology* 10, quoted above. No specific work dealing with Dartmoor in 1086 exists; the figures quoted in the text are derived from entries in *The Devonshire Domesday and Geld Inquest*.

On the Forest and commons the most valuable works, apart from Hoskins, are S. Moore's appendix of documents in P. Birkett's *A Short History of the Rights of Common upon the Forest of Dartmoor and the Commons of Devon-shire* published by the Dartmoor Preservation Association in 1890, and Hansford Worth's chapter in his *Dartmoor* entitled 'Tenants and Com-moners', based on those documents.

CHAPTER 4
(Pages 100–138)
Industry: Frank Booker

Tin Working

THERE is no survey of tin working on Dartmoor comparable with the work of Carew and Pryce for Cornwall. In using them allowance must be made for significant differences due to the smaller and less intensive scale of work-ing on Dartmoor. Hansford Worth dealt with many aspects of the industry on Dartmoor, and his papers, collected in *Dartmoor* (1953), form a good starting point. He is still the standard source for the blowing houses.

Other essential sources include : R. N. Worth : *Historical notes concerning the progress of mining skill in Devon and Cornwall* (1872); G. W. Ormerod : *Traces of tin streaming in the vicinity of Chagford* (1876); R. Burnard : *On the track of the 'Old Men'* (1888) and *The Antiquity of Mining on Dartmoor* (1891); G. R. Lewis : *The Stannaries* (1908); J. V. Ramsden : *Notes on the mines of Devonshire* (1914, but revised in 1952–53); W. S. Lewis : *The West of England Tin Mining* (a valuable and little known survey) (1923); C.

s

G. Moor : *Tin Mining* (a useful text book on tin mining methods) (1928); H. Dewey : *British Regional Geology—South West England* (1948); H. P. R. Finberg : *The Stannary of Tavistock* (1949); W. G. Hoskins : *Devon* and *Old Devon* (1954 and 1966) (both contain useful summaries on which I have drawn for early tin production on Dartmoor); H. G. Dines : *The Metalliferous Mining Region of South West England*, 2 (1956); E. S. Hedges : *Tin; its contribution to social development* (1961); D. B. Barton : *Essays in Cornish Mining History* (1968); D. G. Broughton : *Tin working in the eastern district of the parish of Chagford* and *Dartmoor tin working; its effect upon scenery and land use* (1966). I am indebted to Dr J. C. A. Whetter for the reference to the Plymouth Port Books.

Among more general sources are : S. Rowe : *Perambulation of the antient and royal forest of Dartmoor* (1896); W. Crossing : *A Hundred Years on Dartmoor* (1901) and *The Dartmoor Worker* (1903); Rev D Lysons : *Magna Britannia* (1822); Rev T. Moore : *The History of Devonshire* (1829); L. A. Harvey and D. St Leger-Gordon : *Dartmoor* (1953).

The Rev John Swete's manuscript diary *Picturesque sketches of Devon*, particularly volumes 15 and 16 (1792–1801) has a number of interesting references to tin working while Helen Harris's *Industrial Archaeology of Dartmoor* (1968) is relevant to all the industries mentioned in this chapter.

The Stannaries

The most comprehensive source is G. R. Lewis's *The Stannaries* (1908). He is, however, mainly concerned with Cornwall; a much more complete picture of a Devon Stannary is to be found in H. P. R. Finberg's *The Stannary of Tavistock* (1949) from which the quotations in this section have been mainly drawn. Rowe's *Perambulation* (1896) has some useful references to the militancy of the Devon stannaries, while Hansford Worth in *Dartmoor* deals with the effect of stannary privileges on villeinage. Clapham's *Concise Economic History of Britain* (1949) has some pointed comments on royal trading in tin, and A. L. Rowse's *Tudor Cornwall* (1941) discusses stannary taxation and its effects.

Wool and Cloth

Details about the Dartmoor wool trade have to be pieced together from several sources. The Rev D. Lysons in *Magna Britannia* (1822) has an important chapter on the Devon wool trade generally. Other useful sources are : White : *Directory of Devonshire* (1850); P. F. S. Amery : *Sketch of Ashburton and the Woollen Trade* (1876); Chanter : *The Aulnager in Devon*; Dom John Stephan *The Cistercians and the Woollen Industry*; J. R. A. Pelham : *Fulling Mills*; H. P. R. Finberg : *Tavistock Abbey* (1951); W. G. Hoskins : *Devon*; E. Power : *The Wool trade in English Medieval History*; Joyce Youings : *Tuckers Hall, Exeter* (1969). There is also much interesting material about the wool trade in solicitors' deeds deposited in the Devon County Record Office.

I am indebted to Mr David Seward of the department of Economic History, Exeter University, for information about many of the fulling mill sites and the reference to the South Brent teazle mill. I am grateful also to Mr Michael Dickinson for the references to Chagford wool sales in the

Chagford Churchwardens' Accounts, now in the Devon County Record
Office.

Edge Tool and Other Mills, Peat and Quarrying

A complete description of Finch's foundry is given by Kenneth Major in
Finch Brothers' Foundry (1967), a booklet issued for the foundry restoration
fund. Clues for the site of corn and tanning paper mills can often be found in
parish records, while early directories, particularly White's *Devonshire 1850*,
give an idea of their distribution in the last century. The early files of newspapers frequently contain advertisements for the sale of mills and often give
details of their machinery. Woolmer's *Exeter and Plymouth Gazette* of 10
July 1819 has an advertisement for the Phoenix corn mills at Horrabridge,
describing their machinery, while details of the mill at Two Bridges can be
found in the *Plymouth and Devonport Weekly Journal* of 25 January
1855. In the same paper (2 December 1858) there is a description of papermaking processes at the Ivybridge mill. Helen Harris in *The Industrial
Archaeology of Dartmoor* describes and illustrates the Cherrybrook gunpowder mills as well as peat-cutting processes on Dartmoor. Peat cutting
is also described by W. Crossing in *The Dartmoor Worker* (1903) and there
are further details about peat in *A Survey of the Forest of Dartmore 1786*
(Exeter City Library), in Swete's *Picturesque Sketches* and in Worth's *Dartmoor*. In *Transactions of the Devonshire Association* (73) Worth trans-
cribes some miscellaneous material about Dartmoor in which there are
references to a peat kiln at Two Bridges in 1794, while Brian Le Messurier,
in Vol 97 of the *Transactions*, has a valuable article on the peat passes of
Dartmoor, some of which were cut to reach peat ties. Details about plans
for extracting petrol etc from peat at Rattlebrook appear in *The Western
Morning News* of 19 February and 6 November 1937, 19 March 1940 and
6 April 1965. Diana Woolner in *Devon and Cornwall Notes and Queries* 30,
part 4 (1965) has an informative article on peat charcoal remains. For
quarrying Rowe's *Perambulation* (3rd edition 1896) and G. F. Harris's
Granites and our Granite Industries (1888) are good sources and so is W. A.
E. Ussher's *The Geology of Ivybridge and Modbury* (1912), which contains
some interesting notes by Hansford Worth. W. G. Hoskins's *Devon* refers to
the use of Roborough stone.

D. B. Barton in *Essays in Cornish Mining History* (1968), points out that
peat was regarded as too tender a fuel for smelting, wood charcoal being
generally preferred. On the use of peat as a fuel for pumping engines, C. G.
Moor in *Tin Mining* (1928) refers to a 50in pumping engine at Redmoor,
Callington, which worked at a cost of 8½d for 24 hours off slabs of peat
two inches thick cut off the neighbouring moor.

China Clay

R. M. Barton: *A History of the Cornish China Clay Industry* (1966) has
the most comprehensive treatment of the industry while Kenneth Hudson:
The History of English China Clays (1968) includes the Lee Moor area.
Other sources used have been A. D. Selleck: *China Clay of Devon and
Cornwall* (1948) (an informative manuscript account in the Plymouth
Local History Library); *Working Party Report on the China Clay Industry*

(1948), and W. A. E. Ussher: *Geology of Ivybridge and Modbury* (1912), which contains some useful notes by Hansford Worth. Much helpful information has also been provided by the publicity department of English China Clays Group, St Austell. There is an interesting account of the early days of the Lee Moor china clay industry in the *Plymouth and Devonport Weekly Journal* of 30 September 1858.

I am indebted to Rev E. E. Lamborne for details about the Methodist Chapel and its history. In the garden of the house adjoining the chapel, bricks with Phillips' name stamped on them are still occasionally dug up.

CHAPTER 5
(Pages 139–181)

Dartmoor Farming: Michael Havinden and Freda Wilkinson

1   The Dartmoor Preservation Association, *A Short History of the Rights of Common upon the Forest of Dartmoor and the Commons of Devon*: Report of Stuart A. Moore . . . (Plymouth, 1890) pp 10, 18, 156–9

2   Gray, H. L. *English Field Systems* (Harvard 1915, reprinted London 1959), p 260. The original survey is in the Exeter City Library, and we are indebted to Mr John Somers Cocks for lending us a transcription

3   *Short History*, p 12

4   Hoskins, W. G. and Finberg, H. P. R. *Devonshire Studies* (1952), pp 265–88

5   Gray, H. L. *English Field Systems*, pp 158–60

6   We are grateful to Elizabeth Gawne of Widecombe for information about ancient Dartmoor fields and cultivations, many of which she has mapped

7   Duchy of Cornwall Office, Court of Survey of the Manor of Lydford, 16 August 1608 (copy)

8   *Short History*, p 64

9   *Short History*, pp 156–9

10 Duchy of Cornwall Office, Collections of ancient papers on various matters, 1674–1738, p 16

11 See *Short History*, pp 33–4 for details

12 *Short History*, pp 11–12

13 *Short History*, pp 65–6

14 *Short History*, p 126ff

15 Burnard, Robert. 'The Packhorse on Dartmoor', *Transactions of the Devonshire Association* (1905), p 168

16 Vancouver, C. *General View of the Agriculture of the County of Devon* (1808), p 197

17 Finberg, H. P. R. *Tavistock Abbey* (1951)

18 Vancouver, C. *General View . . .*, pp 228, 345–7

CHAPTER 6

(Pages 182–203)

Roads and Tracks: Robert Groves

1   The best source of information on Dartmoor roads and tracks is the work of William Crossing. In his *Guide to Dartmoor* (1909) he described over eighty tracks on the Moor which he knew at first hand; and Chapter 3 of his *Hundred Years on Dartmoor* (1901), is a description of the Dartmoor roads. Hansford Worth wrote a few pages on the subject of tracks and guide-stones which will be found in his *Dartmoor* (1953), pp 392–402

2   Very early routes are mapped and described in 'Ancient Highways of Devon' by G. B. Grundy, *Archaeological Journal,* 98 (1941), pp 131–64, though some of the routes given there are questionable. For the prehistoric ridgeways near Dartmoor see W. G. Hoskins, *Fieldwork in Local History* (1967), p 147. For Roman roads see Ivan D. Margery, *Roman Roads in Britain* (1955) and later editions, and W. S. Simey, *Roman Roads West of the Exe* (1964)

3   John Swete toured Devon and recorded his experiences in a large number of manscript volumes illustrated with watercolour paintings, now held by the Devon Record Office. The sections relating to Dartmoor date mainly from 1797 and contain much valuable information about the Moor at that time

For the reference by the Rev Sabine Baring-Gould see a pamphlet entitled *Sheepstor* (1912), p 9

4   The best source of information on bridges is *Old Devon Bridges* (1938) by Charles Henderson and E. Jervoise. The Devon Record Office holds many contracts for the building of bridges and also three large volumes of excellently produced plans and elevations of Devon bridges made in about 1854–60. One early nineteenth-century document in the Devon Record Office states that the county was responsible for repairing the road for 300ft in either direction from the county bridges. Wayside stones, apparently marking the limit of the road to be repaired and bearing a large letter C, can be seen at the appropriate distances in either direction from Bellever Bridge and other bridges on the Moor.

Clapper Bridges are described by Hansford Worth on pages 368–71 of *Dartmoor*. The *Shorter Oxford English Dictionary* gives an early meaning of the word 'clapper' as 'heap of stones'—an appropriate description of these bridges. Where the stones used to make a granite structure such as a clapper bridge have been split from a parent block the method of cleavage may give a clue to its age. In the first decade or two of the nineteenth century the old wedge-and-groove method of splitting granite was replaced by a method involving drilling a number of holes along the proposed line of the break. A number of the stones of the clapper bridge at the Powder Mills, for example, have the half-round holes resulting from this later process, and this suggests that, despite the archaic script with which the bridge is named by the

Ordnance Survey, it dates from the years after 1844 when the mills were built

5 Detailed descriptions of the Dartmoor crosses are included in 'Ancient Stone Crosses of Devon', E. Masson Phillips, *Transactions of the Devonshire Association*, 69 (1937), 70 (1938), 71 (1939), 72 (1940), 75 (1943), and 86 (1954). An earlier account, still worth reading, is William Crossing's *Ancient Stone Crosses of Dartmoor and its Borderland* (1902). Only a selection of the Dartmoor crosses, of which there are well over a hundred in various states of preservation, has been given on the map. The crosses indicated on the map, including some now moved or lost but whose original site is known, are those which seem to have had as at least part of their function the marking of a road or track. Crosses clearly having some other purpose entirely, for example village and boundary crosses, have been omitted, and so too have crosses and fragments of crosses whose original site is unknown. Both Siward's Cross (a boundary mark) and the Cross on Childe's Tomb have been included because they probably served as landmarks on a route over the Moor described in the text

6 The following are the most important of the early maps of the Moor :
(a) The fifteenth-century map of the moor was described in a paper entitled 'On the Original Map of the Royal Forest of Dartmoor, Illustrating the Perambulation of Henry III, 1240,' by C. Spence Bate in *Transactions of the Devonshire Association*, 5 (1872), pp 510–48. The map is held by the Royal Albert Memorial Museum, Exeter. A fifteenth-century date was ascribed to it in the Dartmoor Preservation Association's volume *A Short History of the Rights of Common upon the Forest of Dartmoor and the Commons of Devon* (1890), p 36; and this view was supported by Hansford Worth, who thought 1478 a likely date; *Transactions of the Devonshire Association*, 73 (1941), pp 214–5
(b) *Britannia, Volume the First : or An Illustration of the Kingdom of England and Dominion of Wales . . .* , John Ogilby (1675)
(c) *A Map of the County of Devon*, Benjamin Donn (1765), reprinted 1965 with an introduction by W. L. D. Ravenhill (one inch to one mile)
(d) The first edition of the Ordnance Survey one-inch map appeared in 1809. The Exeter City Library holds copies of the larger scale maps from which this edition was prepared, dating from 1784–6 for the south-west side of the moor, 1802–7 for the rest
(e) *Map of the County of Devon*, C. and J. Greenwood (1827) one inch to one mile

7 There still exists a clapper bridge over the Cowsic near Beardown Farm, but it seems too far away and too awkwardly sited to have served this route

8 A charter which probably dates from between 1200 and 1230 and which refers to the section of this route near Cholwich Town as a paved road is described by W. G. Hoskins in *Devonshire Studies* (1952), pp 78–80

9 The trackway indicated by the Ordnance Survey as leading north to Nun's Cross Farm from the Plym and labelled 'Abbot's Way' does not seem even to exist on the ground, much less to have been part of an early routeway

10 John Andrew's papers are the subject of a paper by Hansford Worth in the *Transactions of the Devonshire Association*, 73 (1941), pp 203–25

11 The reference will be found in *The Registers of Walter Bronescombe (AD 1287–1280) and Peter Quivil (AD 1280–1291), Bishops of Exeter* (1889), by the Rev F. C. Hingeston-Randolph, pp 204–5

12 Many of the roadside direction stones on the moor are described in 'Notes on Some Old Roadside Stones in South West Devon', E. Masson Phillips, *Transactions of the Devonshire Association*, 75 (1943), pp 141–65. The reference to the erection of stones on the moor in 1699–1700 is in R. N. Worth's *Calendar of the Plymouth Municipal Records* (1893), p 171. The stones near North Hessary Tor are described by Hansford Worth and Dr David C. Prowse in an article reprinted in Worth's *Dartmoor*, pp 397–402

13 The quotation is from a manuscript book in Exeter City Record Office entitled *A Survey of the Forest of Dartmore belonging to His Royal Highness the Prince of Wales* (1786), William Simpson

14 Turnpike Acts can be located by using the *Index to Local and Personal Acts 1801–1947* (1949) and the index volumes to *Statutes at Large*; and the details of individual Acts found in the *Journals of the House of Commons*, though copies of these Acts can sometimes be found in libraries and record offices

The Devon Record Office has turnpike trust accounts, mainly from about 1820, deposited plans of roads, and conveyances of toll houses and their sites when the trusts were wound up

The Okehampton Turnpike Trust is the subject of an article by E. P. Burd in the *Transactions of the Devonshire Association*, 68 (1936), pp 307–23

15 The Tavistock bridges are described in 'The Bridges over the River Tavy at Tavistock' by Eric V. Kingdon, *Transactions of the Devonshire Association*, 75 (1943), pp 167–70. The Great Bridge, which was in existence from the thirteenth century, was supplemented in about 1540 by the West Bridge. In 1763, under the Act of the previous year, the Great Bridge was demolished and the Abbey Bridge (now called Bedford Bridge) was built a short distance downstream. Under the Act of 1772 Vigo bridge was built in 1773 a short distance upstream

16 We would expect that the road from Dunnabridge through Dartmeet, where a new bridge was built in 1792, and Holne to Ashburton would have been taken over by one of the turnpike trusts and some contemporary maps show it as a turnpike road. It does not, however, appear in any of the turnpike Acts nor were there any toll gates on it.

17 Phillpotts' peat passes are described by Brian Le Messurier in a paper in the *Transactions of the Devonshire Association*, 97 (1965), pp 161–70

CHAPTER 7
(Pages 204–224)

Railways: Michael Ewans

1 *South Devon Monthly Museum,* 7 (March 1836). I am indebted for this reference, and for information especially on the Zeal Tor tramroad, to Mr Somers Cocks
2 Leigham, 620yd
3 Substance of Tyrwhitt's statement to the Chamber of Commerce at Plymouth, 3 November, 1818 (1819). See Worth's *Dartmoor,* Appendix viii
4 Stuart's estimate was for double track; the line as constructed was single, and cost £66,000
5 For letters concerning the 4ft 6in gauge lines, see Plymouth City Library archives
6 See Plymouth and Dartmoor Railway committee minute of 2 July 1821. All the minute books are in British Rail archives, London
7 Clause 4
8 See committee minutes of 23 April 1821 and 25 February 1822
9 Committee minute of 15 April 1822
10 The line eventually had at least six different kinds of rail—all mounted on granite sleepers on the Moor—and short sidings of granite rail on Yelverton Down. See Paley, *Railroad Gazette,* 19 December 1902
11 28 Vict, cap cxxxi
12 For the date see E. C. R. Hadfield's *Canals of South West England* (1967), p 123
13 See agreement of 29 December 1861, Morley—Phillips and Lee Moor Clay Co—SDR (Plymouth City archives)
14 *Exeter and Plymouth Gazette,* March 1834
15 For the location of this see the Plymouth Railway Circle, *Map of the Lee Moor Tramway,* by J. C. Gillham and R. C. Sambourne (revised edition, 1967)
16 For stations on this line see Thomas, *Regional History of the railways of Great Britain* (third edition) 1, (1966), p 193
17 Plymouth City archives

CHAPTER 8
(Pages 225–244)

Recreation: Brian Le Messurier

1 *Transactions of the Devonshire Association,* 66, p 371
2 Crossing's *Dartmoor Worker,* chapter on whortleberry gathering
3 Crossing's *Dartmoor Worker* and *A Hundred Years on Dartmoor.* St Leger-Gordon's *Dartmoor in all its Moods* and *The Way of a Fox*
4 Crossing's *Guide to Dartmoor,* p 112
5 Rachel Evans, *Home Scenes,* p 143

6   I am grateful to Mr H. R. Rivers-Moore for letting me quote from the diary of his mother

7   Other places on Dartmoor now have receptacles containing a visitors' book, rubber stamp and pad, and the Dartmoor National Park Committee (County Hall, Exeter) publishes a leaflet about the custom. It lists Cranmere Pool (603858), Ducks Pool (626679), Fur Tor (588830), and Crow Tor (606787).

8   See the published reports in the *Transactions of the Devonshire Association*, 26–38 (excluding 32 and 36). Two later reports appeared in 67 and 69

9   From a paper 'The Acquisition of the Forest of Dartmoor as a County Park' presented to the Plymouth Institution in 1894. Privately published as a pamphlet

10 From a paper 'Early Western Railroads' presented to the Plymouth Institution in 1888. Reprinted in Hansford Worth's *Dartmoor*, p 483

11 See *A History of the Devon General Omnibus and Touring Company Limited* (1966)

BIBLIOGRAPHY

References to the pastimes of man on Dartmoor many years ago are necessarily widely scattered and few and far between, but a perusal of the *Transactions of the Devonshire Association* has thrown a little light on the subject. There is a chapter 'Devonshire wrestlers' in *Devonshire Characters and Strange Events* (Second series, 1908), by S. Baring Gould. The social history of the last century in the Lustleigh area is well covered by Cecil Torr's three volumes of reminiscences, *Small Talk at Wreyland* (1918, 1921, 1923). An abridged edition was published by the Cambridge University Press in 1926 and 1927.

Apart from the books mentioned in the text notes, hunting is described in the following books :
Collier, W. F. *Harry Terrell: A Dartmoor Philosopher* (1896) and *Country Matters in Short* (1899); Back, Philip *From Terrier Boy to Field Master* (not dated). Besides these books a number of brochures and pamphlets have been published by various Dartmoor hunts, and these can be seen in the Devon County and Plymouth City Libraries.

Fishing topics are covered by *Fishing Facts and Fancies* by H. G. Michelmore (1946) and *Salmon and Trout in Moorland Streams* by Major Kenneth Dawson (1928). D. St Leger-Gordon's *Dartmoor in all its Moods* (1931) has a chapter which is relevant, and the same book should be consulted for references to shooting.

The growth of tourism on Dartmoor is best shown by the changing entries in the various directories for the period from 1850 onwards, and comparing the advertisements in different editions of the Ward Lock and Homeland Association guides to Dartmoor. Other books, notably the early editions of Crossing's *Guide to Dartmoor*, Tickler's *Devonshire Sketches: Dartmoor and its Borders* (1873), *Pictorial Dartmoor* by T. A. Falcon (1902) and *Gems in a Granite Setting* by Crossing (1905) also include advertisements which add to the interest of the illustrations and text.

Two books which are very different from each other, but which are each social surveys for a circumscribed area are *Throwleigh: The Story of a Dartmoor Village* by Emmie Varwell (1938) and *Under Dartmoor Hills* by D. St. Leger-Gordon (1954). The latter is largely concerned with the part of the moor around Belstone, South Zeal, Sticklepath and South Tawton.

The best source book for the growth of railways is *The West Country* by David St John Thomas (1966 edition) in the Regional History of the Railways of Great Britain series, but interesting sidelines can be gleaned from two books by T. W. E. Roche, *Go Great Western* (1966) and *The Withered Arm* (1967).

The national park movement is described in a chapter by Harold Abrahams in *Britain's National Parks* (1959), edited by him.

Rock climbing has its own guide, *Rock Climbing in Devonshire* (second edition 1966). More discursive in its treatment is *A Climber in the West Country* by Edward C. Pyatt (1969).

ACKNOWLEDGEMENTS

I AM indebted to members and friends of Belstone, South Brent and Holne Women's Institutes for information about their own localities. Lady Sayer, Mr A. C. Bulpin and Mr G. E. D. Parsons kindly loaned me photographs, and Mrs W. Osborne was good enough to let me look through, and use, the Chagford material collected by her late husband. I thank them all for their help so freely given.

CHAPTER 9
(Pages 245–276)

Exploitation: John Somers Cocks

A GOOD deal of the essential framework for the chapter is to be found in the files of the Duchy of Cornwall office in London and in those of the Dartmoor Preservation Association, while some of the rest is only available in past issues of newspapers, particularly *The Western Morning News*. Rather more accessible are books of newspaper clippings in the Exeter City Library dealing mainly with the years at the turn of the century.

References to enclosure and the improvers are widely scattered through a number of books such as W. Crossing's *A Hundred Years on Dartmoor* (1901) and *Dartmoor Worker* (1903), Mrs E. A. Bray's *The Borders of Tamar and Tavy* (1836), R. Burnard's *Plundered Dartmoor* (1896) (with comparative maps), the Rev J. P. Jones's *Observations on the Scenery and Antiquities in the Neighbourhood of Moretonhampstead and on the Forest of Dartmoor* (giving details in 1823), E. W. Martin's *Dartmoor* (1958), which in particular has an appreciation of Tyrwhitt, derived from a paper by Brooking Rowe in 37 of the Devonshire Association's *Transactions*, and S. Rowe's *Perambulation of the Antient and Royal Forest of Dartmoor . . . etc* (1896). Burt's preface and notes to Dartmoor : a descriptive poem (1826) by N. T. Carrington are also useful for the earlier period.

R. Fraser's *General View of the County of Devon* (1794), C. Vancouver's *General View of the Agriculture of the County of Devon* (1808), and the Rev T. Moore's *The History of Devonshire* (1829–36), though dealing on a county-wide basis, have some interesting comments. Some references will be found too in various volumes of *Devon & Cornwall Notes & Queries*.

Princetown and its prison have attracted a considerable literature, a good deal of it repetitive, but A. J. Rhodes's *Dartmoor Prison, from War to Convict Prison* (1933), B. Thomson's *The Story of Dartmoor Prison* (1907) and the Rev L. Woollcombe's *Princetown and its Prison* (1926) are amongst those with useful early references, as is H. E. Parsons' pamphlet *Princetown* (1955).

Several other pamphlets are of importance, notably Tyrwhitt's *Substance of a Statement . . . concerning the Formation of a Rail Road from the Forest of Dartmoor to the Plymouth Lime-quarries* (1819), H. Tanner's *Essay on the Cultivation of Dartmoor* (1854) and J. M. Rendel's *Report of a Proposed Line of Railway from Plymouth etc to Exeter over Dartmoor* (1840).

On military training, forestry and water supplies, little is in print apart from the files of newspapers. An article by G. Wycisk 'Dartmoor "fell" in 1875' appeared in *The Western Morning News* of 21 February 1962 and a series of mainly humorous sketches is in H. T. Mackenzie's booklet *Jottings at the Dartmoor Autumn Manoeuvres* (1873). The amenity bodies' petition to the Duchy was printed in *The Western Morning News* of 26 November 1968.

On forestry there is the *Devon Survey* by W. H. Thompson (1932) mentioning the Bellever planting, *Dartmoor* by L. A. Harvey and D. St Leger-Gordon, and G. D. Rouse's *The New Forests of Dartmoor* (1964). Water supplies are mentioned in Hansford Worth's *Dartmoor*, as are military training areas, and an interesting account of the Burrator controversy is to be found in a small pamphlet written by R. N. Worth in 1886 entitled *Plain Facts on the Plymouth Water Question*. For the technically minded, descriptions of the construction of dams appear in the *Journal of the Institution of Water Engineers* and *Proceedings of the Institute of Civil Engineers* (eg Fernworthy in 1946).

My thanks are due to Michael Havinden for readily loaning me his notes of searches made at the Duchy of Cornwall office in London, and to the officials of the Duchy for courteously allowing the searches to be made. I am grateful also to the officers and committee of the Dartmoor Preservation Association for permission to use material in their extensive files.

APPENDIX
(Pages 277–281)

The Forest Boundary: John Somers Cocks

Sources :

Birkett, P. and Moore, S. *A Short History of the Rights of Common . . .*

Burnard R. and Prowse, A. B. 'Place-names in 1 of DPA publications', in *Transactions of the Devonshire Association,* 25

Whale, Rev. T. W. 'Some remarks on the bounds of the Forest of Dartmoor', etc, in *Transactions of the Devonshire Association,* 25

Somers Cocks, J. V. 'The Boundary of the Forest of Dartmoor on the North-East Side', two articles in *Devon & Cornwall Notes & Queries,* 30, pp 214, 284

Index

David & Charles publish a wide range of books on Dartmoor and the surrounding area. Details of some are given below. For later titles, please ask to be placed on the firm's mailing list.

Sheet 90, Tavistock, of the David & Charles reprint of the first edition of the Ordnance Survey covers Dartmoor. It shows the personality of the region in the early nineteenth century but with the details of railways which were subsequently added to the original copper-plate of the map.

THE CHURCHES OF DEVON
J. M. SLADER
9¼ × 7¼in frontis, 160 pp inc 100 plates, maps

7153 4255 X

A survey of the parish churches of Devon covering a thousand years. Chapters: ten Devon churches of outstanding interest; pre-Conquest; Norman; early English; decorated; perpendicular (the great rebuilding, medieval wealth); building stone; roodscreens; pulpits and bench-ends; monuments and brasses; post-reformation (classical and early revival Gothic, Victorian); the 20th century. Appendixes, bibliography, topographical reference, glossary of architectural terms, index (place names, personal names).

CROSSING'S DARTMOOR WORKER
WILLIAM CROSSING
Introduction by Brian Le Messurier
8½ × 5½in 163 pp plus 16 pp plates

7153 4005 0

A collection of twenty articles describing Edwardian life on Dartmoor, originally written for a newspaper series in 1903. New introduction and contemporary illustrations. Chapters: the farmer; the moorman; the labourer; the Newtake wall builder; swaling; peat cutting; the warrener; the miner; the quarryman; the clay labourer; whortleberry gathering; the sportsman; under canvas; the prison officer; the antiquary; the artist; the visitor; coaching; the guide; 'in along' and 'out auver'. Index.

CROSSING'S GUIDE TO DARTMOOR (2nd Ed 1912)
WILLIAM CROSSING
New Introduction by Brian Le Messurier
7¼ × 4¾in xxviii, 529 pp inc maps and illustrations

7153 4017 4

A complete topographical description of Dartmoor, its aim being to acquaint the visitor with the best means of reaching everything worthy of note on the moor from any point. The author gives an arrangement of excursions and routes crossing the moor in every conceivable direction. The main changes on the moor since the book was written in 1909 are described in the new introduction.

David & Charles Reprints
CROSSING'S HUNDRED YEARS ON DARTMOOR
(1901 Ed Reset)
WILLIAM CROSSING
Introduction by Brian Le Messurier

8½ × 5½in 206 pp plus 20 pp plates, text illustrations

7153 4150 2

An account of life on the moor during the 19th century which reveals the lives, work and environment of the ordinary moor people. Chapters: description of the moor; early 19th-century Dartmoor; the moorland roads; industries of the moor; churches of Dartmoor; 19th-century celebrities; the Dartmoor peasant; commoners' rights; social matters; hunting on the moor; notable occurrences; the literature of Dartmoor. New material added for this reprint: introduction and contemporary illustrations. Appendixes, index.

GENERAL VIEW OF THE AGRICULTURE OF THE COUNTY OF DEVON 1808
CHARLES VANCOUVER

8½ × 5½in folding map as frontis, (4), xii, 479 pp, engravings, folding tables

7153 4372 6

A source in trade, agricultural and local history. Contents: geographical state and circumstances; buildings; occupations; implements; enclosing; arable land; grass land; gardens and orchards; woods and plantations; wastes; improvements; embankments; livestock; rural economy; political economy; obstacles to improvement; miscellaneous articles; conclusion, means of improvement. Appendix.
David & Charles Reprints

THE HAYTOR GRANITE TRAMWAY AND STOVER CANAL (2nd Ed)
Incorporating New Material
M. C. EWANS

8½ × 5¼in 72 pp plus 12 pp plates, maps

7153 4020 4

The history of the Haytor Granite Tramway, Devon's first railway, opened 1820, and the connecting Stover Canal. Chapters: background; Stover Canal; granite tramway and quarries; Teign Navigation; coming of the railway; years of peace; new port; the remains of the tramway; the remains of the waterways. Conclusion, notes, bibliography, appendix, index.

THE HISTORY OF ENGLISH CHINA CLAYS
Fifty Years of Pioneering and Growth
KENNETH HUDSON

7153 4655 5

English China Clays Limited, the largest china-clay producing company in the world, is now fifty years old. From 1919, the story of china clay in Britain has been largely that of ECC Limited, and the company is now one of Britain's largest exporters. Though still based at St Austell, Cornwall, its interests include quarrying activities, transport, housing and the manufacture of building and engineering components.

This is the story of the company's growth and expansion, its technical, financial and marketing problems and progress.

THE INDUSTRIAL ARCHAEOLOGY OF DARTMOOR
HELEN HARRIS
8¼ × 5⅞in 239 pp inc 24 pp plates, maps and text figures

7153 4302 5

A study of the remains of the industrial past of Dartmoor. *Part 1*— the beguiling landscape; the early tinners; later mining; industries from granite; peat; mills and miscellaneous; agriculture and kindred pursuits; communications. *Part 2*—gazetteer, bibliographic notes, index.
The Industrial Archæology of the British Isles

THE INDUSTRIAL ARCHAEOLOGY OF THE
TAMAR VALLEY (2nd Ed)
Incorporating new material
FRANK BOOKER
8¼ × 5⅞in 303 pp inc 20 pp plates, maps and diagrams

7153 4106 5

The industrial history and archaeology of the Tamar Valley (the boundary between Devon and Cornwall). Chapters: the strange dichotomy; the Tamar quays and ferries; silver and lead; lime trade; pageantry of the paddle steamers; Tavistock Canal; the canal mines; Devon Great Consols mine; East Cornwall Mineral Railway; Hingston Down mines; coming of the South Western; the vale of plenty. Notes and references, gazetteer of the sites, bibliographical notes, appendixes (mine outputs, Tavistock Canal tonnages, recipe for whitewash), index.
Industrial Archæology of the British Isles

OLD DEVON
W. G. HOSKINS
8½ × 5½in frontis, 208 pp plus 12 pp plates, maps and plans

7153 4049 2

Ten studies concerned with varied aspects of the history of Devon. Chapters: the study of old farmhouses; industrial archaeology in Devon; some old Devon bartons; a sheaf of modern documents; the Elizabethan merchants of Exeter; three Devon families; epidemics in Tudor Devon; the winter of 1963; the wealth of medieval Devon; the farm labourer through four centuries. Index.
Old . . .

TAVISTOCK ABBEY
A Study in the Social and Economic History of Devon
1951
H. P. R. FINBERG
8¼ × 5½in 320 pp, folding map

7153 4335 1

A study concerned with arable and pastoral husbandry, fisheries, tin-mining, cloth production, fairs, markets and the courts of manor and

hundred. Contents: the endowments of the abbey; the agrarian land-scape; the social structure; arable husbandry; pastoral husbandry; fisheries; the stannary of Tavistock; seignorial revenues; the monastic economy; the dissolution. Appendixes (the abbots of Tavistock, the foundation charter of the abbey, the abbey buildings, the Tavistock printing press). List of sources, index.
David & Charles Reprints

WORTH'S DARTMOOR

(1953)

R. HANSFORD WORTH

New Introduction by G. M. Spooner

8¼×5½in col frontis, xviii, 523 pp plus 94 pp plates, maps and diagrams
7153 4096 4

A collection of the author's work on the physical geography, vegetation, and archaeology of Dartmoor (also an account of the activities and customs of the Stannaries) first published in the *Transactions of the Devonshire Association*. Chapters: physical geography of Dartmoor; ancient dwarfed oak woods of Dartmoor; Dartmoor hut circles; pre-historic pounds of Dartmoor; Dartmoor barrows and Kistvaens; stone rows of Dartmoor; Dartmoor stone circles; Dartmoor menhirs; Stan-naries; Dartmoor blowing-house; tenants and commoners of Dartmoor; Moorstone age; on Dartmoor tracks and guide-stones; Dartmoor house; on Dartmoor place-names. Appendixes, general references, locality index, subject index.
David & Charles Reprints

David & Charles
South Devon House
Newton Abbot